INTRODUCTION TO
UHF
CIRCUITS AND COMPONENTS

INTRODUCTION TO
UHF
CIRCUITS AND COMPONENTS

MILTON S. KIVER

D. VAN NOSTRAND COMPANY, INC.

TORONTO   NEW YORK   LONDON

NEW YORK

D. Van Nostrand Company, Inc., 250 Fourth Avenue, New York 3

TORONTO

D. Van Nostrand Company (Canada), Ltd., 25 Hollinger Rd., Toronto

LONDON

Macmillan & Company, Ltd., St. Martin's Street, London, W.C. 2

———

This book is based on an earlier work entitled *UHF
Radio Simplified*, by M. S. Kiver, copyright 1945 by D.
Van Nostrand Company, Inc.

PREFACE

Ever since its inception prior to World War I, electronic communication has steadily advanced into higher and higher frequencies. With the years the pace of frequency increase has accelerated until now communication activities range all the way to 10,000 mc and beyond.

In view of their extensive application, it behooves those who follow the electronic field, either for a livelihood or as a hobby, to understand the operation of ultra-high frequency circuits and components. It is the purpose of this book to point out the underlying equality of all radio, whatever the frequency. The concepts of ultra-high frequency circuits are presented as logical outgrowths of the more familiar low-frequency equipment. With what the reader already knows as a guide, the reasons for modifications become evident and fall more naturally in place.

At various points throughout the book, explanations are presented with more of an eye toward easier comprehension than mathematical rigor. For that, no excuse is offered. However, at no time are the basic principles ever consciously distorted. In keeping with the character of the book, they are merely simplified. There are many excellent theoretical treatises available, and the more inquisitive reader is directed to them.

The book is divided into 12 chapters. At the outset, Chapter 1, the reader is introduced to the higher frequencies by way of the changes that must be made in familiar tuning circuits to adapt them to the higher frequencies. Detailed treatment of specific components then follow in order, with transmission lines in Chapter 2, waveguides in Chapter 3, and cavity resonators in Chapter 4. By this time the reader is ready to consider various methods of generating the higher frequencies, and the next four chapters, 5 through 8, deal with this aspect of high-frequency communication. In Chapter 9, UHF antennas are discussed, both for reception and transmission. Applications discussed range from frequencies below 100 mc to those above 10,000 mc. UHF measurements constitute the subject of Chapter 10, and here again the step-by-step approach is employed in order that each modification may be fully understood.

The final two chapters are concerned with UHF receiving systems. The departure here from conventional low-frequency practice is not as marked as it is in transmission, but differences do exist and these are carefully underscored.

Illustrations are used liberally throughout the text and for many of these the author is indebted to various technical journals and equipment manufacturers. Special acknowledgment is due to the Institute of Radio Engineers, *Radio and Television News Magazine*, Radio Corporation of America, *Bell System Technical Journal*, the General Radio Company, Sylvania Electric Company, Andrew Corp., Technicraft Laboratories, Sperry Gyroscope Co., Inc., and Standard Coil Products, Inc. Every one of these organizations cooperated splendidly and, by their assistance, lightened the task of writing this book.

M. S. K.

November, 1954
Highland Park, Illinois

CONTENTS

Chapter 1

INTRODUCTION TO THE HIGHER FREQUENCIES

Historically, the period from 1940 to 1945 will always be known as the years of World War II, but to those in the field of communications these years will also signify the period during which tremendous advances were made in utilizing the frequencies between 100 and 10,000 mc for transmission and reception purposes. Techniques were evolved in these five years which enabled television and frequency modulation broadcasting to appear on an extensive commercial scale immediately after the war. Since the frequency spectrum below 50 mc was already well occupied by existing A–M services, the only frequencies which could be alloted to these newer broadcasting media were in the very-high-frequency band (30–300 mc), the ultra-high-frequency band (300–3000 mc), and the super-high-frequency band (3000–30,000 mc). At the moment, the major portion of television and all of F–M broadcasting are concentrated in the very-high-frequency band. However, the lower portion of the ultra-high-frequency band has recently been opened to television and, in time, will carry the bulk of such programming.

The Effect of Increasing Frequency. In order to demonstrate what happens to ordinary radio apparatus when the operating frequency is raised, take a common oscillator and attempt to increase its output frequency. The relationship between frequency and coils and capacitors is given by the formula

$$F = \frac{1}{2\pi\sqrt{LC}}$$

where L is the inductance in henries,
   C is the capacitance in farads.
In order to have the frequency F increase, either L or C or both must decrease in value. This means using fewer turns for the coil and fewer plates

1

for the tuning capacitor. But there is a limit to this process, and at the end nothing would remain of the capacitor except two small plates, and of the inductance, a turn or two of wire. In Fig. 1–1 there is shown an oscillator using a small two-plate capacitor and a variety of inductances. The lowest frequency is obtained when the 15-turn coil at the extreme right is connected across the capacitor; the highest frequency, when the single-turn coil at the far left is used.

Fig. 1.1. An oscillator using a small two-plate capacitor and a variety of inductances to cover a wide range of frequencies. (*Courtesy Radio News*)

Throughout this book frequent reference will be made to frequency and wavelength, and the reader should be familiar with the relationship between them. Frequency is related to wavelength by the expression

$$\lambda \text{ (wavelength)} = \frac{300,000,000}{f \text{ (frequency)}}$$

where λ is given in meters,

f is given in cycles per second.

This formula possesses a variety of forms, all of them equivalent, provided that the proper units are used for wavelength and frequency. Thus, if frequency is expressed in megacycles instead of in cycles, the foregoing formula becomes:

$$\lambda \text{ (meters)} = \frac{300}{f \text{ (mc)}}$$

Again, if λ is desired in feet instead of meters, we have

$$\lambda \text{ (feet)} = \frac{984}{f \text{ (mc)}}$$

because there are 3.2802 feet in one meter. Finally, at the very high frequencies it is more convenient to express wavelength in centimeters and frequency in megacycles. The expression for this is:

$$\lambda \text{ (cm)} = \frac{30,000}{f \text{ (mc)}}$$

Other combinations of units are possible, but the foregoing are the ones most frequently used.

The metal and glass tubes that the radio man ordinarily encounters in his everyday work with A–M receivers may appear to be small in comparison to the tubes used in the sets of the early 1930s, but if any one of these

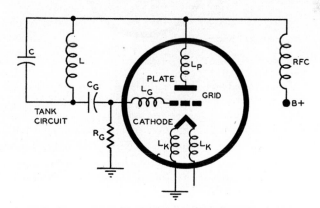

FIG. 1.2. At sufficiently high frequencies, the reactance of the leads within a tube become an important factor in circuit operation.

newer tubes is opened, it will be found to contain connecting leads between the electrodes and the tube base prongs which in some instances are as much as 2 inches long. The wires within a tube are as much a part of the circuit wiring as the external connecting wires themselves. Hence, if we are to indicate properly all of the wiring in a circuit, we must include the leads within the tube. This has been done in Fig. 1–2.

The wiring from the actual element within the tube to the socket terminals is shown as a small inductance. Thus, L_p is the lead from the plate electrode to the base prong, L_g represents the grid wire, etc. At the frequencies employed for low-frequency audio broadcasting, an extra inch or two of connecting wires will not noticeably affect circuit operation. However, if the frequency at which the circuit is to operate is raised high enough, then this inch or two may possess as much inductance as the tank circuit itself. It will be shown in the chapter on UHF measurements that 3 inches of No. 20 copper wire possess an inductance of 0.075 microhenry. At 100 mc, the impedance of this inductance is 47 ohms; at 1000 mc, it is 470 ohms. Since frequencies in excess of 10,000 mc are being used, the impedance of even an inch of wire must be considered.

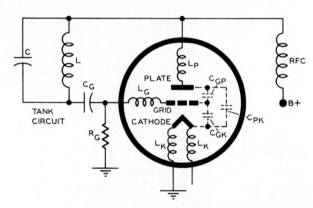

FIG. 1.3. In addition to internal lead inductance, there are also interelectrode capacitances to consider. These are indicated by C_{GK}, C_{PK}, and C_{GP}, above.

Other items which are often ignored in conventional circuitry are the small capacitances scattered about the circuit. Consider, for example, a group of components mounted on a metal chassis. Stray capacitance will exist between the chassis and every section of each component that is not also at chassis potential. Thus, there will be capacitive effect between each turn of the coil and the chassis, between the various prongs of the tube socket and the chassis, etc. It is true that individually the stray capacitances are small—and at frequencies below 10 megacycles their presence may be neglected. The reason for this can be readily seen from the formula for capacitive reactance:

$$X_c = \frac{1}{2\pi f C}$$

Note, as f goes up, X_c goes down. Therefore, the shunting effect of the stray capacitance increases with frequency. However, up to frequencies of 10 mc, with very small stray capacitances, X_c is so large that it can be considered practically an open circuit.

Just as there are capacitances between the various components and the chassis, small capacitances also exist between the various elements within the tube. These are indicated in Fig. 1–3 together with the lead inductances previously shown in Fig. 1–2. Again, at the low frequencies we may disregard them, but above 10 mc, they exert a definite influence on the circuit's operation and must be taken into account.

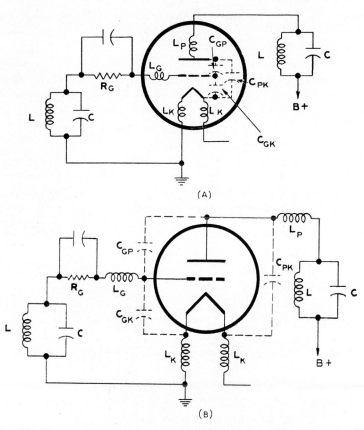

FIG. 1.4. (A) The complete circuit of a tuned-plate, tuned-grid oscillator. (B) The tube inductance and capacitance combined with the external circuit components.

The complete circuit of a tuned-plate, tuned-grid oscillator is shown in Fig. 1–4A. The internal inductances and capacitances of the tube are included in the diagram. In Fig. 1–4B, the internal inductances and capacitances have been moved out of the tube proper and into the circuit. Across the grid tuning circuit we have C_{gk} with C_{gp} and C_{pk} in series. Across the plate tuning circuit we have C_{pk} in parallel with the series arrangement of C_{gp} plus C_{gk}. These capacitances are not constant, but change as the tube warms up, as the plate current varies, and as the tube ages with use. When the circuits are designed to operate at UHF, the internal capacitance of the tube will form an appreciable part of the total circuit capacitance. Thus, with changing internal capacitance, we can expect a drift in frequency and, in general, the circuit will be less stable than when these capacitances form a negligible part of the total capacitance.

Because of the considerable influence which tube elements exert on circuit operation, these were among the first items to receive attention in the drive toward the higher frequencies.

Dimensions were reduced until the tube had shrunk to the "acorn" and "doorknob" sizes. In Fig. 1–5A several high-frequency tubes (9001, 9002, 826, 954, and 958) are shown. Leads from the elements are brought directly through the glass envelope instead of through a base as is customary with ordinary tubes. Isolantite and polystyrene insulators are used throughout to minimize losses due to dielectric leakage.

The subminiature tube shown in Fig. 1–5B is an interesting example of a tube whose dimensions have been reduced far below those of conventional tubes. Overall lengths are between $1\frac{1}{2}$ to 2 inches, and their diameters are about $\frac{5}{16}$ to $\frac{1}{2}$ inch. Leads from the elements extend directly through the glass envelope and either can be soldered into the circuit or, if they are sufficiently rigid, can be inserted into a special socket.

The compactness of the subminiature tube is not only advantageous for UHF operation but is extremely useful in equipment where space is limited. A hearing aid is one such application where subminiature tubes are exclusively employed. The radio proximity bomb fuze is another, and small transceivers or walkie-talkies offer a third illustration. The only bar to more extensive use of these tubes is their low power output due to restricted size. However, where power output is not important, the tubes can be used for electronic circuits ranging from audio amplifiers to UHF oscillators.

By decreasing the area of the various vacuum tube elements, the interelectrode capacitance was reduced. By using very short, direct leads from the elements themselves, the inductance was lessened. And when it was discovered that the materials ordinarily considered as insulators at the low frequencies became partial conductors at the ultra-highs, newer substances such as polystyrene and isolantite were developed. All in all, considerable research was required to attain the proficiency which we now possess in utilizing the UHF's.

In summary, the requirements for efficient operation of electronic equipment at ultra-high frequencies are:

1. Vacuum tubes must be small.
2. Tuning circuits must have small amounts of inductance and capacitance, yet possess sufficiently high Q values to provide good gain and selectivity.

FIG. 1.5A. Number of different tubes that have been designed for ultra-high frequency applications. (*Courtesy RCA*)

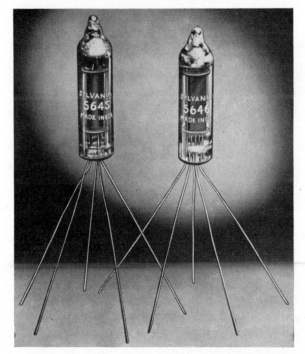

FIG. 1.5B. Two subminiature tubes. (*Courtesy Sylvania*)

3. Insulators must be effective at high frequencies.
4. Wiring between circuit components must be at a minimum.
5. Chassis layout must be carefully planned to minimize stray capacitance.

In the next sections the front-end tuners of receivers operating above 50 mc are explained. They were designed to meet the requirements of these higher frequencies. As a start, let us consider the types of commercial tuners found in F–M and television receivers.

HIGH-FREQUENCY TUNERS

Inductuner. The Inductuner is a wide-range tuner, capable of continuous tuning from 44 to 220 mc. Because of this wide coverage, it is employed in several combination F–M and television receivers.

As can be seen from Fig. 1–6A, the Inductuner consists of three separate variable inductance units mounted on a common shaft. The coils are wound on ceramic forms, with movable trolley sliders for making contact to the coil. At the coil end, an internal stop mechanism limits rotation to ten turns. Each coil is tunable continuously for ten turns producing an inductance variation from approximately 0.02 to 1.0 microhenry. The induc-

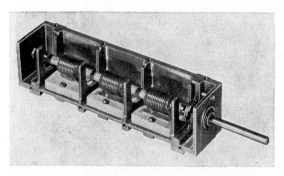

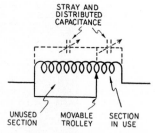

FIG. 1.6A. A continuous tuner used in television and F–M receivers. (*Courtesy P. R. Mallory Co.*)

FIG. 1.6B. Electrical circuit of one inductuner winding.

tance variation of the Inductuner is in the ratio of 1:50 and is the reason for the wide frequency range. If we compare the inductance of this tuning circuit with the 0.04-microhenry inductance of a straight piece of wire 2 inches long and 0.038 inch in diameter, we can again see why all circuit wiring must be kept as short as possible.

The movable trolley contact divides each coil into a used and unused section. (See Fig. 1–6B.) Each section has associated with it stray and distributed capacitances, and these will change as the trolley position changes. It is interesting to note that, even when the entire coil is shorted out by the contact arm (position of minimum inductance), it still contains enough inductance to resonate at approximately 355 mc.

The advantage of using a variable coil instead of a variable air capacitor lies in the wider frequency coverage that is possible. A length of wire and its inductance can be reduced to a smaller value than the minimum capacitance of a variable capacitor. Furthermore, as the inductance decreases, the losses reduce proportionately. In fact, it is even possible for the losses to decrease faster than the inductance, giving a rising Q with frequency. This, in turn, produces a desirable rise in gain at the high-frequency end of the band.

The Inductuner shown contains three windings, which permits three circuits to be controlled at one time: the r-f amplifier, the oscillator, and the mixer circuits at the front end of a receiver.

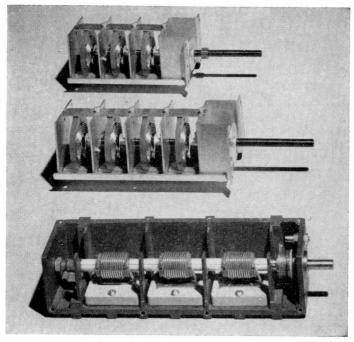

Fig. 1.7.   The comparison of the new spiral inductuners (top two) with the older unit (below).

A more recent version of the Inductuner makes use of a spiral type of winding.   (See Fig. 1–7.)   Operation of this unit is identical to that of the previous Inductuner except that now the contact arm moves around a spiral instead of along a solenoid.   The advantages gained are greater compactness, lower cost, and increased mechanical stability.   The smaller size permits a fourth winding to be added that can be used at the input to the r-f amplifier.

Permeability Tuning.   There are several methods by which the inductance of coils can be varied in order to tune a receiver.   The use of the Inductuner is one method.   Another approach to the problem is through the use of a powdered-iron core.   The position of the core is altered, thereby varying the inductance of the coil. As the iron core is inserted deeper into the center of the coil, the inductance increases. Conversely, as the iron core is withdrawn from the coil, the inductance decreases. This method is known as permeability tuning.

An example of a permeability-tuned coil is shown in Fig. 1–8. Note that a four-strand tinsel wire is used in place of the conventional single-strand wire. The use of four parallel wires is necessary in order to obtain the required inductance change with the small number of turns on the coil. If single-strand wire were employed, the frequency band could not be covered by the maximum movement of the core within the distance allotted to

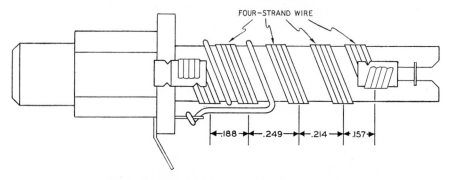

FIG. 1.8. A four-wire permeability-tuned coil. The variable winding pitch produces a linear tuning curve.

it by the tuning dial. To overcome this difficulty, the width of each turn is increased. As the wire width increases, the tuning range is increased. A similar result may be had by winding the coil with parallel wires. This accounts for the four conductors shown in Fig. 1–8.

Application of permeability-tuned coils in a tuner is shown in Fig. 1–9. The antenna, mixer, and oscillator coils are mounted on a bracket fastened to the side of a conventional variable capacitor. The coils cover the F–M band, whereas the variable capacitor tunes over the A–M broadcast and short-wave bands. A cam is mounted on the shaft of the variable capacitor and operates a rocker arm which moves the iron tuning cores in the three high-frequency coils. The unit is very compact, reducing all stray capacitance and inductance to a minimum.

Eddy-current Tuner. Eddy-current tuning is a third method of achieving inductance variation. In this method, nonmagnetic materials, such as copper or brass slugs, are inserted into the core of the coil. Since they are nonmagnetic, inserting them between the turns of a coil lowers the mutual inductance of the coil, with a consequent lowering of coil inductance.

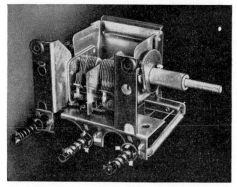

FIG. 1.9. Two views showing how F-M permeability-tuned coils are combined with an A-M variable capacitor in a combination A-M, F-M receiver. (*Courtesy Zenith*)

Furthermore, the slug itself acts as a short-circuited turn, and the current flowing within the slug introduces a loss of power due to heat, which in turn further reduces the inductance of the coil. Hence, the closer the spacing between the slug and the coil, the lower the inductance presented

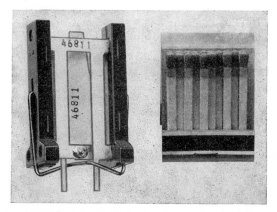

FIG. 1.10. A photograph of the guillotine tuner. Its size can be judged by comparing it with a book of matches. (*Courtesy G.E.*)

to the circuit. Note that this action of the slug is directly opposite to that obtained in permeability tuning.

An eddy-current tuner, developed by General Electric, is shown in Figs. 1–10 and 1–11. Because of its resemblance to the grim French guillotines, it has been nicknamed the "guillotine tuner." The tuner consists of two identical brass frames which form a two-turn inductance when connected at their open ends. To vary the inductance, a brass blade is inserted be-

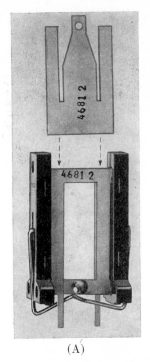

(A)

tween the frames. (See Fig. 1–11A.) As the blade is moved down between the frames, the inductance of the tuner decreases. To obtain the desired tuning curve, *slots* are cut in the blade. The tuner is mounted so that the two terminals project through the chassis, thus providing short leads. Parts of the tuner are shown separately in Fig. 1–11A.

An assembled guillotine tuner is shown in Fig. 1–11B. The blades of the tuner are raised and lowered by a plastic elevator which, in turn, is attached to a windlass. The entire tuner in final form is enclosed in a metal box which shields the unit and keeps out dust.

Transmission-line Tuners. Every radio man is familiar with conventional forms of coils, capacitors, and resistors. These units are said to be "lumped" because the L, C, and R is each concentrated in a small unit.

Now, if we take two closely spaced wires and pass direct current through them, then the only

(B)

FIG. 1.11.   (A) The two sections of the guillotine tuner.   (B) The tuner used in an A-M, F-M receiver.   (*Courtesy G.E.*)

opposition that the d-c will encounter will stem from the resistance in the wires. However, when an alternating voltage is impressed across the lines, the current will encounter not only resistance, but inductance and capacitance as well.

Of the last two quantities, the presence of the capacitance can perhaps be more readily visualized since, by definition, a capacitor is formed whenever two conductors are separated by a dielectric. In this instance the dielectric is air. Since the dielectric is never a perfect nonconductor, it is represented schematically by placing a large resistance across the capacitor, thus denoting leakage.

The presence of the inductive reactance is somewhat more difficult to explain. It is best to go back to the concept of magnetic lines of force and attack the problem from that angle. Whenever current flows through

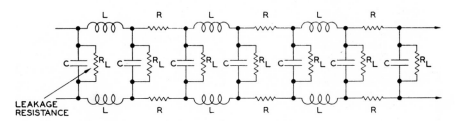

Fig. 1.12.   The electrical components of a transmission line.

a wire, a magnetic field is set up about that wire. Now, as long as the current through the wire is steady (that is, d-c), then the fact that there exists a magnetic field about the wire will have little or no influence on the extent of the current flow. This, of course, ties in with the previous statement that a direct current sees only resistance in the wire.

Should the current change, as it would with a-c, then the rising and falling magnetic field will induce a voltage in the wire that will act in opposition to the voltage already existing there (and which is, of course, responsible for the current flow in the first place). This property of a circuit to develop a counter-voltage because of a varying magnetic field is spoken of as inductance. It is called self-inductance when the counter-voltage is produced in the same circuit in which the original current is flowing; it is known as mutual inductance when the counter-voltage is the result of a current flowing in some other, adjacent circuit.

Thus, two parallel wires present resistance, capacitive reactance, and inductive reactance to any alternating currents that flow through them. And since these components are distributed along the length of the lines, the total amout of such resistance, capacitance, and inductance will depend upon line length.

To represent the foregoing inductance, capacitance, and resistance in schematic form for analytical purposes, a diagram such as shown in Fig. 1–12 is often used in engineering books on transmission lines. Although the various components are shown separate and distinct from each other, they are actually distributed evenly along the line. It is only because of our inability to show these components as they really are that we resort to this method.

Since the transmission line contains exactly the same three components found in any ordinary resonant circuit, it is reasonable to expect that similar

Fig. 1.13. A parallel resonant line tuner. (*Courtesy Approved Electronic Instrument Corporation*)

Fig. 1.14. The parallel-line tuner mounted on receiver chassis. (*Courtesy Approved Electronic Instrument Corporation*)

results can be obtained from each. Hence, the length of the transmission line determines the frequency at which it will operate.

Parallel-wire Tuner. An illustration of a tuner using parallel wires as its tuning elements is shown in Fig. 1–13. The front end of the receiver (an F–M set here) consists of three sets of parallel-wire lines, each set having a movable shorting bar which determines how much of the line is active. The shorting contacts are mounted on plastic bars and then attached to a common shaft. As the shaft is rotated counterclockwise, the bars progressively short out more and more of the lines, raising their resonant frequency from 88 to 108 mc. To permit the three lines to track with each other, each line contains small end inductances and semi-fixed, temperature-compensated, silver ceramic capacitors. At the high-frequency end of the F–M band, the series capacitors are adjusted for maximum output. At the low end of the F–M band, 88 mc, the end inductance coil turns are either spread apart or squeezed together to achieve tracking of the three separate parallel-wire lines. The entire tuner is rubber-mounted to give freedom from microphonics. Miniature tubes are used to provide good frequency, stability, and sensitivity.

The unit, mounted on the receiver chassis, is shown in Fig. 1–14.

Coaxial-line Tuner. Coaxial transmission lines, in which one conductor is placed inside and at the center of an outer conductor, have also been employed as tuners. One problem encountered here is the method of varying the resonant frequency of the line. A shorting bar arrangement, as employed with parallel-wire lines, is not as readily carried out. It is possible to resonate the inductance of the transmission line with a variable capacitor placed across the end of the line. However, since the magnitude

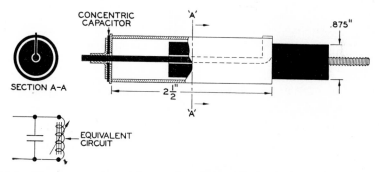

Fig. 1.15. The construction of the coaxial tuner. The equivalent coil-and-capacitor tuning combination is also shown.

of the inductance is low, the use of a gang capacitor—one section for each transmission line tuner—would in itself introduce too much additional inductance to prove useful. We can, however, resonate the inductance of the transmission line with a small fixed capacitor, and then vary the inductance of the line by means of a powdered-iron core. In other words, we would have permeability tuning, but in a form which is substantially different from the previous unit.

An arrangement of this type has been employed by one manufacturer in his F–M receivers. (See Fig. 1–15.) Here an iron core is mounted on a threaded rod and its position in the coaxial line is adjusted by rotating the head or top of the threaded rod. The Q of the tuner, with the iron core, at 100 mc is 335. The tube load reduces the effective Q of the circuit to 195 and this is approximately its final value, although the antenna loading lowers the Q somewhat. In the same diagram the equivalent conventional circuit is shown.

F-M COAXIAL
TUNERS

An expensive, high-quality, concentric capacitor has been developed for this particular unit and is shown in Fig. 1–14. The capacitor is of silver-on-mica construction. A highly desirable feature of the tuner is that the unit can be constructed as a mechanical assembly, without the necessity of electrical checking. The coaxial line and capacitor type of construction forms a very compact unit. This reduces considerably the importance of the inductance present in leads connecting the tuned lines in the circuit. At 100 mc, the problem of confining the desired signal pick-up to the antenna terminals of the receiver is quite difficult. Chassis pick-up, for example, tends to degrade the image and adjacent channel attenuation.

FIG. 1.16. Transmission-line tuners mounted in receiver. (*Courtesy Motorola*)

FIG. 1.17. The Standard Coil rotary turret tuner. The two sets of coils for one channel are shown below.

However, when the entire unit is confined within the coaxial cable, the undesired pick-up becomes negligible. Removing the antenna completely kills the receiver output even in the presence of a strong signal.

Application of the tuner to an F–M receiver is shown in Fig. 1–16.

Selector Switch Tuning for Television Receivers. Although some tuners in television receivers are of continuous tuning construction like the Inductuner and permeability types, most of the tuners are of the selector switch type. Each channel is switched in by rotating the selector switch to the desired channel number. This automatically brings in the proper coils (and capacitors, if any are used). Most selector-switch television tuners thus consist of 12 relatively distinct tuning circuits. Two selector-switch tuners currently being employed in television receivers are shown in Figs. 1–17 and 1–18.

In the tuner of Fig. 1–17, known as a turret tuner, separate tuning circuits are employed for each channel. Provision is made on the turret to mount 12 sets of tuning circuits, thereby enabling any receiver to tune to each of the 12 channels. The antenna and r-f amplifier input tuning circuits are mounted on one strip; the mixer and local-oscillator tuning circuits are placed on a separate strip. These two units then constitute the complete set for one channel. The mounting strips are of the snap-in type and can readily be changed by a technician to receive any desired channel.

The wafer-switch tuner represents another type of selector-switch tuning. This tuner employs rotary switches with the tuning coils mounted between each set of contact switches. To accommodate the different r-f, oscillator, and mixer tuning circuits, multisection switches are required. There are a number of wafer-switch tuners in use, with the unit shown in Fig. 1–18 typical of their mechanical structure.

Printed Circuits and Tuners. The development of printed circuit techniques in the production of electronic components is a recent and important advance in UHF circuitry. Such items as conductors, resistors, capacitors, and inductances are changed from their normal three dimensions to two dimensions. This results in reducing the overall bulk of any electronic device containing these components, and it lends itself admirably to UHF circuits where small physical size is necessary.

The process of printing circuits is basically simple. A conductor, for example, is made by depositing a metallic paint in a line on an insulating surface. One end of this conducting line connects with one part of the circuit and the other end with another part of the circuit. Current can then flow along this thin line, just as it would through an ordinary wire conductor.

A resistor is formed in essentially the same manner, except that the metallic paint used presents a higher resistance to the flow of current. An inductance is produced by depositing the conducting material in a spiral.

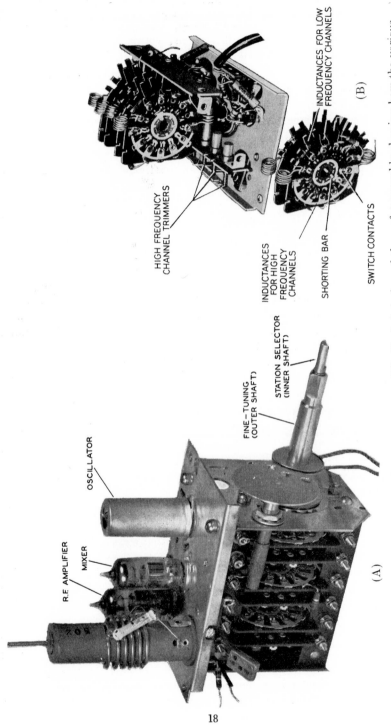

OSCILLATOR

MIXER

R.F. AMPLIFIER

FINE–TUNING
(OUTER SHAFT)

STATION SELECTOR
(INNER SHAFT)

(A)

HIGH FREQUENCY
CHANNEL TRIMMERS

INDUCTANCES FOR LOW
FREQUENCY CHANNELS

INDUCTANCES
FOR HIGH
FREQUENCY
CHANNELS

SHORTING BAR

SWITCH CONTACTS

(B)

Fig. 1.18. (A) A rotary wafer-switch television tuner. (B) Exploded view of the wafer assembly showing how the various low- and high-frequency coils are mounted between switch contacts. (*Courtesy RCA*)

18

Fig. 1.19. An illustration of the size reduction achievable using printed circuit techniques. At the left is a 2-stage conventionally built amplifier and at the right is its printed circuit counterpart. (*Courtesy Bureau of Standards*)

A capacitor is formed by applying metallic paint to both sides of the insulating base being used to hold all the circuitry. Deposition methods for coating the insulator with these chemicals include painting, spraying, electroplating, and die stamping. When conducting wires from different portions of a circuit must cross each other, undesired contact is avoided by having one of the conductors go through the base plate and continue on the other side. Or the same situation may be handled by going around an edge, or by cementing or spraying a thin layer of insulating material over the lead crossed.

A startling illustration of the size reduction that can be achieved by using printed circuit techniques is shown in Fig. 1–19. At the left is a 2-stage amplifier conventionally built and at the right is its printed circuit counterpart.

Size reduction is one advantage of this process. It will lead, also, to uniformity of production, reduction of assembly and inspection time and costs, and reduction in rejects. Because of these favorable aspects, increasing use of printed circuits is being made in electronic systems. Fig. 1–20, for example, shows a television printed circuit tuner. The coils used here were made by a photoetching process on copper sheets. Briefly, this process

FIG. 1.20.   The printed circuit TV tuner. (*Courtesy RCA*)

begins with the photographing of a drawing of the circuit. A contact print is then made from the negative in a copper-covered sheet of phenolic plastic which has been sensitized. The print of the plastic sheet is developed and placed in an etching solution. The solution dissolves away that part of the copper not covered by the circuit pattern. What is left is the copper circuit on the plastic sheet. The sheet is then placed on a die and cut into separate sections and pierced.

The thin copper strips are formed into individual coil strips for the various channels. All tuned circuits are printed this way except the oscillator coils for channels 2 to 6. These are wound in the normal manner.

Butterfly Tuners. The butterfly tuner is another attempt to bridge the gap between lumped components on the one hand and distributed circuitry

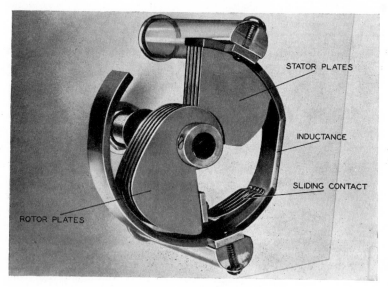

FIG. 1.21.   A tuner capable of covering the range from 60 to 660 mc. (*Courtesy General Radio Co.*)

on the other. The butterfly tuner contains a rotor and a stator that could roughly be compared to the rotor and stator elements of a conventional variable capacitor. However, the same assembly also contains inductance, and there is no clear-cut division between the two. In fact, as the rotor is turned, it varies inductance and capacitance simultaneously.

To understand the operation of a butterfly circuit, it might be best to trace its development from the conventional capacitor and inductor combination. In Fig. 1-21, there is shown a variable capacitor possessing a sliding contact on the end of the movable or rotor plates.

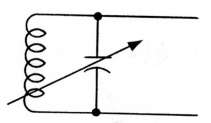

FIG. 1.22. The equivalent electrical circuit of the tuner in Fig. 1.21.

This sliding contact moves over a single-turn inductance. The stator or stationary plates of the capacitor connect to one end of this single-turn inductance and the sliding contact furnishes

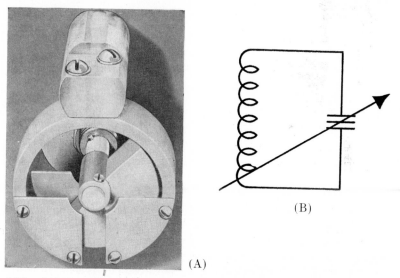

(B)

(A)

FIG. 1.23.   (A) A tuning unit without contacts covering the range from 400 to 1200 mc.   (B) The equivalent electrical circuit.

the other connection to the inductance. The effective or acting inductance, therefore, is the length of the inductance ring contained between the stator plates and the sliding contact. When the rotor plates are turned by the capacitor shaft, not only does the capacitance of the capacitor change, but the inductance as well, because of the altered position of the sliding contact. The equivalent electrical circuit is shown in Fig. 1-22. The

capacitor can be moved through an arc of **270** degrees and the contact
is so arranged that the inductance and capacitance increase and decrease
together.

The next step in the development of the butterfly circuit was the combining of the inductance and capacitance into a single unit and the removal

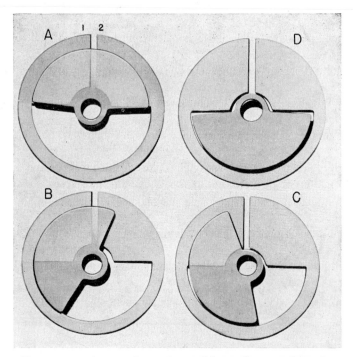

Fig. 1.24.   The stator and rotor plates of a semi-butterfly tuner in various positions.
(*Courtesy General Radio Co.*)

of all sliding contacts.   Such a unit is shown in Fig. 1–23A.   In this, the
so-called "semi-butterfly" circuit, the stator plates are split in half and
are connected to each other by a semi-circular band which represents the
inductance of the circuit.   Schematically, this portion of the butterfly circuit
can be drawn as shown in Fig. 1–23B.   The rotor plate is semi-circular, too,
and forms a capacitive coupling link between each of the stator plates.

In Fig. 1–24A, the rotor plate is shown in the position which produces
the lowest resonant frequency for the tuner.   The capacitance of the tuner
is maximum because the full area of the rotor is directly above both halves
of the stator.   Inductance, too, is maximum.   As the rotor plate is moved
to position B, tuner capacitance decreases because part of the rotor has been
turned away from the stator sections.   Inductance decreases because the
presence of the rotor within the magnetic field region developed by the

inductance ring restricts or reduces the number of magnetic lines since the rotor acts as a shorted turn.   This action is similar to the previously described guillotine tuner and is eddy-current tuning.   As the rotor occupies more and more of the open area of the inductance loop, less and less of the inductance is actually effective in the circuit.   The effect is to reduce

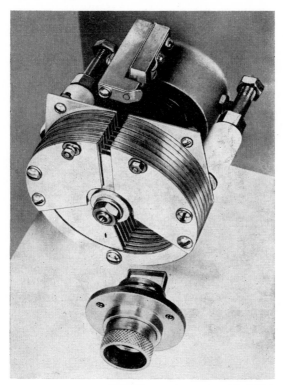

FIG. 1.25.   Inductive coupling to a butterfly tuner.   To vary the degree of coupling, the small coupling loop is rotated in position. (*Courtesy General Radio Co.*)

the resonant frequency.   Finally, in position D, the rotor plate has all but filled up this region, and the lines of magnetic flux are now confined to the very small air clearance between the rotor plate and the rest of the circuit structure.   In this position, the butterfly tuner is set for its highest frequency.

In a conventional coil and capacitor tuner, the connecting points to the circuit are made between rotor and stator of the capacitor.   In the semi-butterfly arrangement, connections are made to points 1 and 2 shown in Fig. 1–24A.   No connections are made to the rotor, which may be mounted on an insulated shaft.   This minimizes the flow of any undesirable currents in the rotor shaft and keeps losses low.

To obtain energy from this circuit, we can employ either electrostatic or magnetic coupling. Electrostatic coupling is recommended when one terminal is grounded. Direct connection can then be made from the other terminal to whatever circuit is designated to receive the energy. If the circuit is floating, that is, there is no ground connection, then magnetic coupling is recommended. To accomplish this, a small loop of wire is placed near the inductance loop of the butterfly circuit. (See Fig. 1–25.)

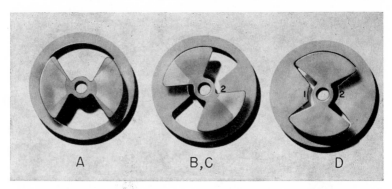

Fɪɢ. 1.26. The rotor and stator plates of a true butterfly tuner. The frequency is highest at D and lowest at A. (*Courtesy General Radio Co.*)

The second type of butterfly circuit, known as the true butterfly, is shown in Fig. 1–26. The two stator sections now are symmetrically placed, with inductance arms between them. The approximate equivalent circuit is shown in Fig. 1–27, and it is to be noted that the two inductance arms are in parallel with each other and connected across the capacitance. The explanation of circuit operation follows closely that previously given for the semi-butterfly circuit. In Fig. 1–26A, the two rotor plates are directly above the two stator sections and the circuit capacitance and inductance are at a maximum. In Fig. 1–26B, C, the rotor plates have been rotated slightly so that they extend partially into the inductance region. At the same time, less rotor plate area is directly above the stator plates and consequently the capacitance has decreased. In Fig. 1–26D, the inductance and capacitance values are at their lowest point. Connections to this tuner would be made at terminals 1 and 2. In Fig. 1–28, we have a 220-to-1100-mc butterfly circuit designed to be used with a special UHF tube. Grid and plate terminals of this tube fit into the spring clips provided on the two stator sections.

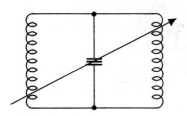

Fɪɢ. 1.27. The approximate equivalent circuit of the true butterfly tuner.

Increased tuning range can be obtained by constructing butterfly circuits with a number of stacked stator and rotor sections, and this is the form in which these units are generally seen. Too much stacking of plates is not feasible because the resonant impedance decreases with increase in the number of plates. While butterfly resonators have been built to tune as high as 3000 mc, they are seldom used extensively above 1000 mc. In order to reach these high frequencies, the size of the unit decreases, the

Fig. 1.28.   A 220–1100 mc butterfly tuner designed to be used with special UHF tube. (*Courtesy General Radio Co.*)

number of stacked sections increases, and spurious frequencies begin to appear throughout the tuning range.

A comparison of semi-butterfly and true butterfly circuits reveals the following.

1. For low-frequency applications (up to 300 mc) the semi-butterfly circuit is more suitable than the true butterfly. This is because the semi-butterfly possesses a single inductance arm—instead of two in parallel as in the true butterfly—and for any given size could be constructed to contain more inductance. In addition, the inductance arm of a semi-butterfly can be opened and a small external coil inserted to further increase the inductance. In the true butterfly, both inductance arms would have to be opened, leading to mechanical as well as electrical balancing difficulties.

Finally, the semi-butterfly rotor can be varied through an angle of 180° against 90° in true butterfly, providing a greater tuning range.

2. For high-frequency applications, the true butterfly is preferred because of its symmetrical construction which places the rotor in the true

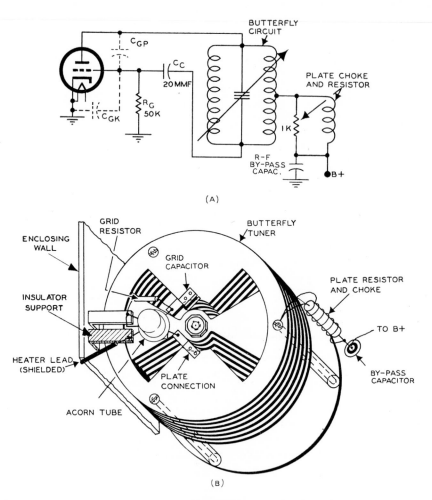

Fig. 1.29. (A) Electrical circuit and (B) physical appearance of a butterfly oscillator.

butterfly at ground potential at all times. Hence, less trouble is likely at very high frequencies. At these extreme frequencies, exceptional care must be taken to prevent spurious frequencies from being developed in the circuit. These spurious frequencies may be due to portions of the rotor forming series resonant circuits with stray capacitances to ground. This is less likely to occur when the rotor is at r-f ground potential at all times (as in the true butterfly) than in the semi-butterfly (where the rotor is at ground potential only at the lowest frequency).

There are other features which distinguish the two types of butterfly circuits, but the foregoing are the most important.

It might be instructive to examine an electrical diagram of a butterfly oscillator and then see how this circuit is physically constructed. The electrical circuit, shown in Fig. 1–29A, is that of an ultraudion oscillator. The butterfly circuit is connected between grid and plate of an acorn-type 955 tube. In the physical diagram, Fig. 1–29B, these plate and grid connections are made to two clips, each clip being fastened to one stator section of the butterfly. Grid coupling to the butterfly is accomplished with a small 20-$\mu\mu$f capacitor. The capacitor is formed by inserting a thin mica sheet between the top stator section and the grid clip. The plate of the tube is connected directly to the opposite stator section and receives its B+ voltage through the plates. A plate resistor and choke connect to the center of one inductance arm, bringing the B+ to the plate. At the other end of the resistor, there is a small by-pass capacitor. One heater lead and the cathode terminal are grounded directly to a small plate which is fastened to the shield wall enclosing the oscillator assembly. (The shield wall is only partially shown.) The other heater receives its d-c power through a shielded lead.

Energy can be abstracted from this oscillator by magnetic coupling to one of the inductance loops. Although not indicated here, we could place another butterfly circuit so that its inductance loop is close to one of the inductance loops of the oscillator circuit and thereby transfer energy from the oscillator to a mixer, if the set is a receiver, or to an amplifier, if the circuit is used in a transmitter. We would not employ electrostatic coupling by attaching a capacitor to the butterfly resonator because this would upset the balance of the tuner.

Selective Tuning—Q. The desirability of having high Q tuning circuits has been stressed in the previous discussion of high-frequency tuners. Since Q, at times, may become quite puzzling, a brief discussion may be helpful.

A tuning circuit, consisting of a capacitance and an inductance in parallel with each other, presents across its terminals an impedance that varies with the frequency of the signal applied to the circuit. If we plot the variation of this impedance with frequency, we obtain a curve such as shown in Fig. 1–30A. At a single frequency, known as the resonant frequency, the impedance will reach a maximum value. At all other frequencies, the impedance presented by this circuit will be less than this maximum value, how much less depending upon the difference between the frequency applied and the resonant frequency.

The effect of adding resistance in either capacitive or inductive branches of this network is indicated by the curves of Fig. 1–30B. As more and more resistance is added, the top of the curve tends to flatten out, and the variation in impedance about the resonant frequency becomes less sharp.

Now, it is the general purpose of any tuning circuit to pass a desired frequency (or narrow range of frequencies) and to suppress or ignore all others. Looking at the curves in Fig. 1–30, we can see that the ability of a tuned circuit to discriminate depends upon the amount of internal resistance it contains. The greater the resistance in its circuit, the less ability it possesses to discriminate against undesired signals. Since, in a tuning circuit, almost all the resistance is associated with the inductance, the ratio of the inductive reactance of a coil to its resistance has been called Q. This ratio may be looked upon as a relationship between the amount of energy stored in the magnetic field of the coil to the energy lost in the coil's resistance.

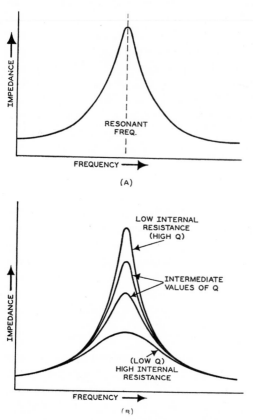

FIG. 1.30.   (A) The variation of impedance with frequency of a resonant circuit.   (B) The effect of resistance in the resonant circuit.

The greater this ratio, the sharper will be the resonance curve and the more selective the circuit. Furthermore, a parallel tuning circuit possessing little internal resistance will have a high impedance, permitting it to develop more voltage when connected in the output circuit of a tube. Since voltage amplification in an amplifier is directly proportional to the impedance of its output circuit, the benefits of a high Q circuit are evident.

While the modifications of reduced tube size and special tuners permit us to raise the frequency that can be generated, circuit efficiency drops rapidly in the region above 500 mc. Values of 15–20 per cent are not uncommon and, thus, to develop 1000 watts of r-f output power, 6700 watts of d-c power must be supplied to the oscillator. The chief reason for this poor efficiency is not due to the so-called radio frequency losses (that is, skin effect, dielectric loss, eddy-current loss in adjacent conductors, or even radiation loss), but rather to something else—something which in ordinary tubes is completely disregarded—namely, the time of flight of an electron from the cathode to the plate, called transit time.

Transit Time. At the low frequencies, the time it takes an electron to travel from cathode to plate is negligible, because this time represents a very small portion of the interval necessary to complete one cycle of the grid or input r-f wave. As the frequency of the input wave is increased, however, the time for one complete cycle of the r-f wave becomes less and less, and soon the electron transit time becomes comparable to the period of the alternating wave. An example will make this clearer. Suppose that it takes an electron 0.000,000,001 sec to travel from the cathode to the plate. This may be ignored when the frequency of the input wave to the grid is, say, 1000 cps, for then one complete cycle requires 0.001 sec. This is a very long interval compared to the electron transit time given just above. But suppose that the frequency of the wave is raised to 1000 mc. Now, one cycle is completed in 0.000,000,001 sec or in the same time that it takes the electron to travel from filament to plate. When this happens, two major effects occur in the circuit. First, the operating efficiency of the circuit drops. Second, the grid-to-filament (or cathode) impedance decreases from its ordinary value (which is so high it can be considered as infinite). This affects the whole grid tuning circuit because the grid-to-cathode impedance is actually in parallel with this tuner. The same effect is obtained as though a low resistance were placed in parallel with the resonant circuit. The Q is lowered, and with it goes the selectivity of the circuit.

Electron Flow—Revised. In order to help visualize the entire process, some ideas on electron flow will be revised or extended. Ordinarily, it is unusual to think of current flowing in either the plate or grid circuits until the electrons from the cathode hit these elements. Actually, however, this is the point that completes a cycle begun when the electron first left the cathode. The charge of the electron is negative, and at the moment it leaves the cathode the conditions shown in Fig. 1–31A prevail. It can be seen that upon leaving the cathode the electron left an equal and opposite (positive) charge on the cathode. At the same time a very small positive charge is induced on the plate. This is because the cathode electron is slightly closer to the plate and an electron at the plate has been repelled a small distance from the plate surface. As the cathode electron gets closer and closer to the plate, the positive charge of the plate will increase, correspondingly, and the electron that was originally at the plate will be farther

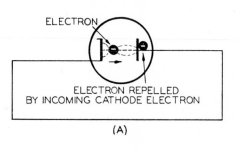

ELECTRON REPELLED
BY INCOMING CATHODE ELECTRON

(A)

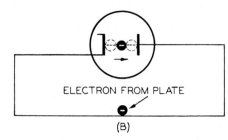

ELECTRON FROM PLATE

(B)

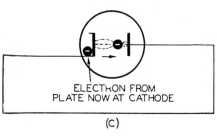

ELECTRON FROM
PLATE NOW AT CATHODE

(C)

FIG. 1.31. A simplified illustration of electron flow in a vacuum tube and its external circuit.

and farther repelled from the plate toward the cathode through the wire. (See Fig. 1–31B.) When the cathode electron finally reaches the plate, it neutralizes the positive charge there, and likewise the plate electron by this time has reached the cathode.* The positive charge on the cathode is now also neutralized. The circuit is then in equilibrium and the current flow has ceased (see Fig. 1–31C). Multiply this electron by the billions that actually flow and there are the comparatively large plate currents observed in tubes.

The foregoing concepts are not new, but are not always mentioned because, at the low frequencies, results obtained agree with the ordinary ideas of electron flow in tubes. With increase of frequency, however, the transit-time effects require that this more general idea be used. Now the effect of this transit time on the efficiency of the circuit will be determined.

In any oscillator or power amplifier, high efficiency (which means conversion of d-c input power into r-f output power) is achieved when the tube is operated so that plate current is allowed to flow only when the plate voltage is low. This is shown in Fig. 1–32. In Fig. 1–32A, we see the r-f voltage variations appearing on the plate of the tube. The grid voltage variations are shown below, in Fig. 1–32B. Now, if the grid voltage is properly chosen, then

---

* This is not wholly true. Actually, the electron which left the plate only traveled a small distance, but it did succeed in pushing other electrons along until one finally did reach the cathode and neutralized the positive charge left there by the departing cathode electron.

the grid bias will permit electrons to pass only when the grid voltage is at its most positive peak. For all other values of grid voltage, the grid is below cut-off and no current flows through the tube. Thus, the total plate current can be shown as indicated in Fig. 1–32C, and we see that it flows only when the r-f plate voltage is at a minimum. Under these conditions, the amount of energy lost as plate dissipation within the tube is at a minimum because power is equal to current times voltage $(P = E \times I)$, and if E is low, the power lost at the plate in the form of heat is likewise low. Consequently most of the input power appears across the output circuit. These are very desirable conditions.

Now let us see how transit time disrupts this state of affairs with a

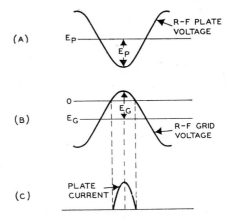

FIG. 1.32. The phase relationship between the plate voltage, grid voltage, and plate current in an r-f oscillator or amplifier. Electron transit time is considered negligible.

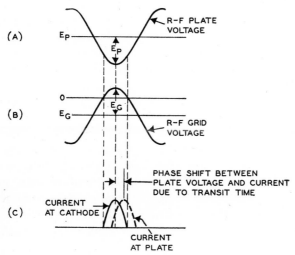

FIG. 1.33. The same illustration as Fig. 1.32, when electron transit time is not negligible.

consequent reduction in the operating efficiency of the circuit. In Fig. 1–33, we have shown the r-f plate voltage, the r-f grid voltage, and the current. The electrons leaving the cathode will do so under the influence of the grid voltage, just as in Fig. 1–32. This means that the maximum number of electrons will be drawn from the cathode when the grid voltage is maximum. So far the conditions shown in Figs. 1–32 and 1–33 do not differ from each other. But, when the r-f operating frequency is high enough, the time required for the electrons to travel from the cathode to the plate of the tube cannot be considered instantaneous. During this flight time, the voltage on the plate will change, with the result that, when the effect of the electrons is felt at the plate, the r-f plate voltage will no longer be minimum, but at some higher value. The consequence of this is an increase in the amount of energy lost at the plate of the tube (that is, plate dissipation), leaving less of the total energy available for the output circuit. The net result is a decrease in operating efficiency. Obviously, the greater the lag due to transit time, the greater the energy lost within the tube.

This is one detrimental effect of electron transit time. The other concerns the decrease in input impedance which also tends to lower circuit efficiency.

When an electron from the cathode approaches the grid, an electron on the grid is repelled. The closer the electron from the cathode is to the grid, the greater the repelling action, causing the grid electron to move along the grid wires. When this action is multiplied by the enormous quantities of electrons emitted by the cathode, it can be seen that an appreciable current is set up in the grid wires and consequently the grid circuit. This induced current flow is reversed when the electrons pass the grid and recede toward the plate. Now, if the time required for the r-f grid voltage is slow compared to the velocity of the electrons traveling between cathode and plate, there will be just as many electrons approaching the grid as there are receding from it and going toward the plate. The induced currents due to these two groups of electrons will be equal and opposite and the induced currents will cancel each other.

As the frequency of the grid voltage increases, however, the grid voltage will change noticeably while the electrons are traveling between cathode and grid and between grid and plate and, in general, there will *not* be the same number of electrons approaching the grid as there are receding from it. The two induced currents will not be equal, leaving a resultant current which, traveling back and forth through the grid circuit, will introduce voltages that will tend to counteract the applied r-f signal, reducing its effectiveness.

To see this more clearly, consider the circuit shown in Fig. 1–34A. An r-f voltage is applied between grid and cathode of the tube. At the time under consideration, suppose the grid is driven in the positive direction, attracting more electrons to the grid. These electrons traveling toward the grid will tend to repel the electrons existing in the grid wires, with the result that there will be a displacement of electrons away from the grid and toward the cathode through the grid resistor, R_g. Electrons flowing down through the resistor will cause a voltage to develop here, with the grid end of the resistor negative and the cathode end positive. Since the polarity of this voltage is opposite to the applied r-f voltage, it will, to a certain extent, offset the effect of this voltage.

Now, if the electrons receding from the grid equaled in number the electrons approaching the grid, then the induced currents due to these two

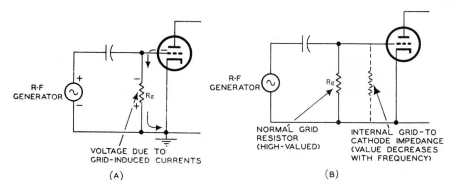

FIG. 1.34. (A) Grid-induced currents develop a voltage across the grid resistor that acts in opposition to the applied voltage. (B) The effect of the grid-induced currents can be indicated schematically by a shunting resistor between grid and cathode.

groups of electrons would cancel each other and no voltage due to the induced currents would be obtained across R_g. But when the r-f grid voltage changes rapidly enough, there will be more electrons approaching a positive grid than receding from it and, by the same token, there will be more electrons receding from a negative grid than there are approaching it. Under these conditions, resultant induced grid currents will flow, working in opposition to the applied voltage as demonstrated above and effectively decreasing it.

Note again that this effect occurs only when the r-f voltage between grid and cathode has a very high frequency. When the frequency is low, the voltages change so slowly, in comparison to the time required by an electron to travel from cathode to plate, that there will be equal numbers of electrons found in the space between cathode and grid and between grid and plate. This does *not* mean that the total number of electrons flowing from cathode to plate remains the same. Far from it. When the voltage is positive, the total number of electrons exceeds the total number traveling when the voltage is negative. However, regardless of whether the total number is more or less, half of this total will be found between cathode and grid and half between grid and plate. And the induced grid current will be zero. It is only when the signal frequency becomes so high and its value changes appreciably while electrons are traveling between elements that unequal numbers of electrons will be found between cathode and grid and grid and plate.

To indicate this lowering effect schematically, we place a resistor between grid and cathode of the tube. (See Fig. 1–34B.) This places the resistor in parallel with, or across, any tuned (or other) circuit existing between grid and cathode. The value of this resistor decreases as the frequency of the signal rises, since the higher the frequency, the greater the transit-time effect. Since this resistance shunts the input tuned circuit, the lower it goes in value, the greater will be its loading effect on the circuit, decreasing the ability of this tuned circuit to develop any r-f voltage. At a sufficiently high frequency, the loading effect of the tube approaches a few hundred ohms or less, permitting little or no voltage to develop across any circuit connected between grid and cathode. At this point the tube is valueless as an amplifier.

Mathematical formulas have been derived giving the relationship of the resistance between grid and cathode to frequency. One such relationship is given here and is due to W. R. Ferris:

$$R_{gk} = \frac{1}{Kf^2T^2g_m}$$

where R_{gk} = input resistance between grid and cathode,

K = constant of the tube,

g_m = mutual conductance of the tube,

f = frequency of the input signal,

T = time required by electron to travel from cathode to plate.

Inspection of the Ferris equation reveals that the resistance decreases rapidly as the frequency is raised because the frequency term is squared.

Minimizing Transit-time Effects. One way to overcome the effect of transit time is to increase the electron velocity until the time required by an electron to travel from the cathode to the plate is negligible in comparison with any r-f voltage applied to the grid. A method of accomplishing this consists in applying higher voltages to the plate so as to attract the electron that much more and thus cause it to travel with greater speed. The electron, however, now that it has this added speed, will hit the plate harder and cause it to get hotter. Means must be devised to cope with this increased plate dissipation.

Another method employed involves the moving of the electrodes closer together. This would again counteract transit-time effects of electrons because now the electron has less distance to travel and any voltage placed on the plate will attract the electron more strongly. Probably the best example of the frequency extension that can be achieved by closer element spacing is the disk-seal, or lighthouse, tube. These tubes are useful up to 3000 mc and are used extensively at the ultra-high frequencies.

The Lighthouse Tube. The basic construction of a disk-seal tube is shown in Fig. 1–35. The heater wire is enclosed in a cylinder at the top end of which is deposited an oxide material from which the electrons are emitted. The grid is a mesh which is mounted horizontally and placed very close to the cathode, the spacing being no more than 4.0 mils, or 4 thousandths of an inch. It is supported by a circular flange which, in turn, rests upon a glass cylinder. The anode cylinder is mounted directly above the grid mesh. The separation between these two elements is 12 mils. Again the supporting structure for the anode is a glass cylinder which, itself, is mounted on the grid structure. It is thus seen that the cathode connection, the grid connection, and the anode connection are all pyramided on each other and indented so that the tuning units to be described presently can be readily attached to the tube.

The particular construction of the lighthouse tube permits a very close spacing between grid, cathode, and plate which minimizes electron transit time. Furthermore, the actual area of each of the elements is quite small and this helps to reduce interelectrode capacitance. Lead inductance is kept low by the direct connection between the elements and their external connections. The cathode, grid, and plate connections are made to circular disks which can be designed with extremely low inductance. The tube base is a standard octal, 6-pin base, which permits all d-c connections to be made through a standard octal socket. The seals between each disk and the glass enclosing the tube are made by using a special glass. The expansion of the glass is essentially the same as low-carbon steel, permitting seals to be made directly to the silver-plated steel parts.

The cathode connection is unique in that there is a d-c connection which is available through one of the base pins and an r-f connection which is the metallic cylinder just above the base. This r-f connecting point is separated from a d-c connection to the cathode by a mica by-pass capacitor. In many high-frequency applications it is desirable to separate the r-f and d-c currents flowing to the cathode, and this construction permits such a separation.

Tube operation remains identical with the conventional low-frequency tube. A signal voltage applied between grid and cathode controls the number of the electrons passing the grid and reaching the plate. Because of the reduced distance between elements, the grid exerts a greater influence

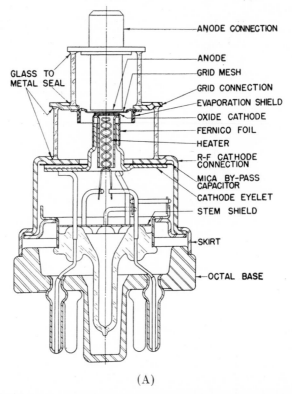

(A)

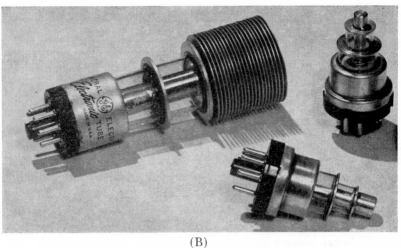

(B)

FIG. 1.35. The internal construction (A) and external appearance (B) of the disk seal or lighthouse tube.

over the cathode and hence tube conductance (g_m) is high. For the same reason, a positive potential at the plate exerts a greater attractive force over the same electrons, causing them to attain a greater velocity and reach the plate in less time. All this is helpful for high-frequency operation.

At low frequencies it is customary to distinguish carefully between the tube and the circuit into which it is connected. As we increase the operating frequency, and the interelectrode capacitance and tube lead inductance begin to assume an increasingly important role in the functioning of the circuit, the sharp line of demarcation between tube and tuned circuit begins to disappear. In the range from 300 to 3000 mc, which is the region in which the lighthouse tube is most effective, we reach the point where the tube and the tuning circuits must be combined as intimately as possible.

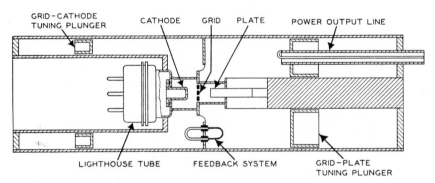

FIG. 1.36. A microwave oscillator using a lighthouse tube and two tunable concentric lines.

An illustration of this is the microwave oscillator shown in Fig. 1–36. The circuit consists of a lighthouse tube plus two tunable concentric lines. One line is placed between the grid and the plate of the tube and the other line between the grid and cathode. Tuning is accomplished by a movable circular plunger in each line. Feedback of energy between the two resonant circuits is provided by a small single turn of link coupling. This is indicated more clearly in the equivalent low-frequency circuit of this unit, Fig. 1–37. Power output is obtained from the grid-plate line by means of a loop connected to another smaller coaxial cable.

The wide frequency range of the butterfly tuner and the satisfactory operation of the lighthouse tube at frequencies of 1000 mc make it desirable to combine both these components. To accommodate the lighthouse tube, it is necessary to alter the construction of the original butterfly circuit to the form shown in Fig. 1–38. The unit consists of a coaxial line shorted at one end and open at the other. The grid and plate of a lighthouse tube are then connected across the open end, acting as a capacitive load.

The outer conductor of the butterfly coaxial tuner is not a complete cylinder but has two sections cut away. Between the inner and outer conductor are two 75-degree sectors that rotate and, in so doing, they vary the

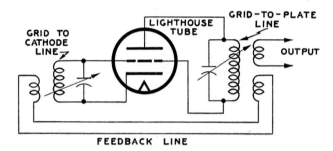

FIG. 1.37. The low-frequency equivalent circuit of Fig. 1.36.

frequency of the tuner. In Fig. 1–39, the coaxial butterfly unit is designed to have the lighthouse inserted into it. Spring fingers slide over the grid and plate, making good electrical and mechanical contact.

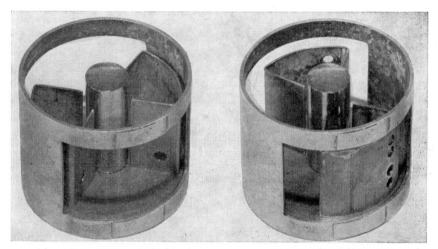

FIG. 1.38. The basic form of the coaxial butterfly circuit.
(*Courtesy General Radio Co.*)

Other Disk-seal Tubes. The lighthouse tube represents one form of disk-seal type of construction; other designs are also available. Fig. 1–40 shows several disk-seal triodes developed and marketed by Sylvania Electric Company. The type 2C37 is designed for use as a pulse-modulated oscillator at frequencies up to 1200 mc. The tube fits into a coaxial-line circuit and has a built-in internal feedback circuit between cathode and

anode.   The type 5766 is designed primarily for use as a continuous oscillator at frequencies up to 3300 mc.   This tube is identical with the 2C37
except that the plate disk is folded and the grid disk is flat.   This allows
the tube to be used in cavity shapes different from those used with the 2C37.

FIG. 1.39.   A butterfly tuner designed to be used with a lighthouse tube. (*Courtesy General Radio Co.*)

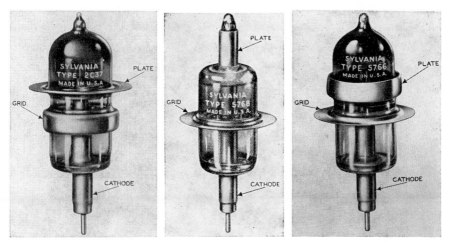

FIG. 1.40.   Three disk-seal triodes developed by Sylvania.

Finally, the type 5768 was designed for use as an amplifier at frequencies
up to 3000 mc.   The cylindrical anode design of this tube lends itself to
use in high-impedance output cavities.

   Radio Corporation of America has developed a pencil-type UHF triode
which is also a form of disk-seal tube.*   These will function as amplifiers
or low-power oscillators at frequencies from 300 mc to more than 3000 mc.

* "Pencil-Type UHF Triodes," by Rose, Power, and Harris. *RCA Review*, September
1949.

A typical pencil-type triode is shown in cross-section in Fig. 1–41A and physically in Fig. 1–41B. The upper cylinder is the anode, the lower cylinder is the cathode, and the center disk is the grid connector. Two glass cylinders at the center of the tube serve to join the various metallic

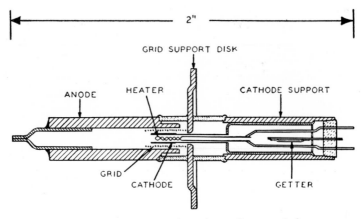

FIG. 1.41A.   Cross-section of pencil-type triode.

components together. An idea of tube size can be gained from the fact that the plate and cathode cylinders are only $\frac{1}{4}$ inch in diameter, while the overall length of the tube is but 2 inches. Because of the particular shape that these tubes possess, they are readily adaptable to coaxial circuits.

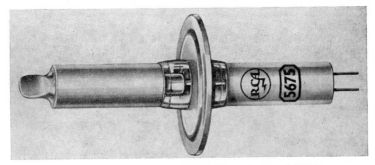

FIG. 1.41B.   A pencil-type triode. (*Courtesy RCA*)

Internally, the elements are concentrically placed with the heater and cathode at the center of the tube structure. The cathode is completely surrounded by the grid and this, in turn, is surrounded by the anode. Electrons radiate from the cathode in all directions, passing through the grid wires and striking the anode cylinder. This type of construction is more efficient than the conventional triode because, first, the cathode can utilize all of the heat radiated by the heater and, second, the plate can receive all of the electrons emitted from the cathode surface.

The radical construction of the disk-seal type of tube permits it to be used successfully up to approximately 3000 mc. However, it still functions in the same manner as a conventional tube and therefore is subject to the same limitations of transit time. It was necessary, therefore, to evolve some other type of electronic circuit in which this limitation was removed entirely or else utilized in such a manner that it did not interfere with the circuit operation. Such is the case with the klystron, magnetron, and resnatron tubes to be described presently.

QUESTIONS

1. In an ordinary tuning circuit, reducing the capacitance by one fourth has what effect on the frequency? (Assume that the inductance remains fixed.) State your answer numerically and prove whatever values you get.

2. What is the wavelength of a signal whose frequency is 500 mc? State your answer in meters, feet, and centimeters.

3. Draw the schematic circuit of a pentode tube showing all interelectrode capacitances and lead inductances.

4. Why can miniature tubes be used successfully at the ultra-high frequencies?

5. Describe the operation of the Inductuner.

6. What are printed circuits?

7. What is permeability tuning? Why does the coil shown in Fig. 1–8 of this chapter use four parallel wires?

8. How does eddy-current tuning differ from permeability tuning?

9. Describe two types of transmission line tuners.

10. Would the television tuners shown in Figs. 1–17 or 1–18 of this chapter be feasible for F–M receivers? Explain your answer.

11. What factors led to the development of the butterfly tuners?

12. Explain the operation of the semi-butterfly tuner. Where would connections be made to this tuner?

13. In what respects does the true butterfly tuner differ from the semi-butterfly? Could the two units be used interchangeably? Explain.

14. What is meant when it is stated that the Q of a coil or tuning circuit is low?

15. How would energy be coupled away from the butterfly tuners (both types) magnetically? Electrostatically?

16. The Q of a certain tuned circuit is found to be too high. How could this be lowered?

17. What is meant by the transit-time effect?

18. What are some of the more common ways that can be used to overcome its effect in ordinary tubes?

19. Describe the revised ideas of electron flow within tubes.

20. Can currents flow in the grid or plate circuits if no electrons actually reach these elements? Explain.

21. What features does the lighthouse tube possess that enable it to operate more efficiently at the ultra-high frequencies than tubes conventionally constructed?

22. Describe several methods of combining the lighthouse tube with resonant circuits to form an oscillator or an amplifier.

Chapter 2

TRANSMISSION LINES AT THE UHF'S

In the first chapter of this book, when the transition in operation from the low to the high frequencies was traced, frequent mention was made of transmission lines. However, only a brief explanation was given concerning their basic operating principles. It is the purpose of this chapter to amplify that portion of the preceding material. In order to best accomplish this end, the operating principles of transmission lines at the low frequencies will be given. Then the ultra-high frequency transition will be more understandable.

Although transmission lines at low frequencies find their most extensive use in radio as coupling systems between a transmitter or receiver and its antenna, at ultra-high frequencies their use becomes more extensive. Not only do they transfer energy from one point in a circuit to another, but they are employed as interstage coupling devices, tuning circuits, inductances, capacitances, and even as high- and low-pass filters. And all this is achieved by simply varying the length and load impedance of the transmission line.

It was previously noted that transmission lines possess distributed resistance, inductance, and capacitance, and these may be represented schematically as shown in Fig. 2–1. Now, since a transmission line possesses these various reactances and resistances distributed along its length, there must be some definite value of impedance that a generator, or other electrical circuit, will "see" when it is connected into one end of the line. Let us assume that there is some sort of circuit or load connected to the opposite end of the line. (As we will see presently, the end of the line may be left unconnected. However, at this point the use of a definite load is desirable, since this conforms with the low-frequency concept of a "complete" circuit.) If the value of the load is correctly matched to the transmission line, all the power put into the line will be absorbed by the load* and none will

---

* The transmission line will absorb some of the energy itself through its line resistance. However, the inductance and capacitance in a line cannot absorb energy but only store it. Whatever energy they do receive is periodically returned to the line.

be reflected. But if there is a mismatch of impedances, some power will be reflected and some absorbed. Naturally, this does not represent the maximum power transfer, and a loss in efficiency will result. Also, the reflected energy produces standing waves of voltage and current along the transmission line—a condition that may or may not be desirable, depending upon the requirements of the particular case. For the ultra-high frequencies it is often (although not always) desirable.

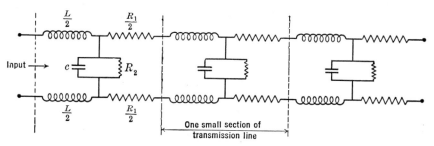

FIG. 2.1. The components of a transmission line. Although shown as separate, they are actually distributed.

The subjects of reflection and standing waves in transmission lines are important ones, and a thorough understanding of them is necessary if the radio man is to be able to use transmission lines properly. Energy, and by this is meant voltage and current, will decrease gradually as it travels along a transmission line if no change in line construction occurs. But suppose that the end of the line is reached and the load does not match the impedance of the line. In this case the energy that remains will be broken up into two portions, one portion being dissipated in the load and the other sent back down the line from whence it came. The situation is analogous to that of light waves striking a piece of glass. Part of the light rays penetrate the glass and part of the rays are reflected. A new condition or medium was hit and this called for a redistribution of energy. Some energy is absorbed and some sent back. Every radio man knows that the output transformer in a radio set must be matched to the voice coil of the speaker, or distortion results. This distortion may be thought of as being due to the rearrangement of the energy (current and voltage) in the circuit due to the mismatching. At broadcast frequencies, when transmission lines are used, care is taken usually to see that all systems match. But at the ultra-high frequencies there are many occasions where the reflected wave is knowingly set up because certain effects are desired. These will be discussed shortly in more detail.

Characteristic Impedance. When any electrical circuit contains inductance, capacitance, and resistance, it will possess a certain value of impedance.

In a transmission line, the value of this impedance is known as the characteristic impedance and is denoted by the symbol Z_0. It is given this particular name because it is a characteristic or constant of the line. If we take any section of a uniformly constructed cable, say, a foot or an inch, and connect an impedance across one end of this section which is equal to the characteristic impedance of the line and attach a generator to the other end of the line, then all of the energy which the generator puts into the line will be absorbed by the load. Any transmission line which is terminated by a load having an impedance equal to its characteristic impedance will represent a matched circuit. And in such a circuit, whatever power is fed in will be completely absorbed by the load. There will be no reflection of energy. However, when an impedance other than the characteristic impedance is used for the load, the matching is not complete and reflection occurs.

When a transmission line is matched, the current and voltage decrease very gradually as we proceed from the generator end of the line to the load end. In Fig. 2–2, let the current that leaves the generator be labeled I. As this current travels along the line, part of it (I_1) is diverted through the leakage resistor and capacitor. The remaining current (I_2) is equal to the original current I minus the amount diverted (I_1). Farther on, the same process occurs again, resulting in the smaller current I_4. The diminution is very gradual, decreasing slowly along the line until the load is reached, at which point all of the remaining current passes through the load and back to the generator.

Investigation of the voltage between the wires as one progresses along the line reveals the same sort of diminishing effect due, of course, to the various voltage drops which occur across the series resistance in the line. These are indicated in Fig. 2–3. It can be seen that the voltage across the line at any point becomes less and less the greater the distance from the generator.

When a transmission line is to be used for communication purposes, the ideas just developed with regard to terminating the line in Z_0 is usually observed as closely as possible. However, if the characteristic of the line and its load should suddenly change as, for example, by terminating the line in an impedance other than Z_0, then the current and voltage decrease will no longer be gradual but will, in general, tend to vary sharply from point to point. While this may prove to be unwise when intelligence is to be transmitted, it may be very desirable if the transmission line is to be used for some other purpose, perhaps as a tuned resonant circuit or even as an inductance or as a capacitance. This will be discussed very shortly and is mentioned here only to point out that, at the ultra-high frequencies, transmission lines may be used for a variety of purposes. In order to achieve

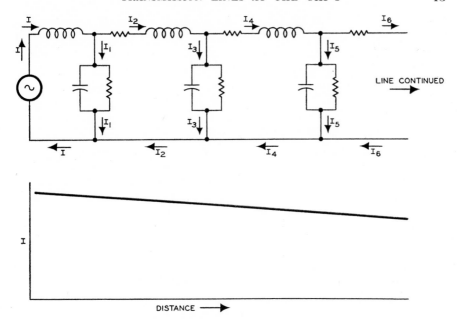

FIG. 2.2. The diminution of current with distance from a generator along a transmission line.

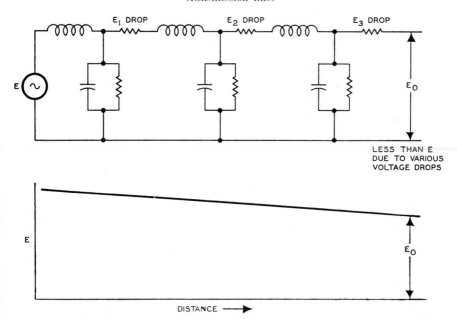

FIG. 2.3. Voltage losses in the line resistance cause the voltage across the line to diminish as the distance from the generator increases.

these other applications resort must be made to different terminations of the transmission lines.   But the distinction between matched and unmatched lines should be remembered.

Attenuation and Phase Shift.   Loss of efficiency due to mismatching the transmission line at its load is but one of several considerations.   There is loss due to attenuation of the signal or voltage as it travels down the line and this is due to the resistance which is part of the line wire.   There is also phase distortion.   When a signal containing several frequencies is transmitted down a line, it is found that in the output signal these same frequencies bear a different phase relationship to each other than they did at the input end of the line.   This should not be strange since a line has inductive and capacitive reactance and these reactances vary with frequency. The symbol used for attenuation is α and that for phase shift, β.   Usually both are expressed as having such-and-such a value per foot or per mile or other unit of length of the transmission line.

There are two widely used methods that are employed to minimize the attenuation and phase distortion.   One method extensively used in telephone lines is to insert networks at various points in the line that tend to accentuate the frequencies that have been the most attenuated by the transmission line.   In other words, these uints have properties that are just the opposite of the properties of the line.   They are sometimes referred to as compensators.   The second method is usually more expensive and involves the use of specially constructed cable.   This cable is built so that the attenuation constant is not dependent on frequency, and the phase constant is made linearly proportional to frequency.   With these two changes very little distortion of the signal will result.

The three constants—Z_0, α, and β—are not separate and distinct from the really fundamental units of the line—resistance, inductance, and capacitance.   They are introduced to simplify the equations for the various properties of the line and can always be expressed in terms of the three really basic units.

Before continuing with the discussion of transmission lines, there are several conventions concerning transmission lines with which the reader should be familiar.   Every transmission line consists of two conductors. Whenever power is fed into these conductors, voltage differences develop across the conductors and currents flow through them.   However, the voltages and currents in one conductor are equal and opposite to the voltages and currents existing in the other conductor.   Thus, suppose that at any one instant of time, the current in conductor No. 1 is as shown in Fig. 2–4. Between points A and B, the current wave is shown as positive, which means that it is flowing away from the generator.   From B to C, the wave is negative, and the current is now flowing back to the generator.   Finally, from points C to D, the wave is again positive, and the current flow is away from the generator. Throughout each of these distances (A to B, B to C, and C to D) the amplitude or amount of current present at each point varies.

Now consider the conditions existing on conductor No. 2 at the same instant. Between points A and B, the current wave is negative, and so the current is flowing toward the generator. This is precisely opposite to its action in conductor No. 1 over the same distance. Further comparison between these two conductors reveals that this is true at all points; whenever

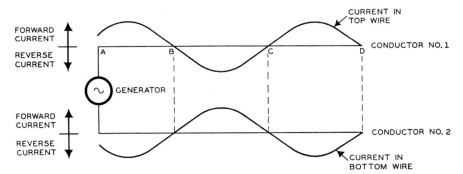

FIG. 2.4. The voltages and currents in each conductor of a transmission line are equal in magnitude (at similar points) but opposite in polarity.

one conductor is positive, the other is negative, and by the same amount. While only the current is indicated, it is reasonable to expect the voltages to function similarly because the voltages and currents are interrelated.

Since the conditions in these wires are equal and opposite, it is not necessary to draw the voltage and current waves for both conductors. Simply indicating these waves for one wire is sufficient to convey to the reader as much information as if the waves for both wires were shown. Hence, only one wave is generally seen. In fact, sometimes a transmission line is shown with only one conductor. Again, the reader must know that actually two are meant.

Mismatched Transmission Lines. We have dealt with the advantages of properly terminating a transmission line in a load equal to its characteristic impedance. There are many instances, however, when it is not desirable to terminate a transmission line in its characteristic impedance, but rather to go to the extreme of placing a direct short across the end of the line or else leaving it entirely open. The line is then mismatched. We shall consider these conditions to see why they are important.

The voltage and current values along a matched transmission line vary smoothly from one end of the line to the other. To determine the voltage and current distribution for a mismatched condition, let an r-f oscillator be connected to one end of a line which is several wavelengths long and let the other end of the line be left open or, what is equivalent, terminated in an infinite impedance. Any energy sent out from the generator will hit this open end and bounce back, so to speak, somewhat as a sound wave hitting a stone wall is reflected. There can be no absorption of power at the open end because there is nothing there to receive this power. The reflected wave

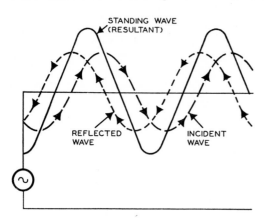

Fig. 2.5. The incident, reflected, and resultant standing waves along an open-ended transmission line.

of energy will travel away from the open end of the line and meet other waves coming from the generator. We now have two waves traveling in opposite directions along the line where in a matched line only one existed. Everywhere, the two waves will combine to form a new wave having values which vary from point to point. At some points this new wave will have a maximum value; at other points the wave will be zero. The oncoming wave requires a certain amount of time to reach the open end of the line and the reflected wave also requires time to travel. Thus, there will be phase differences between these waves wherever they meet along the line. At some points the two waves will be in phase and aid each other while at other points they will be 180 degrees out of phase and cancel. Where they completely cancel each other we have zero amplitude, and where they reinforce each other the result is a maximum. In between, the reinforcement or cancellation is only partial and intermediate values are obtained.

Fig. 2–5 illustrates the relative phase of the reflected and incident waves at one instant of time when the end of a line is open-circuited. The current wave is used in the illustration. If the values of these two waves are combined at each point, we would obtain the resultant wave shown.

The resultant wave in Fig. 2–5 possesses two positive and two negative peaks, all at one instant of time. Let us consider the first positive and negative peak from the open end. (See Fig. 2–6A.) If we were to stand and watch this resultant wave and were somehow able to see the changes occurring in it, we would see the wave go through the changes indicated in Fig. 2–6B. At time 1, the wave is the same as shown in Fig. 2–6A. At time 2, the peaks begin to decrease, the positive peaks becoming less positive and the negative peaks less negative. The wave continues to go through successive changes at times 3 and 4, finally reaching zero at all points at time 5. From times 6 through 9, the various sections of the wave reverse their polarity, and at time 9 the former positive peaks are now negative and the former negative peaks are now positive. This change in polarity is a continuous process and exists for as long as energy is fed into the transmission line and reflected. Note, however, that points which are zero are always zero, while points which are maximum always attain the same peak value. This is why the resultant wave is known as a standing wave. The wave remains in one position, but in this position varies alternately from positive to negative or negative to positive values. The only exception to this occurs at the zero points. These always remain zero.

The voltage distribution along an open-ended line will have the same form as the current distribution, but the maximum voltage points will not coincide with the voltage peaks. (See Fig. 2–7.) Thus, at the open end of the line, the current is reduced to zero since there is no complete path for the current to travel. The magnetic field due to this current collapses at this point and produces a voltage

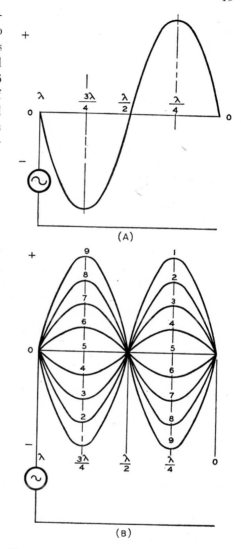

(A)

(B)

Fig. 2.6. (A) One cycle of a standing wave. (B) The changes in amplitude and polarity occurring in this wave from instant to instant.

which adds to the existing voltage in an attempt to maintain the current flow. Consequently, the voltage appearing across the open end is a maximum. The voltage distribution will also vary in a sinusoidal manner, but the voltage maxima will always occur where the current is zero. Hence the waves, as depicted pictorially, will be displaced as in Fig. 2–7A. Using the ratio of voltage to current to define the impedance ($E = IZ$), it is possible to calculate the impedance at any point along an open-ended

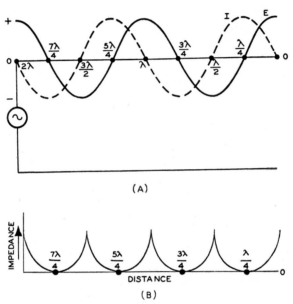

(A)

(B)

FIG. 2.7.   (A) The current and voltage standing waves and (B) the impedance variation along an open-ended transmission line.

transmission line.   At the current nodal points, the value of the impedance will be very high since

$$\frac{\text{large voltage}}{\text{small current}} = \text{large impedance}$$

At current maxima points, the opposite situation occurs and the impedance is low.   In general, then, the value of the impedance along the line will tend to vary as the voltage, being high when the voltage is high and low when the voltage is at low.

If, instead of having the end of the transmission line open, it is now short-circuited, the voltage and current standing waves formed along the line will differ from the previous open case and, similarly, the impedance at various points will be changed.   Fig. 2–8 shows the voltage, current, and impedance relationships when the line is short-circuited.   By comparing Figs. 2–10 and 2–11 these differences will be immediately discernible.

We can pause now and re-examine the properties of mismatched transmission lines. When a line is properly matched, any signal, voltage, or current fed to the line will travel down the line and be completely absorbed by the load. If we could see the r-f variations along the line, we would see a wave which is continually traveling forward. If no loss existed along the line, then an r-f voltage meter would indicate essentially one value of voltage all along the line.

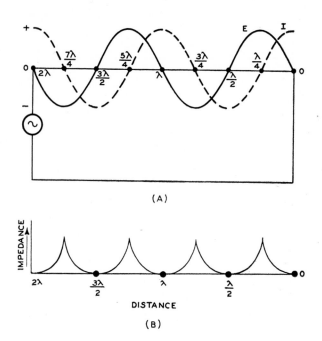

FIG. 2.8. (A) The voltage and current standing waves and (B) the impedance values along a short-circuited line.

However, when a line is mismatched, part (or all) of the energy reaching the point of mismatch is reflected back along the line. This energy, coming in contact with the oncoming signal, combines to form a resultant wave which has peaks and valleys and which remains in position. If, now, we moved an r-f voltmeter along the line, it would indicate a maximum value at some points and a minimum value (near zero) at other points.

We thus have here a very simple test for determining whether or not a line is properly matched. Suppose we connect an r-f oscillator to one end of a line and either do not know what is at the other end of the line or, if we know what is there, we do not know whether or not the line is matched. To find out, simply take an r-f voltmeter and move it along the line, noting the meter readings as it progresses down the line. If the line is matched, the meter reading will not change appreciably. If, however, the meter reading varies from point to point, then the presence of standing waves is indicated.

To indicate the amount of mismatch on a line, a ratio known as the standing-wave ratio is often used. This is the ratio of the peak r-f voltage

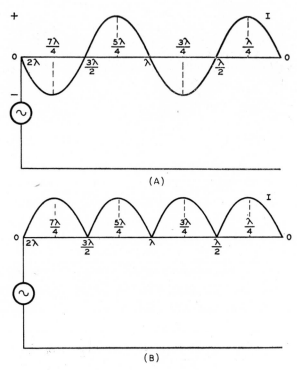

FIG. 2.9. (A) The relative polarity of the standing-wave peaks along a line at one instant of time. (B) A frequently used method of illustrating standing waves.

on the line (as indicated by an r-f meter) to the minimum voltage. Thus, if a 6 to 1 standing-wave ratio exists, it indicates that the voltage peaks have 6 times the amplitude of the voltage troughs or valleys. Lines are generally said to be matched for ratios of 1.5 to 1 or less. A perfect match occurs when the ratio becomes 1 to 1.

The standing-wave ratio can be used to determine whether a load is higher or lower than it should be to match the characteristic impedance of the line. Suppose that the standing-wave ratio turns out to be 6 to 1. To determine whether the load impedance is too high or too low, measure the voltage across the load. If a maximum voltage reading is obtained, the load is roughly 6 times greater than the line impedance. If a minimum reading is observed, the load impedance is $\frac{1}{6}$ of the line impedance. This generalization becomes more inaccurate, the more reactance (capacitive or inductive) that the load possesses.

In the case of a mismatch, the meter will indicate only the resultant or standing wave. Thus, only the resultant need be shown in any of the diagrams. Keep in mind, however, that the incident and reflected waves

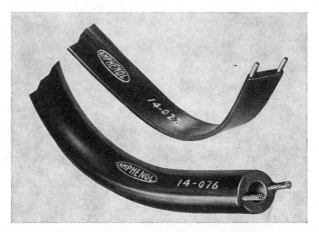

FIG. 2.10. Several types of shielded and unshielded parallel-wire transmission lines. (*Courtesy Amphenol*)

combine to form this wave. Furthermore, since positive and negative peak values have little significance in standing waves, due to the fact that these peak values are continually changing from one polarity to the other, it has become customary to show standing waves as indicated in Fig. 2–9 where all the peaks are placed above a zero reference line or level. In spite of this notation it might be useful for the reader to remember that, at any one instant, consecutive peaks have opposite polarity.

Characteristic Impedance of Typical Lines. There are principally two types of transmission lines in common use, the two-wire parallel conductor line and the coaxial or concentric line. Each type comes in a variety of sizes, construction, and characteristic impedances, some of which are shown in Figs. 2–10 and 2–11.

Formulas are available by means of which the characteristic impedance

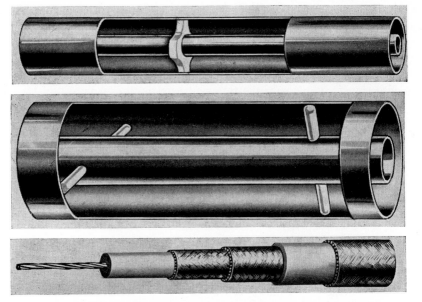

Fig. 2.11.   Several types of coaxial transmission lines. (*Courtesy Andrew Corp.*)

of a line may be computed.   Thus, for a two-wire parallel conductor line using air dielectric, the characteristic impedance is:

$$Z_0 = 276 \log_{10} \frac{2S}{d}$$

where S is the separation distance of the wires and d is the wire diameter.

In a coaxial line, the formula for characteristic impedance is:

$$Z_0 = 138 \log_{10} \frac{D}{d}$$

where D is the inner diameter of the outer conductor and d is the outer diameter of the inner conductor.   Note that these formulas apply only when the wires are separated by air.   If polystyrene or some other dielectric is used, the characteristic impedance will be less.   In the formulas, this will be taken care of by reducing the value of the constants preceding the logarithmic expressions.

The foregoing formulas are useful primarily for roughly determining the impedances of lines, where these values are not known, or for comparing lines of similar construction but differing in line spacing, diameter, dielectric constant, etc.   If the occasion should arise where the characteristic impedance of a line must be determined, the following method will provide the answer quite accurately.

Connect a variable, noninductive resistor across the end of the line and couple an r-f signal into the line. (See Fig. 2–12.) This may be done either by extending a wire from an r-f oscillator or generator close to the line or, if the output available is quite small, connecting the line directly to the generator.

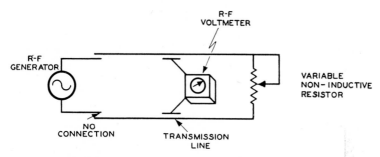

FIG. 2.12. How to determine the characteristic impedance of a high-frequency transmission line experimentally.

Now, with an r-f meter, measure the standing-wave ratio along the line. If this ratio is greater than 1 to 1, vary the resistance until a 1:1 ratio is obtained. At this point, no standing waves are on the line, and a matched condition exists. Disconnect the resistance and measure it with an ohmmeter, the value indicated being the characteristic impedance of the line.

We are now in a position to consider some practical applications of transmission lines. This will be done under three categories: quarter-wave lines, half-wave lines, and lines possessing lengths other than a quarter or a half wave.

PRACTICAL APPLICATIONS OF THE QUARTER-WAVE LINE

Tuning Circuits. Before we examine the applications of the quarter-wave line, the significance of the term "quarter-wave" should be fully appreciated. We say that a transmission line is a quarter of a wave long when the standing wave developed on that line, by feeding in a signal, varies from a maximum at one end to a minimum at the other end, with no other maxima or minima in between. This represents one quarter of a full cycle as can be seen by comparison with any sine wave. As the signal frequency increases, the wavelength decreases. Thus, if a section of line is a quarter wavelength at one frequency it could not be a quarter wavelength at any other frequency unless its physical length was changed.

We have here a situation which is very similar to coil and capacitor resonant circuits. For any set value of capacitance and inductance, this combination will be resonant at only one frequency. If we desire another resonant frequency, then we must change either the capacitance or the inductance, or both.

With transmission lines, the capacitance and inductance is distributed evenly along the line and, therefore, to change the overall amount of either

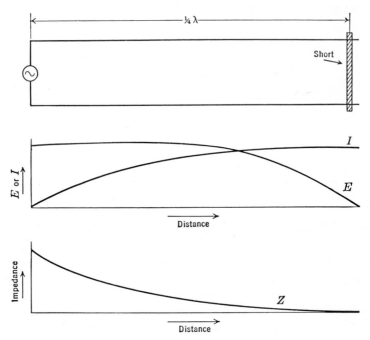

FIG. 2.13. Current, voltage, and impedance values on a short-circuited, ¼λ transmission line.

of these components, a change in line length is necessary. In fact, transmission line tuners utilize movable shorting bars which are moved back and forth along the line to attain different resonant frequencies.

To employ a transmission line as a resonant circuit, use is made of the standing waves to produce, at the input, either a high impedance or a low impedance, depending upon whether a parallel or a series resonant effect is desired. To show this graphically, start with Fig. 2–13, in which a quarter-wave section has been shorted at one end. By drawing the voltage and current distribution along the line and, from them, the impedance curve, we see that, when one end of the quarter-wave line is shorted, the input will present a high resistive impedance to anything connected to it. (Impedance = E/I and if E is high and I is low, impedance will be very high.)

The quarter-wave line is now equivalent to a parallel tuned circuit. However, this high value is obtained at only one frequency; at frequencies on either side of this resonant value, the impedance decreases.

For the open-ended quarter-wave line, the conditions depicted in Fig. 2–14 are obtained. With the far end open, the input end of the line will present a very small impedance and the impedance will be resistive just

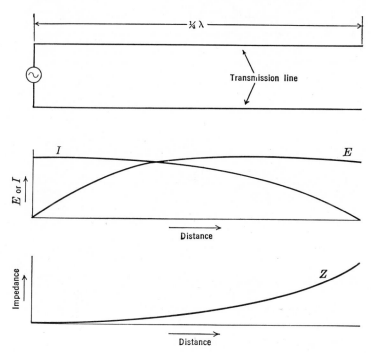

FIG. 2.14. Voltage, current, and impedance values on a ¼λ transmission line that is open-circuited.

as it is in a series-tuned circuit. From the preceding discussion, it can be seen that quarter-wave transmission lines make a load appear opposite to what it is as, for example, short-circuiting one end will make the input end show a high impedance. This is called load inversion or impedance transformation and is an important property of quarter-wave lines.

An illustration of a quarter-wave line employed as a high-frequency tuner is shown in Fig. 2–15A. The grid of a tube is connected to the open end of the line. The shorting bar connects to ground. In a push-pull arrangement, each grid would connect to a line at the open end and again the shorting bar would go to ground, completing the electronic path. (See Fig. 2–15B.) Equivalent low-frequency circuits are shown for each case.

In a high-frequency receiver, this quarter-wave line might conceivably be the input tuning circuit, in which event connection to the antenna would be required. Fig. 2–16 demonstrates how this might be done. The antenna lead-in, if balanced, would be connected across the tuned line at a point

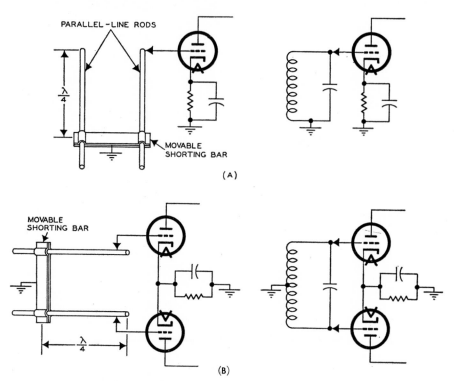

Fig. 2.15. Quarter-wave sections of transmission lines employed as high-frequency resonant circuits.

where the line impedance equaled that of the lead-in. A common example would be a 72-ohm dipole antenna connected to a 75-ohm parallel lead balanced line. This line reaching the receiver should be attached to the quarter-wave tuner at a point where its impedance is 75 ohms. Now, if we examine the current, voltage, and impedance curves of such a section of line (Fig. 2–14), we note that the impedance starts from zero at the shorted-end of the line and increases to a fairly high value at the open end. The antenna lead-in, therefore, would be connected to the tuning circuit at a point near the shorted end where the impedance is low. The illustrations shown in Fig. 2–16A and B represent capacitive coupling between lead-in and tuned circuit. For inductive coupling, a loop of wire is used, its position close to the shorted end of the tuned circuit where the magnetic field is strongest. (See Fig. 2–16C.)

The impedance at the open end of the quarter-wave line will depend upon what is connected across it. At sufficiently high frequencies, the input impedance of a tube decreases to a value of several hundred ohms and

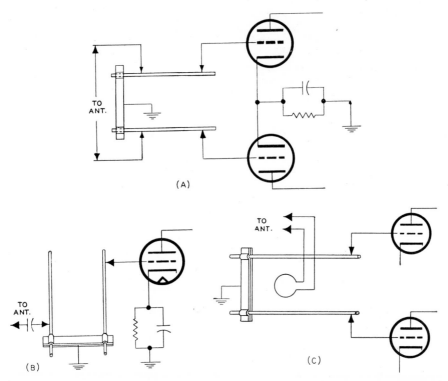

TO ANT.

(A)

TO ANT.

TO ANT.

(B)

(c)

FIG. 2.16. Three ways of feeding energy to a quarter-wave line: (A) balanced input; (B) unbalanced input; (C) loop coupling.

placing this tube across the end of the line would reduce the value of this end impedance to the same low value and affect the impedance values at all other points along the line. On the other hand, when the open end is not loaded down, impedance values of several hundred thousand ohms may be measured.

In order to minimize the loading effect of the tube, it is common practice to connect the grids not directly across the open end, but at some point where the line impedance more closely matches the tube input impedance. The advantage of this arrangement is that it does not reduce the Q or selectivity of the line and therefore does not impair its ability to discriminate sharply against signals with frequencies other than that of the desired signal. When the tube is connected across the end of the line, the Q is decreased considerably, resulting in a broad tuning curve. This makes it easier for unwanted signals to pass through the receiver.

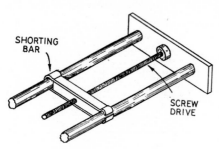

FIG. 2.17.   A movable shorting bar is one means of tuning transmission lines.

Wide-range tuning of these quarter-wave resonant circuits is best accomplished by moving the shorting bar. The bar is connected to a screw drive which is extended to the front panel. (See Fig. 2–17.) By rotating the handle, the shorting bar can be brought to any point along the line. If the tuning range is restricted, it may be accomplished by inserting a small variable capacitor across the open end of the line. Variation of the capacitor will then alter the total capacitance of the circuit and cause the frequency to change.

Impedance Matching. A second property of a quarter-wave line is its ability to serve as a matching section between two different impedances. It can be shown that if Z_{out} is the impedance used to terminate a line, then the impedance presented at the other (or input) end of the line, Z_{in}, is related to Z_{out} by the formula

$$Z_{in} \times Z_{out} = Z_0{}^2$$

where Z_0 is the characteristic impedance of the matching section and is, of course, a constant.

As an illustration, suppose a television serviceman wishes to match a 75–ohm dipole antenna to a 300–ohm twin-lead transmission line. Using the foregoing formula and substituting for Z_{in} 75 ohms and for Z_{out} 300 ohms, the following result is obtained.

$$Z_0 = \sqrt{75 \times 300}$$

$$Z_0 = \sqrt{22,500}$$

$$Z_0 = 150 \text{ ohms}$$

Thus, a quarter-wave section of a line whose characteristic impedance is 150 ohms will properly match a 75–ohm dipole to a 300–ohm line. (See Fig. 2–18.)

If two coaxial lines possessing different characteristic impedances have to be connected, a match may be effected as shown in Fig. 2–19. The central connecting cable possesses an outer diameter which is equal to the outer diameter of the cables to be matched. Its inner conductor, however, has a diameter which is larger than the inner conductor of the left-hand cable but smaller than the same conductor in the right-hand cable. Just what diameter the inner conductor of the matching section should possess will depend upon the characteristic impedances of the coaxial cables to be matched. For coaxial cables, the characteristic impedance depends upon the ratio of the outer and inner conductors. In measuring these

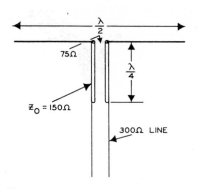

Fig. 2.18. A quarter-wave matching section between a half-wave dipole (impedance approx. 75 ohms) and a 300-ohm line.

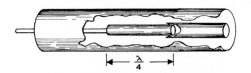

Fig. 2.19. How to match two coaxial cables possessing different impedances.

diameters, we use the inner diameter of the outer conductor and the outer diameter of the inner conductor. The reason for this is the fact that the energy transported by the line exists *between* the inner and outer conductors. Very little energy exists *beyond* the inner diameter of the outer conductor or *below* the outer diameter of the inner conductor.

Quarter-wave Lines as Insulators. The property of a quarter-wave section to present a high impedance at one end when the opposite end is shorted enables us to use such a line as an insulator. Thus, suppose that a two-wire transmission line carrying very-high-frequency signals has to be supported, and conventional polystyrene or porcelain insulators are found to be unsuitable because of the large amount of leakage they present at these frequencies. If copper conductors are cut to a quarter wavelength at the frequency of the r-f signals and connected as shown in Fig. 2–20A, they will not only support the two-wire line, but will also not divert any current from the main line.

A similar arrangement can be employed in coaxial cables to support the inner conductor with negligible loss. (See Fig. 2–20B.)

The quarter-wave insulator will only function as such at the frequency for which it was cut. Its impedance at all other frequencies will be less, the actual value decreasing rapidly the greater the difference between the frequency used and the resonant frequency of the section. At these other frequencies, the quarter-wave section represents a shunt across the main line, drawing off energy and reducing its usefulness. To make the stub less sensitive to frequency, it is constructed with a lower charac-

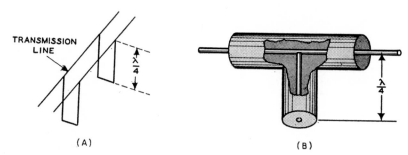

FIG. 2.20. (A) Shorted quarter-wave stubs acting as insulated supports for a parallel-wire transmission line. (B) The supporting stub in a coaxial cable.

teristic impedance than the line to which it is attached, and its length is extended for one-quarter of a wavelength in either direction along the main line from the point of support. (See Fig. 2–21.) It is now able to function as an insulator over a frequency range of 20 per cent above and below its resonant frequency.

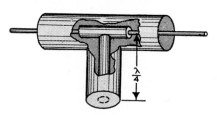

FIG. 2.21. A broad-band quarter-wave supporting stub.

Matching Balanced to Unbalanced Lines. There is frequently occasion to match balanced to unbalanced transmission lines. Simply connecting a balanced line to the inner and outer conductors of a coaxial cable would not produce a match, even if the characteristic impedances of the two lines were equal, because currents from the balanced line would tend to flow along the outer surface of the coaxial line, resulting in a considerable loss of radiated energy. To connect the two lines, without permitting the currents to stray from the desired paths, a special converter known as a bazooka may be employed.

A coaxial cable and a balanced twin-lead transmission line are shown in Fig. 2–22A. In the balanced line, each conductor possesses the same potential and the same impedance to ground; which is why the line is said to be balanced. In the coaxial line, the outside surface of the outer conductor is at ground potential while the r-f voltages and currents are confined to the inner surface of the outer conductor and to the inner conductor. The purpose of the bazooka is to prevent any of the r-f energy passing between the coaxial and the balanced line from reaching the outer surface of the coaxial cable. It accomplishes this by presenting a high impedance, at the point of connection, to any currents desiring to reach the outer surface of the cable. Here is how this high impedance is formed.

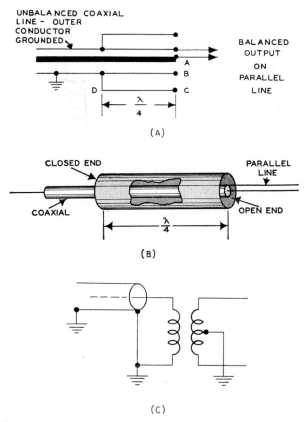

Fig. 2.22. (A) Bazooka formation. (B) Physical appearance of bazooka.
(C) Equivalent low-frequency network.

A shield is placed around the outer conductor of the coaxial line and is connected to the outer conductor at a point one quarter-wave from the end of the line where the balanced line is to be attached. Now this second shield and the outer conductor form a quarter-wave section. Since the end of this section, at point *D*, is grounded, the other end presents a high impedance between points *B* and *C*. Any currents desiring to flow from the balanced line to the outer surface of the coaxial cable encounter this high impedance and are thereby prevented from doing so. The inner conductor is unaffected by this second shield and retains the impedance it previously possessed. The bazooka isolates point *B* from ground, even though the outer conductor of the coaxial cable is grounded at one or more points below point *D*. (See Fig. 2–22B.)

The equivalent low-frequency circuit of the bazooka is shown in Fig. 2–22C and is seen to be similar to a transformer in which one side of the

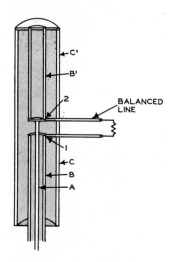

Fig. 2.23. A modification of the bazooka of Fig. 2.22. This unit possesses better electrical balance over a range of frequencies.

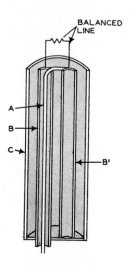

Fig. 2.24. A compact version of the bazooka in Fig. 2.23.

primary and the center-tap of the secondary are grounded. Insertion of the bazooka has not affected the impedance of either line, and the characteristic impedance of the cable should be chosen to equal that of the balanced line. If the bazooka is employed at frequencies other than that for which the distance *C–D* is not one quarter-wave, then the impedance between points *B* and *C* will not be high, resulting in an unbalance with resultant loss of power due to standing waves and radiation.

To overcome the limitation of narrow band width which is characteristic of the foregoing bazooka, the modified unit shown in Fig. 2–23 was devised. This is similar to the bazooka except that an additional coaxial section *B'*, *C'* has been added. This section has the same impedance and characteristics as the section formed by *B* and *C* of the bazooka. This means that whatever impedance is presented to the incoming balanced line between point 1 and ground, due to section B and C, will be exactly equal to the impedance developed between point 2 and ground, due to section B', C'. This will be true at all frequencies, enabling the incoming balanced line to remain undisturbed.

It is possible to reduce the physical dimensions of this unit in half by folding the upper section (B'–C') back on the lower section. (See Fig. 2–24.) This compact unit, at UHF frequencies, will seldom exceed 5 inches in length.*

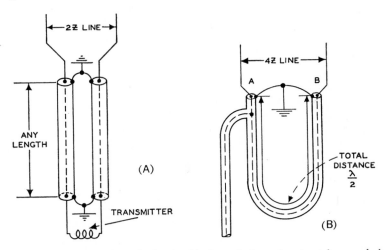

FIG. 2.25.   Two additional methods of achieving a balanced output from unbalanced coaxial lines.

There are additional methods for connecting coaxial cables to balanced lines. Several such arrangements are shown in Fig. 2–25. In the first illustration, two lengths of coaxial lines are run side by side (from a transmitter to an antenna, for example), with the inner conductors connecting to the circuits at either end. The outer shields of both lines are at ground potential at all points. In this arrangement, we are effectively placing the line impedances of both cables in series, producing an impedance at either end which is equal to twice that of either cable.

The second illustration of Fig. 2–25 is sometimes mistaken for the bazooka, although its method of matching is entirely different from that of the bazooka. The end of a coaxial cable is folded back on itself for a half wavelength in such a manner that the inner conductor at each end

---

*The bazooka is a special device in a general class known as baluns. The word *balun* is a contraction of *bal*anced and *un*balanced and signifies a device which will match balanced impedances to unbalanced impedances.

may be connected to a balanced line.   The ends of the inner conductor are points A and B in Fig. 2–25B.   Since these two points are separated from each other by a half wavelength, the amplitude of their voltages (with respect to ground) will be equal but 180 degrees out-of-phase.   This is the condition desired for proper connection to a balanced line.

The impedance presented across points A–B is four times the impedance of the coaxial cable.   The reason for this is as follows: The voltage between point A and ground is equal to the voltage between point B and ground. Therefore, the total voltage between points A and B is $2E$, or twice the voltage carried by either coaxial cable alone.   Now, the power obtained across points A and B must equal the power fed in by the single coaxial cable at the left.   Thus

$$P_{in} = P_{out}$$

But, P_{in} is equal to

$$P_{in} = \frac{E^2}{Z_1}$$

where Z_1 is the impedance of the coaxial line.   By the same reasoning, P_{out} is equal to

$$P_{out} = \frac{(2E)^2}{Z_2} = \frac{4E^2}{Z_2}$$

where Z_2 is the impedance between points A–B.   Since the power has not changed, Z_2 must be equal to $4Z_1$ because only in this way can $P_{in} = P_{out}$. Thus,

$$P_{in} = P_{out}$$

Substituting for each, we have

$$\frac{E^2}{Z_1} = \frac{4E^2}{Z_2}$$

or

$$Z_2 = 4Z_1$$

To summarize the important properties of a quarter-wave line:
1. The line can act as a resonant circuit, either series or parallel tuned.
2. When one end is shorted, the opposite end presents a high impedance.
3. Because of its inverting properties, a 90-degree phase shift is obtained.
4. Also due to its property of inversion, it can match two impedances that differ in value.

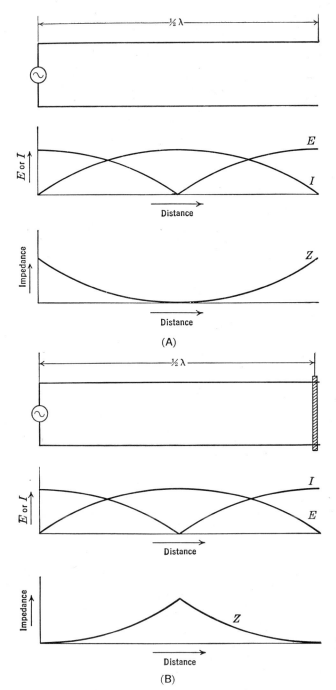

Fig. 2.26. (A) Voltage, current, and impedance values along an open-circuited, ½λ line. (B) Voltage, current, and impedance values along a short-circuited, ½λ line.

Half-wave Lines. If the foregoing discussion is extended to lines which
are one-half wavelength long, very little difficulty in understanding will be
encountered if the half-wave line is regarded simply as two quarter-wave
lines joined end to end. Since a quarter-wave line inverts the load, two
joined together will introduce another inversion which will bring it back
to its original form. Thus, as indicated in Fig. 2–26, the same conditions

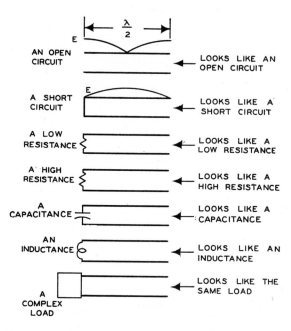

FIG. 2.27. Half wavelength sections of transmission lines act as 1:1 transformers.

prevail at both ends of the line. A half-wave line short-circuited at one
end will present an extremely low impedance at the other end; similarly,
if one end is open, the other end will present a high impedance. Thus there
is a 1 to 1 impedance transformer action here. This property is useful if
it is desired to match two sections of a circuit which are widely displaced
from each other. If the two have equal impedances, then by using a half-
wave line (at the frequency of the signal) we can connect the two points
and afford a correct match. In this case the characteristic impedance of
the line is not important; it may be any value. What must be observed,
however, is the length of the line; this must be precisely one-half wave long
at the frequency at which the circuits are operating. The property of a
half-wave line to act as a 1:1 transformer applies to any electrical component, as Fig. 2–27 reveals.

An exception to the foregoing generalization exists where the load impedance is equal to the characteristic impedance of the line itself.   In this case, of course, the line is matched and does not depend upon standing waves for its action.   The line is now said to be nonresonant and any length may be used.   When the load is not equal to the characteristic impedance of the line, the line is said to be resonant.

Half-wave lines can also be used as phase-inverters.   If we examine the voltage relationships at either end of a half-wave line, we see that their amplitudes are equal, but they are 180 degrees out of phase with each other. This was pointed out previously when the concept of standing waves was introduced.   It was stated then that consecutive peaks of any standing wave established along a transmission line always possessed opposite polarity. We need not, however, confine this only to the peaks of the standing wave. Any two points one-half wavelength apart have opposite polarities.

Lengths Other than One-quarter or One-half Wavelength.   Thus far, the entire emphasis has been on either quarter or half wavelengths of transmission lines.   There are, however, numerous applications where lines having lengths other than either of these values are used and, therefore, the radio man should be familiar with the behavior of transmission lines of any length.

It is easiest to commence with line lengths which are multiples of either quarter- or half-wave sections.   Any *even* multiple of a quarter-wave line is either a half-wave line or some multiple of it.   Thus, two quarter-wave sections represent a half-wave line, four quarter-wave sections represent two half-wave lines or a full-wave line, etc.   If, as we have seen, a half-wave line is simply a 1 to 1 impedance transformer, then adding any number of half-wave lines together does not change the value of any load connected to either end.   Thus, if a 100-ohm resistor is placed across one end of a half-wave line, 100 ohms will be the impedance "seen" at the other end. Adding any number of half-wave lines will not change the input impedance of the line.   However, one half-wave line will reverse the *polarity* of any voltage appearing at one end; two half-wave sections will bring the polarity back to its original phase, etc.

Extensions of quarter-wave lines fall into two categories.   As stated above, even multiples of quarter-wave lines are actually half-wave lines and may be considered as such.   Odd multiples of quarter-wave lines may be considered as sections of half-wave lines plus a single quarter-wave line. Thus, a ¾-wave line can be considered as a half-wave section and a quarter-wave section.   If the quarter-wave section is short-circuited at one end, then the impedance seen at the opposite end of the quarter-wave line would be high.   Connecting a half-wave section to this will simply transfer this high impedance to the opposite end of the half-wave section.   Adding additional half-wave sections will not change the character of this high impedance.

When we come to consider lengths of transmission lines other than one-half or one-quarter wavelength long, or multiples thereof, we must of necessity turn to certain mathematical equations. It is quite logical that the input impedance of a transmission line will vary as the length of the line is changed since, by this process, more or less resistance, inductance, and capacitance are brought into the circuit. Of interest is the relationship between the input impedance Z_{in} and the length of line used. For a short-circuited line the relationship turns out to be

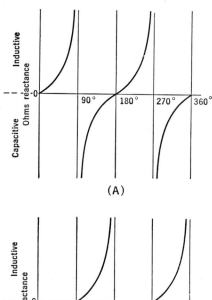

(A)

$$Z_{in} = Z_o \tan \theta$$

where Z_o is, as usual, the characteristic impedance of the line. As mentioned previously, Z_o is a constant. The angle θ requires a little more explanation since it might not at first be obvious that the length of a transmission line can be measured both in feet and in degrees, the two being equivalent. To demonstrate this, consider a line that is 2 feet long and at a certain frequency has one complete standing wave on it. A complete wave has 360 degrees and, for this one particular frequency, 360 degrees are equivalent

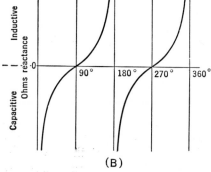

(B)

Fig. 2.28. (A) Input impedance for short-circuited line. (B) Input impedance for open-circuited line.

to 2 feet of this line. One foot would allow only one half-wave to be put on the line, again at this frequency, and now there are only 180 degrees. The words "at one frequency" are important because the amount of line needed to resonate at one frequency is different from that required at any other frequency. It is analogous to an ordinary tuning coil and capacitor which will resonate at one frequency but which must be changed before they will respond to any other wave, except a harmonic.

The plot of the above equation, in Fig. 2–28A, shows that when the length of the line used is less than one-quarter wave length, or 90 degrees, the value of Z_{in} is positive (above the zero line) and so shows inductive properties. For values of θ between 90 and 180 degrees, the value of Z_{in} is negative, and a capacitive effect is obtained. The remaining lengths will give rise to either inductances or capacitances, depending upon whether Z_{in} is positive or negative. At exactly 90, 180, 270, and 360 degrees, the line is neither capacitive nor inductive but acts as either a series or parallel tuned circuit, depending upon the angular length involved. If this seems strange, remember that, in ordinary coil and capacitor tuned circuits, whenever you tune above the resonant frequency, the combination has a capacitive reactance whereas, if the circuit is tuned below resonance, an inductive effect is obtained. Since a transmission line is a tuned circuit, it is only natural to expect the same behavior.

For the open-circuited line, the equation differs from the above and is given by

$$Z_{in} = Z_o \cot \theta$$

The same interpretation should be given to this set of curves as in the previous case. (See Fig. 2–28B.)

Transformer Action with Transmission Lines. Not only can a transmission line act as an inductance, capacitance, or resonant circuit, but it can also be used either as a step-up or step-down transformer, depending again upon the type of load across the end of the line. For example, take a line that is an odd number of quarter wavelengths long and draw the voltage and current distribution along the line. This has been done in Fig. 2–29A for a short-circuited, quarter-wave line. Now, if at some point PP' a resistive load is connected across the line, it will be subjected to a voltage that is less than the voltage across the input of the line. And, as is true in all step-down transformers, if the voltage is decreased, the current will be increased in like proportion. Fig. 2–29B shows the similarity of the transmission line to the ordinary tuned circuit, where the same effect may occur. For voltage step-up purposes an open-ended line can be used if it is also any number of odd quarter wavelengths long and is connected as shown in Fig. 2–30. The load that is shunted across the line should not contain too much reactance nor should its impedance be too low, as either case will disrupt the conditions as shown in the preceding diagrams and result in voltage and current distributions that will vary with each case.

Matching Stubs. There are applications where more than one property of a line is utilized. An excellent example is the quarter- or half-wave matching stub that is widely used by amateurs on short-wave antennas. To facilitate the explanation, refer to Fig. 2–31 where a transmission line and a matching stub are shown connected together at points AA. The load at the end of the transmission line, Z_L, may be an impedance; in

amateur work it is usually the antenna. The point of this entire arrangement is to help couple the transmission line to the load and to have both
impedances match as closely as possible for maximum power transfer.
In most applications at the high frequencies, the characteristic impedance
of the transmission line can be represented by a pure resistance while that

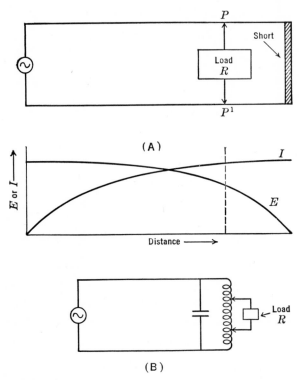

Fɪɢ. 2.29. Showing similarity between transmission line and step-down transformer.

of the load may not be. It is the purpose of the matching stub to cancel
any reactive component in Z_L and thus have it appear as a resistance to any
generator feeding the transmission line. If the distance from the load
to the points AA is properly adjusted, the resistive component of the load
will match Z_o and so leave its reactive component to be neutralized. The
matching stub is now introduced to eliminate this unwanted load reactance.

To adjust the length of the matching stub, short-circuit one end (which
is also near one-quarter wavelength) and move the shorting bar until
standing waves which are present on the transmission line due to the un-
neutralized reactance of the load Z_L disappear. When this happens, the
reactive component of Z_L has been neutralized and the load presents an

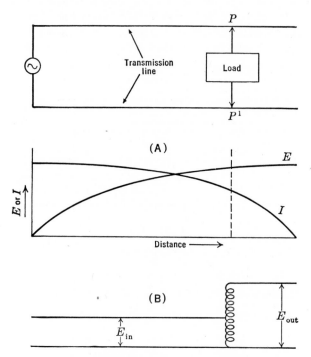

FIG. 2.30.   (A) Using a transmission line as a voltage step-up transformer.
(B) Low-frequency analogy.

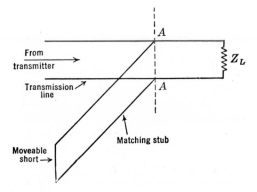

FIG. 2.31.   Method of using a quarter-wave stub to neutralize any reactance in the
load Z_L.

impedance matching that of the transmission line. Sometimes amateurs use a half-wave matching stub where the end is not short-circuited but left open. The wire is cut off until the line is adjusted. Those readers

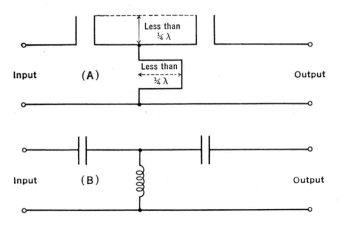

FIG. 2.32. (A) An ultra-high frequency high-pass filter. (B) Low-frequency equivalent.

who desire to use this arrangement on the amateur frequencies should consult the *Radio Antenna Handbook* published by the American Radio Relay League.

Perhaps it has occurred to some readers that, since resonant lines can take the place of coils and capacitors, such systems may be used to act as high-pass, low-pass, and bandpass filters. Such use has already been suggested. A typical circuit may look like that of Fig. 2–32A, where a high-pass filter is shown. The corresponding, conventional, low-frequency circuit is shown in Fig. 2–32B. Comparison of the two will aid in bringing out again the equivalent circuits developed at the beginning of this section. Many other arrangements will probably occur to the reader and it would help considerably if these were put on paper and practised. It might be mentioned that all of the preceding material will also apply to concentric cables, as well as to parallel wire systems.

A consolidated summary of the various properties of the transmission line is given in pictorial form in Fig. 2–33.

Standing-wave Measurements. The determination of the standing-wave ratio along a transmission line is an important consideration if any work is to be done on the line. This ratio may be determined using either the voltage or current standing waves, the value being the same in each instance. Generally, however, it is the voltage ratio which is determined because most measurements are made using coaxial lines and this component is more easily measured.

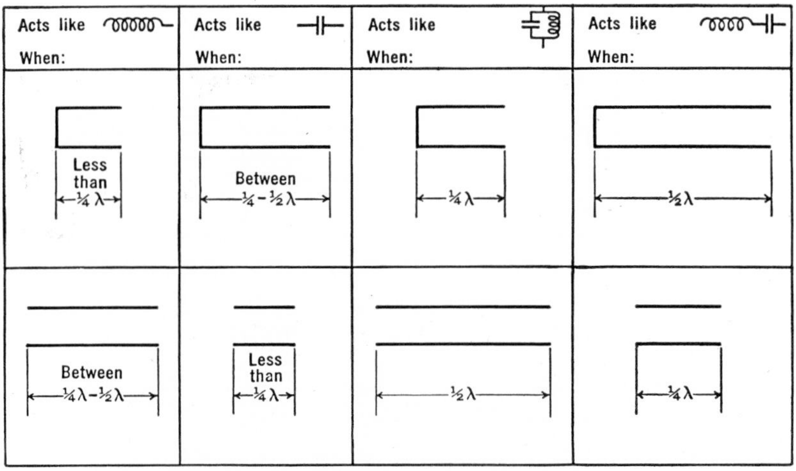

Acts like 〰️ When:	Acts like —⊣⊢— When:	Acts like ⊟ When:	Acts like 〰️⊣⊢ When:
Less than ¼ λ	Between ¼ – ½ λ	¼ λ	½ λ
Between ¼ λ–½ λ	Less than ¼ λ	½ λ	¾ λ

FIG. 2.33. Summary of properties of transmission line ½ λ or less.

For very simple measurements, where only a rough indication of the standing-wave ratio is desired, either of the measuring devices shown in Figs. 2–34 or 2–35 may be employed. In the first illustration, a small

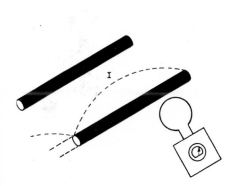

FIG. 2.34. One method of roughly determining the standing-wave ratio along a transmission line.

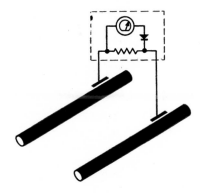

FIG. 2.35. Another method of roughly determining the standing-wave ratio along a line.

coupling loop of wire is series-connected to a crystal rectifier and a sensitive d-c microammeter. The loop is placed only as close to one conductor of a twin-lead line as is necessary to obtain a suitable indication. If the loop is placed too close to the line, there exists the possibility of either burning the meter out or disturbing the operation of the line due to the presence of the loop and its circuit. The loop is moved along the line, and the value of the meter reading at successive maximum and minimum points is

Fɪɢ. 2.36. The mechanical arrangement of a slotted transmission line designed to measure the voltage distribution along the line. (*Courtesy Collins Radio*)

recorded. Their ratio will then give the required standing-wave ratio for the line.

An even simpler arrangement than the foregoing is merely a loop and a small incandescent lamp bulb in series. The intensity of the lamp filament will then serve to indicate the strength of the standing wave.

To obtain the voltage ratio for a twin-lead line, the set-up shown in

Fig. 2–35 is employed. The ends of the indicator are capacitance-coupled to each conductor of the line, this coupling again kept as loose as possible. For precise measurements on transmission lines, a slotted coaxial cable and a probe are employed. The slot, running the length of the line, is made to accommodate a small narrow probe which extends through the slot and for a very small distance into the line between the inner and outer conductors. In this way it comes in contact with the electric field existing between these two conductors, developing an induced voltage which is proportional to the field strength. A crystal rectifier and a sensitive d-c meter complete the indicating circuit.

The probe is mounted on a movable carriage (Fig. 2–36) containing a drive mechanism which slowly moves the probe along the slot. In the unit shown, a gear rack is engaged by the drive wheel pinion. From an accurately marked scale along the side of the line, the exact distance traveled by the probe can be determined.

QUESTIONS

1. What are the common uses for a transmission line at the low frequencies?
2. Name the components of a transmission line. How are these usually stated?
3. Define characteristic impedance and explain what happens when a line is terminated in its characteristic impedance.
4. How can the action of an infinite line be simulated without actually using an infinite line?
5. What factors of a transmission line other than characteristic impedance exert influence over a signal traveling down the line? How?
6. What occurs to a signal if a line is not terminated in its characteristic impedance?
7. Draw the voltage, current, and impedance relationships on a quarter-wave line, both open-ended and shorted.
8. Why can a quarter-wave line act as a resonant circuit? Describe, using the two types of terminations.
9. How does a quarter-wave line introduce a phase shift? Explain either graphically or mathematically.
10. Name two additional applications of quarter-wave lines.
11. How does the action of a half-wave line differ from that of a quarter-wave line?
12. Could a half-wave line, either open-ended or short-circuited, be used in place of the quarter-wave line for tuning purposes? Explain.
13. Why is it desirable to use these lines in place of coils and capacitors at the ultra-high frequencies?
14. What factors determine whether a line will act as either a capacitance or inductance at any one frequency?
15. For question 14, does the end termination make any difference? If so, how?
16. Draw a diagram of a high-pass filter, using appropriate sections of transmission lines.
17. Do the same for a low-pass filter.

18. How do amateurs sometimes use lines to eliminate standing waves on antenna feeders? Illustrate.

19. Compare the advantages and disadvantages of open-wire transmission lines and coaxial cables.

20. What phase shift is introduced when a half-wave line is connected into a circuit? Three-quarter wave line?

21. Draw the voltage and impedance relationships on a half-wave line that is open-ended; short-circuited.

22. Describe a simple test for determining whether or not a transmission is terminated in its characteristic impedance.

23. Describe several methods of tuning transmission lines.

24. How could a resistance of 50 ohms be matched to a resistance of 250 ohms, using a transmission line? Give full details in your answer, including the length of the transmission line and its characteristic impedance.

25. How is it possible to obtain a balanced output from a coaxial line? Show several methods.

26. Describe how accurate standing-wave measurements are made on transmission lines.

Chapter 3

WAVEGUIDES

The Old Way. If a radio man were asked how he would transfer power from a transmitter to an antenna, his answer would most likely be: "By using a transmission line." And that would be correct for most frequencies, at least until the ultra-highs were reached. And even at these frequencies transmission lines could be used. However, a waveguide method of conveying UHF energy from point to point has been devised which introduces considerably fewer losses than even well-constructed coaxial cables. As a result, waveguides have completely replaced transmission lines at frequencies above 1000 mc. Below 1000 mc, transmission lines are preferred because the size of the conductors required by the new system becomes too large.

The New Way. In the usual method of low-frequency power transmission, one end of the transmission line is connected to the transmitter output and the other end is connected to the antenna. As the signal frequency increases, the size of the antenna decreases, until at 1000 mc the length of a half-wave dipole is only 6 inches. Now suppose that, instead of employing a long transmission line with which to conduct the energy from the oscillator to the dipole, a very short length of line is used and the antenna is placed close to the set itself.

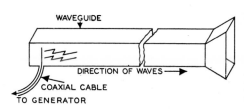

FIG. 3.1. A rectangular waveguide being employed to direct energy from a UHF generator to open space.

Since the generating equipment is usually contained somewhere within a building, direct radiation from this point would introduce high losses. Instead, let the small antenna be enclosed in a rectangular (or circular) pipe, with the other end extending into the open. The waves emitted by the antenna will travel through

79

the pipe and out into space when the end is reached. (See Fig. 3–1.) The pipe acts as a guide, confining the radiated energy until it leaves the pipe and travels forward into open space. It is because of this guiding action that the name "waveguide" has been bestowed upon these rectangular or circular pipes.

The idea that radio waves can be made to follow a certain path is, in reality, an old one. In short-wave transmissions up to 10 and 20 meters, long-distance communication depends upon the reflection and refraction* of the radio signals from the ionosphere and from the ground. (See Fig. 3–2.) By successive reflections and refractions the signals are guided from the transmitting antenna to distant receivers, the distance depending upon the radiated power, the frequency of the signal, and the losses suffered by the wave at each point of reflection. We can, very easily,

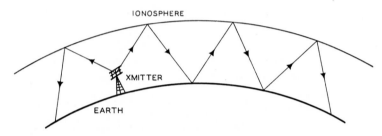

FIG. 3.2.   The ionosphere and the earth act as a gigantic waveguide for low-frequency radio signals. This is directly responsible for long-distance short-wave communication.

consider this as an enormous waveguide, with the ionosphere functioning as the top of the guide and the ground forming the bottom. Side walls to this guide do not exist and hence the waves may travel horizontally in all directions. However, in man-made waveguides, complete limiting of the radiated energy may be achieved by inserting side walls and forcing the energy to follow a definite path until the end of the guide is reached.

Why Waveguide Loss Is Low. The superiority of waveguides to transmission lines can best be seen by an analysis of the losses which commonly exist in transmission lines. There are three types of losses: resistive loss, radiation loss, and dielectric loss.

Resistive loss in transmission lines arise in the conductors through which the current flows. In the twin-lead, parallel-wire line, both wires possess the same diameter and both contribute equally to the loss of power.

* Reflection refers to an abrupt change in direction, as light striking a mirror. Refraction refers to a gradual change, as light passing through (and being bent by) a prism. Radio waves are subjected to both reflection and refraction in the ionosphere,

In coaxial cables, most of the resistance is contained in the smaller center conductor and hence most of the power loss occurs here. The outer conductor has a greater surface area and since resistance is inversely proportional to area, less resistance is offered by this conductor. A waveguide is superior in this respect to either type of transmission line because it contains only one conductor—the sides of the guide. This is equivalent to the outer conductor of the coaxial cable; there is no inner conductor in a guide.

Radiation loss is present to a considerable extent in the parallel-wire type of line, especially when the frequency reaches such a value that the separation between the conductors represents an appreciable part of a wavelength. The coaxial cable and the waveguide each have negligible radiation loss because in both the energy is confined within a shielded enclosure.

The third loss, dielectric loss, arises chiefly at the insulating beads in a coaxial line or the supports in a twin-lead, parallel-wire line. In a waveguide no such supports are necessary and therefore no such loss occurs.

An additional advantage of the waveguide is its ability to handle greater amounts of power than an equivalent-sized coaxial line. A coaxial line and a circular waveguide are shown in Fig. 3–3, each possessing the same outer diameter. In the coaxial line, maximum voltage is developed between the inner and outer conductors. In the waveguide, there is no inner conductor, and the distance separating points of maximum voltage is equal to the diameter of the outer conductor. The separation is thus greater in a guide, permitting it to handle higher voltages. Since power is proportional to voltage, a guide is able to handle larger amounts of power without voltage arc-over.

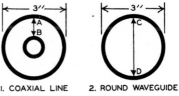

1. COAXIAL LINE 2. ROUND WAVEGUIDE

Fig. 3.3. The relative voltage breakdown path of a circular waveguide and a comparable coaxial line.

Twin-lead and coaxial lines find application up to 1000 mc; beyond this waveguides are used almost exclusively. A graph comparing the attenuation of a 3-inch coaxial line with that of a 3-inch circular waveguide is shown in Fig. 3–4. The guide has a frequency cut-off at 2500 mc below which waves cannot be propagated. Above 2500 mc, however, its attenuation is appreciably less than that offered by the coaxial line. This phenomenon of frequency cut-off will be examined in more detail in a later paragraph.

The limitation of size restricts the use of waveguides below 1000 mc. Generally speaking, the minimum width of a guide must be equal to one-half wavelength of the signal to be transmitted through it. At 1000 mc,

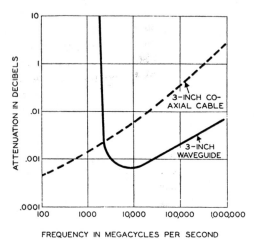

FIG. 3.4. The attenuation characteristics of a 3-inch circular waveguide and a comparable coaxial cable.

this means a width of at least 6 inches; at 500 mc, 12 inches, etc. A waveguide a foot wide is a fairly bulky piece of equipment. A coaxial cable, on the other hand, may have an outer diameter of an inch or so.

Electromagnetic Waves — How They Travel. The primary purpose of waveguides is to conduct electromagnetic waves from one point in an ultra-high-frequency system to another. In its most usual application, the energy is introduced into the waveguide by a small antenna rod at the transmitter, and then conducted by the guide to another antenna from which point it is radiated into free space. At the receiving point, the signal is picked up by an antenna and fed to the receiver through a connecting wavguide.

The electromagnetic energy radiated by an antenna is the same whether the antenna is inserted in a waveguide or placed atop a tall building. A difference exists, however, in the direction in which the energy radiated by these antennas will travel. When the antenna is out in the open, energy may be propagated in all directions; with a confined antenna, the energy is forced to remain within the limits established by the walls of the guide. The nature of the energy itself, however, is unaffected and is the same in both cases. This is true at the low frequencies as well as at the high frequencies.

The signal radiated by the antenna is developed by the r-f currents flowing in the antenna. The mathematical laws which govern the behavior of these electromagnetic waves were first formulated by Maxwell and have since become known as Maxwell's equations. While the derivation and specific application of these laws are quite complex, requiring a considerable background in calculus, the basic nature of electromagnetic wave travel through space can be more easily understood.

Energy radiated by an antenna contains two components. There is an electric field (such as we find between the plates of a charged capacitor) and a magnetic field (such as surrounds a coil of wire carrying current) and each field is dependent on the other. It is impossible to have one without the other.

Every radio man is undoubtedly familiar with the fact that, when currents flow through a wire, they establish a magnetic field about the wire and the magnetic field varies directly with the current. It is also known that varying magnetic fields, when they cut across a conductor, will induce an electromotive force (emf) in this wire. These basic facts were generalized by Maxwell as follows:

1. Changing magnetic fields produce varying emf's or, what is the same thing, varying electric fields or forces.

2. And changing electric fields will give rise to varying magnetic fields, and both will exist together.

These statements are true whether we are discussing circuits containing wire conductors or the space between antennas where the electrical conductivity is low. If a magnetic field cuts across a nonconductor, just as much voltage is induced in it as there would be in a conductor having the same size. Place a block of wood in a varying magnetic field and it will be subjected to an induced voltage. Replace the wood by a block of copper and the copper will receive the same induced voltage or electric force. The only difference between the two will be that current will flow within the copper whereas no measurable amount of current would be noted in the block of wood. The resistance offered by the wood is so high that only a minute amount of current can flow.

Now let us apply this to wave propagation through an electrically nonconducting space. At the antenna the high-frequency currents are rapidly moving back and forth along the wires. The moving currents set up changing fields that alternately expand and contract (or collapse) about the wire in accordance with the rise and fall of the currents in the antenna wire. When the fields expand, energy is being transferred from the antenna to these fields. When the fields collapse, the energy is returned to the antenna.

Now, if all of the energy transferred by the antenna to the space surrounding it were returned, there would be no radio wave communication. It is found, however, that, as we increase the frequency of the currents flowing in the antenna wire, an increasing amount of energy transferred to the fields is not returned to the antenna. Instead, this energy travels away from the antenna with the velocity of light (approximately 3×10^{10} cm per sec). Let us focus attention on the magnetic field for an instant: as this wave travels outward, it will, because it is changing in magnitude, induce an electric field in the surrounding space. But this electric field will not only appear in the same place where the magnetic field is, but it will also appear a little beyond; and the electric field will, as it travels outward, produce a magnetic field—also slightly removed from the agent that produced it. It is by having these fields sustain each other, and at the same time move outward, that the mechanism of wave propagation may be pictured in a general way.

In space, the energy in the wave is divided equally between the electric and magnetic components and these fields are at right angles to each other. The balance of energy is disrupted only when the wave enters a different medium, such as the ionosphere layers found from **70 to 250** miles above the earth. Since no new energy is added to the wave, the only way that a readjustment can occur is for some of the energy already in the wave to be redistributed. For example, if some of the energy is returned in the direction from whence it came, then we say that reflection has taken place. On the other hand, if some or all of the energy is made to partially alter its direction of travel, then refraction has occurred.

Depicting Electric and Magnetic Forces by Arrowed Lines. Electromagnetic waves traveling through space require, for an adequate presentation, a three-dimensional picture. Since the written page possesses only two dimensions, it has become customary to illustrate the electric and magnetic components of electromagnetic waves by means of lines. The idea of a line or series of lines to represent a field stems from the basic definitions of electric and magnetic forces in terms of flux lines. The stronger the field, the greater the number of lines. Actually, of course, magnetic and electric fields are continuous throughout the space in which they act and do not possess lines of any sort. However, the concept of lines appears to make it easier for the engineer to visualize and work with these fields and they are used extensively.

The forces in electric and magnetic fields are directed in certain directions according to the way the fields are produced. To indicate direction of these electric or magnetic forces, arrows are used, these being drawn on the ends of the lines. (See Fig. 3–5A.) When a certain region possesses a greater electric or magnetic force, more lines are drawn here than in some other region where the force is not as great. In Fig. 3–5A, electric forces are acting. The forces may be due to a group of electrons or any other charged body that is capable of exerting an electrical force. At the center of the diagram the field is strongest, and this is shown by grouping four lines together. On either side of the center the number of lines becomes progressively less, indicating that the strength of the field is decreasing. There are no lines at the extreme right- and left-hand margins, indicating that here the strength of the field has diminished to zero. The same variation in electric field strength is shown graphically in Fig. 3–5B. This is equivalent to one half-cycle of an a-c wave, where the same conditions exist, with a maximum value at the center and zero at either end.

Fig. 3–6 shows the electric field distribution when there is a full-wave variation from one side wall of a waveguide to the other. For the positive half of the wave, the arrows point in one direction, while for the negative half of the wave the arrows are drawn in the opposite direction, just as the current reverses during each half-cycle in ordinary a-c circuits. The process is continued in one more illustration, Fig. 3–7, where the variation in electric field strength is a wavelength and a half. By following this line of reasoning, any number of cycles can be drawn.

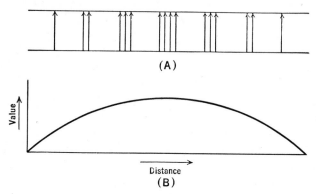

(A)

(B)

FIG. 3.5. (A) Using arrowed lines to show strength and direction of arrowed fields. (B) Equivalent half-wave curve.

Since, in any illustration of an electromagnetic wave, there are both magnetic and electric lines of force, the magnetic lines are shown as dashed in order to distinguish them from the electric lines of force. Magnetic lines of force, however, are always drawn as complete rings, whereas electric lines need not be. This difference is due to the fact that, although electrons are readily separated physically from their molecules, leaving the latter with a positive charge, north and south magnetic poles cannot be similarly separated. However, if such a separation could be achieved, then magnetic lines would not necessarily have to form complete rings.

The existence of a strong electric field, say at the center of a guide, Fig. 3–5, means that there is a large potential difference in this region between the top and bottom plates of the guide. Since the electric lines of force must extend from positive to negative charges, we would find a concentration of positively charged atoms on the surface at the mid-section of the bottom plate. The electrons that are ordinarily part of these atoms (when no electric field is present) would be repelled away from the atom, possibly moving into the plate for a short distance.

The lines of force, extending up from these positively charged atoms, would attract a similar number of electrons at the top plate and by this action produce a concentration of electrons on which to terminate.

Now, although the electric field distribution is shown with all lines pointing upward, this condition exists only for one half-cycle of the applied

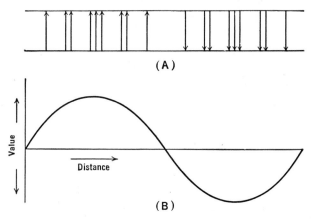

Fig. 3.6.   Same as Fig. 3.5 except for full wave variation in field strength.

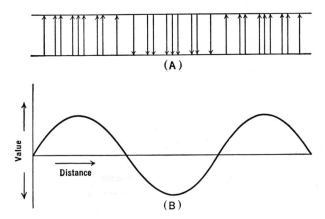

Fig. 3.7.   Full wave and a half variation in electric field strength.

signal.   During the following half-cycle, the polarity of the field reverses and the arrows on the lines of force should be reversed, also.   During this second half-cycle there is a concentration of electrons at the center of the bottom surface and a positive charge at a similar point on the surface of the top plate.   The field, however, is still strongest in the center, tapering off to zero at the side walls.   This remains the same, differing only in polarity from half-cycle to half-cycle.   Since the concentration of electrons along the top and bottom surfaces of the guide will change as the electric field goes through its variations during each cycle, we will have the equivalent of an electron flow in these surfaces. As we expand this picture to include wave propagation down the length of the guide, it will be seen that current flow exists on all surfaces in the interior of the guide. The current flow does not extend very deeply into the surface because the skin effect, because of the extremely high frequencies of the signals, forces it to remain near the surface. The depth of current penetration for copper is given by

$$d = \frac{0.0026}{\sqrt{f \text{ (mc)}}} \text{ inch}$$

and, as f increases, d decreases. Since resistance will rise as the current is forced to flow in a narrower layer, the power lost will also rise with frequency.

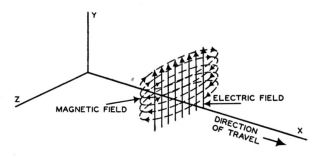

FIG. 3.8. A polarized electromagnetic wave, shown at one instant of time.

Polarization of Radio Waves. The electric and magnetic fields of an electromagnetic wave may extend in all directions. Many times, however, one field (say, the electric field) is active in only one direction, perhaps along the Y-direction in Fig. 3–8. The magnetic field, associated with and developed by this electric field, would then exist at right angles to it. This could be either along the X-axis or the Z-axis, both of these being at right angles to the Y-axis. By restricting the fields of radio waves to special directions and not allowing them to expand in every direction, a process known as polarization has taken place. A field so restricted is said to be polarized. In waveguides, the polarization of a wave has an important bearing on the behavior of the wave as it travels through the guide.

The direction of polarization is always taken to be the same as that of the electric vector. Vertical antennas send out vertically polarized waves and, if these waves do not change their sense of polarization as they travel, they may best be received or picked up by a vertical antenna. This is true in waveguides just as much as it is in radio broadcasting. In commercial broadcasting, however, we lose control of a wave once it has been transmitted and it is common to find that the polarization of part of the wave changes, either by the ionosphere or by reflection off near-by objects. In transmission through waveguides, greater control is exercised and change of polarization is kept to a minimum. This insures maximum transfer of power.

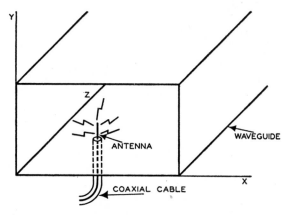

Fig. 3.9.   A small antenna in a waveguide.

Wave Travel in Guides.   The introduction of r-f energy into a waveguide is usually accomplished by inserting the inner conductor of a coaxial cable into the guide in the manner shown in Fig. 3–9. The electric field radiated from this antenna establishes a distribution of electric field intensity across the guide in which the field strength is maximum at the center, decreasing to zero at the side walls of the guide. (See Fig. 3–10.) This condition, it will be recognized, represents a standing wave in which the maximum value appears in the center, gradually tapering down to zero at the sides. Physically, we can simulate the field distribution by fastening the ends of a short section of rope to two rigid pillars, then grasping the rope at its center and moving it up and down rapidly. The section grasped will travel the greatest distance, the next adjacent section a little less, etc. The ends of the rope, which are fastened firmly each to a post, will, of course, not move at all.

Electrically, the situation indicated in Fig. 3–10 represents the only stable condition for this wave. At the sides of the guide the electric field intensity must be zero because the sides are conductive and would short-circuit any vertical electric field present here. An electric field, between any two points, represents a difference of potential. If this difference of potential exists across a conductor containing a negligible amount of resistance, a large current will flow, effectively short-circuiting the potential and preventing it from existing at this point. This is analogous to the destructive effect which a short circuit has on any d-c or a-c generator. In order for the attenuation to remain small, the electric fields established by the antenna must decrease to zero at the side walls and this can occur only when the width of the guide is at least one-half wavelength of the transmitted signal.

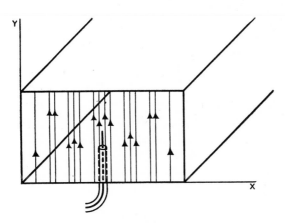

FIG. 3.10.   The electric field distribution developed by the antenna of Fig. 3.9.

Here we encounter one of the limitations that must be observed in wave-guides if they are to be used successfully for transmitting electromagnetic signals.   Maxwell indicated that, for electromagnetic waves to exist in any space enclosed by conductors, two conditions would have to be met.   The first was that the electric field should be zero at the surface of a conductor if the field is parallel to that surface.   In the above waveguide example, this occurred at the side walls.   However, the electric lines of force may be perpendicular to a conducting surface without affecting the field.   This condition exists for the top and bottom plates of the waveguide in Fig. 3–10.

The second condition requires the magnetic lines of force to be parallel to a conducting surface at all points because only in this way would they be unaffected by the surface. Otherwise, whenever magnetic lines of force cut across a conductor, a voltage is induced which, in turn, produces a current. The current sets up its own magnetic field in opposition to the original field, reducing the strength of this original field and otherwise altering the over-all magnetic field distribution. But, when magnetic lines of force are parallel to any conductor, no such induced emf appears.

If either of the two conditions is violated, the electromagnetic waves will be attenuated rapidly, thereby preventing them from traveling through the guide.

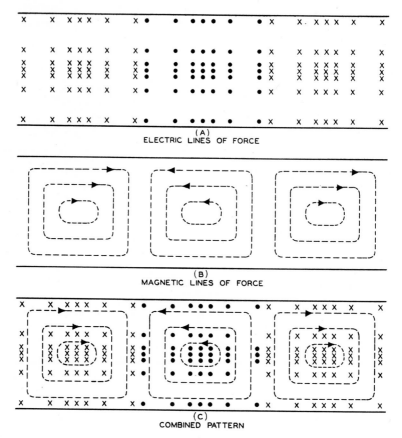

FIG. 3.11. A top view of a waveguide showing the electric and magnetic lines of force.

In waveguides containing nothing inside but air, the magnetic lines of force will everywhere be at right angles to the electric field. These magnetic lines of force encircle the electric lines of force in precisely the same manner that they encircle any wire carrying current.

A top view of the waveguide will bring out the relationship between the vertical electric field and the accompanying magnetic lines of force. Looking down on the guide, Fig. 3–11A, we see the electric field either pointing up toward us (the dots in the center of the diagram) or pointing away from us, (the ×'s at the ends of the illustration). We can call the electric field positive when the lines point toward us and negative when they point away from us. Since these lines are continually changing in direction, we have the equivalent of a varying emf, producing a magnetic field that encircles the electric lines of force. (See Fig. 3–11B.) As is true of current flow in wires, so it is true of these lines of force that, whenever they change direction, the magnetic field also reverses. Fig. 3–11C shows both fields combined.

As the wave travels down the guide, the field varies sinusoidally from a positive to a negative maximum just as it does in every a-c wave. If we were to stand at any one point along the length of the waveguide, and we could somehow see the electric field passing by, we would see it varying in intensity and polarity from instant to instant. A photo of the conditions

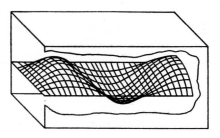

FIG. 3.12. An illustration of the electric field of a wave traveling along a waveguide at one instant of time. (*Courtesy I.R.E.*)

existing at any one moment along this guide would appear as shown in Fig. 3–12. An instant later, the various positive and negative peaks would have moved to some other position along the guide with the magnetic field moving in step with the electric field. Note that no standing waves are set up down the length of the waveguide because we are assuming that the energy continues to travel along the guide without any backward reflection. If a wall is inserted at the far end of the guide, so that the forward traveling energy is reflected, then standing waves along this dimension would also appear and the waveguide would now become a cavity resonator.

The wave shown in Fig. 3–13 is called the $TE_{1,0}$ wave. (The method of labeling the waves will be considered presently). The distribution of the electric and magnetic fields for the next higher order wave is shown in Fig. 3–14. This is the $TE_{2,0}$ wave. Its frequency is double that of the $TE_{1,0}$ wave as indicated by the fact that the width of the waveguide can accommodate a full wavelength of this wave and only a half wave of the $TE_{1,0}$ type. The $TE_{1,0}$ wave possesses the lowest frequency that can be propagated down the guide since nothing less than a half wave can exist across the guide and satisfy the condition that the electric intensity will be zero at each side wall. A wider waveguide will accommodate a signal of lower frequency. Decreasing the guide dimensions will raise the frequency of the lowest frequency signal that could be sent down the guide.

Since we are accustomed to having radio waves travel in a straight line through space, it is natural to believe that the same action takes place

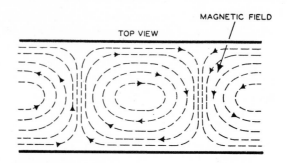

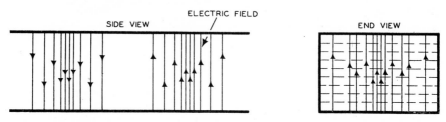

FIG. 3.13. The distribution of the electric (solid) and magnetic (dashed) lines of force for the $TE_{1.0}$ mode. To simplify the illustrations, only the end view contains both magnetic and electric fields. The other views show only one field each, although both are present at all times. (See Fig. 3.11.)

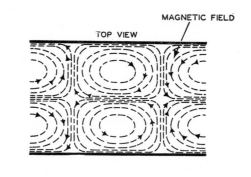

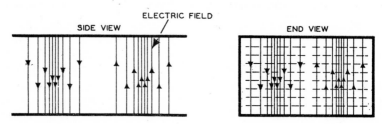

FIG. 3.14. The electric and magnetic field distribution for the $TE_{2.0}$ mode.

in a waveguide. If this were true, and if the dielectric employed was air, there should be no difference between the travel time of a wave inside or outside the rectangular guide. But it has been found that the measured time inside the guide is always greater than the time for the corresponding distance in free space. This difference can be explained only if the path inside is longer than the outside distance, and this, in turn, could be true only if the interior waves followed a zig-zag path, reflecting back and forth off the walls as the wave moved forward.

Still another reason for doubting that the path of travel through the guide is a straight line is the fact that a standing wave must exist *across* the guide, at all points, in order to satisfy the condition that the electric field intensity be zero at the side walls. We originally noted this standing wave across the mouth of the guide, Fig. 3–10, near the antenna. The same type of sidewise standing wave must exist at all points along the guide. Thus we are faced with the following situation. The electric field intensity must be zero at the side walls and to do this requires a standing wave *across* the guide, at all points. At the same time this energy must be traveling down the guide. Standing waves can be obtained only by combining two waves—a wave that hits a surface and a reflected wave. In the present instance, the standing wave is sidewise, across the mouth of the guide; hence the reflection must occur off the side walls of the guide. We are thus forced to accept the conclusion that wave travel in a guide is characterized by two conditions:

1. The wave follows a zig-zag path down the guide.

2. Reflections occur off the side walls to develop the sidewise standing waves needed to insure zero electric field intensity at each side wall.

In order to gain a more precise conception of wave travel in guides, let us trace the path of a signal down a waveguide.

Exact Wave Paths in Guides. A convenient system of wave notation for this purpose is shown in Fig. 3–15. The positive and negative maxima are drawn in heavy lines and indicated by either $(+)$ or $(-)$ signs, depending upon their polarity. In between each positive and negative maximum is a zero point in the wave and this is represented by a lightly drawn line. The direction of travel of the wave is perpendicular (or normal) to the wave-front and arrows pointing in the direction of travel show this. Now let us take the wave and send it down a waveguide. For the sake of simplicity we will consider first the foremost section of the wave-front and follow it partially down the guide. Then, we will gradually add sections to this wave front.

To start, consider the four illustrations in Fig. 3–16. In part A the wave-front is moving into the waveguide in the direction indicated by the arrowheads. Only the positive maximum portion of the wave-front is shown at the moment.   As the wave-front penetrates deeper into the wave-guide, the foremost edge will reach the guide side wall and be reflected.

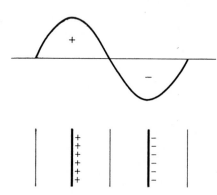

FIG. 3.15.   A method of representing the variations in a sine wave by several heavy and light lines.

The angle at which the wave-front hits the side wall and the angle at which it bounces off are equal.   Stated differently, the angle of incidence (arriving) and the angle of reflection (departure) are equal—a fact which holds true for light rays as well as radio waves.   This is understandable since both are electromagnetic in character.   Furthermore, because the side walls are conductors, the reflected wave will have the reverse polarity of the incident wave.   The reflected wave is due to the voltage induced in the side wall by the incident wave.

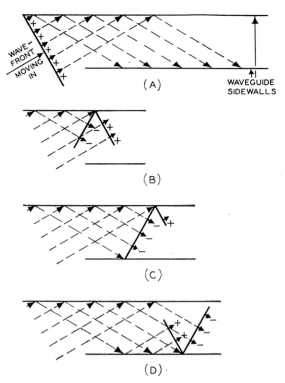

FIG. 3.16.   The manner in which a wave-front moves through a guide.   For simplicity, only part of the wave is shown.

Since an induced voltage is in opposition to the voltage which produced it, the polarity of the reflected wave will be opposite to the incident wave. Thus, if, as shown in Fig. 3–16, the incident wave-front is positive, when it is reflected from the side walls, the polarity becomes negative. At the point of reflection, we have the arriving positive field and the departing

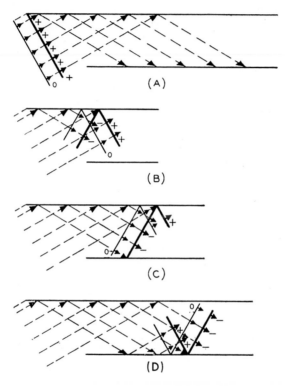

Fig. 3.17. An extension of the illustration of Fig. 3.16. The line marked "O" possesses zero potential or no polarity.

negative field neutralizing each other's effect to produce a resultant zero field. This is necessary at the side walls and was one of the conditions previously specified.

The remainder of the illustrations in Fig. 3–16 show the same wave-front at various moments as it travels down the waveguide. As each section of the wave-front hits a side wall, it rebounds with a reversed polarity. We can, if we wish, consider that from the original incoming positive wavefront, we now possess two waves, one negative and the other positive.

The next illustration, Fig. 3–17, includes the maximum positive peak of the wave and the zero level, at which point there is no electric field.

(The reader should understand, of course, that, between the maximum positive value and zero, the electric field intensity diminishes gradually in a sinusoidal manner. This diminution is not shown for the sake of simplicity.) The path of travel is readily followed in Fig. 3–17, being exactly similar to the preceding diagram. Since the electric field intensity is zero at the light line, there is no polarity reversal at each reflection point.

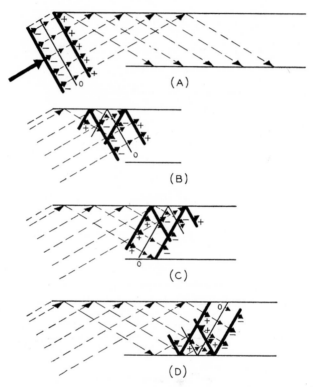

FIG. 3.18. The addition of more sections of the wave-front shown in Fig. 3.17.

The illustration is extended, in Fig. 3–18, to include the negative peak. At each side wall rebound, the negative wave reverses polarity, becoming positive. As with the positive wave, the angle of reflection is equal to the angle of incidence.

Finally, in Fig. 3–19, we have a more complete illustration of the wave traveling down a guide. The incoming energy is continuous, and so the pattern shown in Fig. 3–19 should be a continuous one, stretching as far to the right as the eye can see. Along both side walls, the net electric field intensity is zero, increasing to a maximum (positive or negative) at the center. As we look down the center of the guide, we can see that the electric field intensity varies periodically, going from maximum value of one polarity to a maximum value of the opposite polarity. In between each of these peaks the field intensity changes sinusoidally to zero.

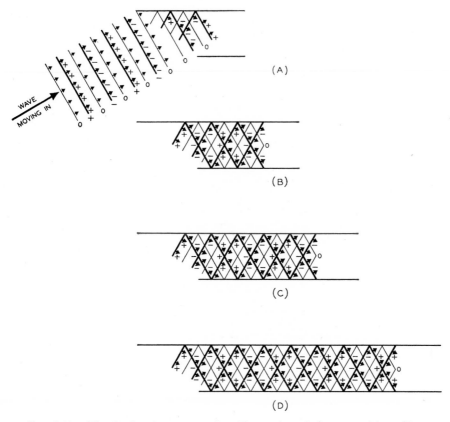

(A)

(B)

(C)

(D)

Fig. 3.19. The final and most complete illustration of wave travel in guides.

Phase and Group Velocity. Because of the zig-zag motion of the electromagnetic wave in the waveguide and the redistribution of energy that occurs, the wavelength of a signal in the guide appears to become longer than the wavelength of the same signal in free space. Now, by definition, the length of any wave is the distance from one positive maximum to the next positive maximum or from one negative peak to the next negative peak. (Note: It is not the distance from one zero value to the next zero value as examination of any simple sine wave will indicate). In Fig. 3–20, the wavelength of the wave down the guide is labeled λ_g, extending from one positive peak to the next positive peak. The distance between similar points in the wave, if it were traveling in free space, is indicated in Fig. 3–20 by λ. That this is the wavelength in free space may readily be seen if we remove the side walls of the guide and permit the wave to travel in a straight line without rebounding. From a simple comparison of the lengths of λ and $λ_g$ it is seen that the wavelength of a wave in a guide is longer than the wavelength of the same wave in free space. Now it may be asked, Has the wavelength of the wave actually increased? And, if so, how does this affect the frequency? In answer to the first

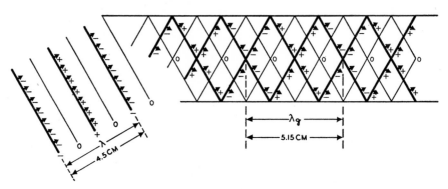

Fig. 3.20.   The wavelength of a signal within a guide ($λg$) is always greater than its free space wavelength ($λ$).

question, if we retain the definition for wavelength, then it has increased. However, since this new wavelength exists only in waveguides, a specific notation must be adopted ($λ_g$) to distinguish it from the wavelength in air ($λ$). Actually one wavelength is no more its "true" value than the other. However, since most communication work is carried on in free space or along wires where the conditions are similar to those of free space, it is customary to consider the free space wavelength as the so-called "true" wavelength.

Concerning the second question, wavelength and frequency are related by the expression:

$$λ \text{ (meters)} = \frac{V}{f \text{ (cycles)}}$$

where V is the velocity of the wave. In free space this is 300,000,000 meters per second. It is also the velocity of the wave in a guide containing air, as the wave travels from wall to wall across the guide. However, due to this zig-zag motion, the actual forward velocity of the wave will be less. Thus, in a waveguide, the apparent wavelength increases and the forward velocity of the wave decreases. Now, in order for the foregoing relationship to hold, then apparently the frequency must decrease. Yet, there is nothing in the guide which would cause such a decrease. This has been proved experimentally. At no time has the frequency ever been observed to change when passing either from free space into a waveguide or from a guide into free space. We are thus led to the conclusion that

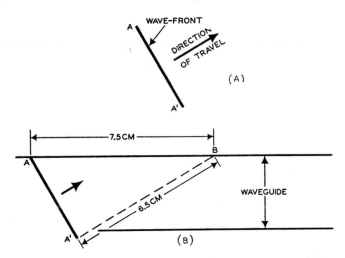

FIG. 3.21. A diagram to illustrate the difference between group and phase velocity. While the wave, as a group, moves from A′ to B in the waveguide (a distance of 6.5 cm), the phase moves from A to B (7.5 cm). Therefore, the phase velocity exceeds the group velocity by a factor of $\frac{7.5}{6.5}$ or 1.15.

either the relationship between frequency and wavelength, as given above, is not valid in waveguides or else we are not associating the proper velocity with the "new" wavelength.

To reconcile these apparent contradictions, let us examine wave travel in free space and compare this with the conditions existing in waveguides. Consider a wave which has been radiated by an antenna and is traveling forward with the velocity of light. All portions of this wave-front (Fig. 3–21A) are traveling forward at the same speed and all points have the same phase.

Now let this plane wave-front enter a waveguide, Fig. 3–21B. Its path of travel here will no longer be forward along the guide, but at an angle, as previously described. To show this wave-front we will resort to our previous notation of a straight line. This is shown as A–A′. At all points along A–A′ the phase conditions are the same and the entire front moves as indicated by the arrow—which is at right angles to the wave-front.

As the wave travels deeper into the guide, point A reaches the side wall first and rebounds. Following it in close succession are the remainder of the points along the wave-front A–A', the last point (A') striking the wall at point B. Since A and A' possess the same phase, we see that in the time required for point A' to move to point B (or the distance $A'B$), points having the same phase have moved from A to B. And since the distance AB is greater than the distance $A'B$, then obviously the phase velocity of this wave (described as the velocity at which points of equal phase travel) is greater than the velocity of the wave itself (known as the group velocity).

When the wave is traveling in free space, the velocity of the wave itself and the phase velocity are equal because both are traveling in the same direction and their velocities are measured along the same direction. In the guide, however, the wave travels at an angle to the wall, and the various sections of the wave-front having equal phase reach the side walls at different times. If we compare the forward phase velocity with the velocity of the whole wave as it moves forward, we find that the phase velocity is greater. If now we use the value of the phase velocity in the wavelength-frequency formula, we will obtain an equality where wavelength times frequency will equal velocity. In a guide, as the wavelength increases, the phase velocity does too, in similar proportion, maintaining both sides of this equation equal to each other.

This distinction between phase velocity and actual wave velocity should be kept carefully in mind. In phase velocity we are measuring the rapidity with which a series of points having equal phase move forward. A–A' in Fig. 3–21B represent such a series of points and this line of constant phase moved from A to B in the time that the actual wave itself moved from A' to B.

If we are concerned with the distance the wave itself and the line of constant phase travel in the same direction—as we generally are with waves in free space—then the phase and group velocity will be the same. In the guide, however, the wave travels from side to side while we measure phase velocity along the guide. Because of this difference in direction along which the measurements are made, different velocities are obtained.

Remember, however, that the energy in the signal travels at the group velocity and this determines how fast a signal will travel through the guide.

Cut-off Frequency. The zig-zag path taken by a wave in traveling down a guide depends upon the width of the guide and the wavelength of the signal being transmitted down the guide. As the wavelength changes, the distribution of energy must rearrange itself in order that the electric field intensity at the sides of the guide will be zero. When the frequency of the signal is low and the wavelength is long, the situation shown in

Fig. 3–22A obtains. As the wavelength becomes shorter, or the frequency of the signal increases, the path changes from Fig. 3–22A to Fig. 3–22B and finally to Fig. 3–22C. If the frequency of the signal is lowered sufficiently, a value will soon be reached where the wave just bounces back and forth across the waveguide and is not propagated forward at all. This value is known as cut-off frequency of the guide and represents the lowest frequency that can be transmitted by this particular guide. Here we have a

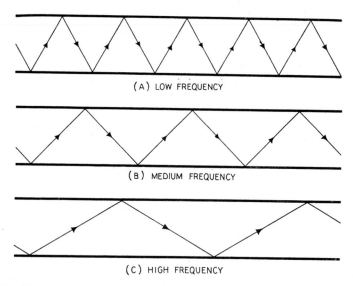

(A) LOW FREQUENCY

(B) MEDIUM FREQUENCY

(C) HIGH FREQUENCY

Fig. 3.22. The number of reflections off the side walls in a guide increases as the frequency of the signal traveling through the guide decreases. The lines in the above illustration represent one component of the wave shown in Fig. 3.19.

most important property of a waveguide. All waves above a certain frequency will be transmitted more or less freely, whereas waves with frequencies below cut-off will suffer a high attenuation and will not be propagated at all, or at least not very far.

To illustrate, take the case of a small rectangular waveguide where the dimension X (Fig. 3–9) is 10 cm. For the $TE_{1,0}$ wave, there must be a half-wave variation in electric field from one side of the guide to the other. In this case the distance is 10 cm. If the frequency of the wave being sent into the guide is low, a half-wave will occupy more space than the allowable 10 cm, a situation that will not be tolerable by the rules formulated by Maxwell. Thus the problem is to find the frequency for a $TE_{1,0}$ wave which will give a half wavelength of 10 cm so as to enable this wave to fit into the dimension X of the waveguide.

The formula that can be used is

$$f = \frac{\text{velocity of light}}{\text{wavelength } (\lambda)}$$

which, when solved for the frequency in the example above, gives an answer of

$$f = \frac{30,000,000,000}{2 \times 10}$$

$$= 1500 \text{ mc}$$

Any wave having a frequency less than this would have a correspondingly longer wavelength, and it would then be impossible to fit a half wavelength into 10 cm. This wave cannot be propagated down the guide. But a wave having a higher frequency will be propagated down the guide with very little attenuation. Thus it can be seen that a waveguide provides a filtering action. The initial conditions must, at all times, be completely satisfied.

Now take the same rectangular waveguide and decrease the previous X dimension of 10 cm to 5 cm. Using the above formula, we obtain

$$f = \frac{3 \times 10^{10}}{2 \times 5}$$

$$= 3000 \text{ mc}$$

The cut-off frequency has now gone up, and no wave having a frequency less than 3000 mc will be propagated down the guide. Here is a peculiarity connected only with waveguides since there is nothing comparable to it in transmission lines. An interesting sidelight on wave travel in guides is the fact that, as the frequency of a signal increases, the time required for it to pass through a section of waveguide becomes less. The reason is indicated in Fig. 3–22. Ultimately, if the signal frequency is high enough, this time equals the time required by the wave to travel an equivalent distance in free space.

The relative sizes of waveguides used at 3000 mc, 10,000 mc, and 30,000 mc are illustrated in Fig. 3–23. The two waveguides at the right have the same cut-off frequency, this being determined by the distance across the mouth of the guide. The unit at the extreme right, however, is capable of handling more power by virtue of the greater separation between top and bottom walls.

The foregoing example has dealt with a relatively simple type of wave which allowed the direct usage of the ordinary formula giving the relationship between frequency and wavelength. However, when the electric or the magnetic fields extend in more than one direction, special formulas become necessary. While such modes may be employed, they seldom are because of the difficulty encountered in properly designing waveguides to operate efficiently with them. However, whether the waves are in the X-direction alone (such as the $TE_{0,1}$ wave) or also in the Y-direction, the rules laid down by Maxwell's equations must still be followed. In the previous discussion, the electric fields in the X and Y directions are meant;

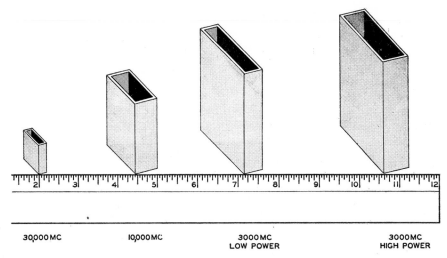

FIG. 3.23. An illustration of the relative sizes of rectangular waveguides used at 3000 mc, 10,000 mc, and 30,000 mc.

the Z-axis contains the magnetic field at right angles to the electric field or fields.

Energy attenuation in waveguides has been disregarded in the preceding discussion. Since all practical conducting surfaces do have some resistance associated with them, energy is abstracted from the wave as it travels down the guide. Energy is lost each time the wave-front bounces off a side wall. It is evident from Fig. 3–22 that, as we lower the frequency of the signal, the losses rise because of the increase in the number of reflections off the side walls. It would thus appear advantageous to operate at as high a frequency as possible in order to keep the attenuation at a minimum. However, as the frequency rises, the resistance of the side wall surfaces rise due to skin effect. If the losses versus frequency are charted, it will be found that the attenuation is least at some intermediate frequency, rising as we approach the cut-off frequency and rising at the higher frequencies.

Wave Notation. In order to distinguish the various types of waves from each other, a special labeling system has been developed based upon the difference between longitudinal and transverse waves. To demonstrate longitudinal wave motion, take an ordinary tuning fork and hit it sharply, causing it to vibrate. This motion will force any air particles near the fork to vibrate, and the resultant waves will travel outward in all directions. The vibrations of the air particles will be in the same direction as the

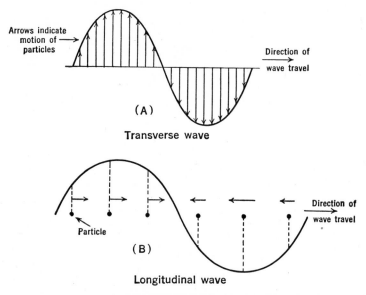

FIG. 3.24. (A) Motion of particles is up and down. (B) Motion of particles is back and forth.

propagation of the sound waves, causing their paths to be parallel. This action is the defining characteristic of a longitudinal wave. It should, of course, be remembered that the air particles vibrate about a mean point while only the energy is expanding outward. It is somewhat analogous to a situation where a straight row of billiard balls is tapped at one end. The energy is transmitted forward by the balls while they themselves remain relatively fixed in position.

For the case of a transverse wave, consider the motion obtained by means of a rope, one end of which is secured and the other end moved up and down by hand. Here the rope particles move up and down while the wave itself is propagated forward. The two motions, that of the rope and that of the wave, are at right angles to each other. This combination of motions defines a transverse wave. Fig. 3–24 emphasizes pictorially the difference between the two types of waves.

TE **Waves.** Transferring our attention from sound waves and rope waves to electromagnetic vibrations, we can use this information to label the various types of waves in rectangular guides. As mentioned before, every electromagnetic wave may have electric and magnetic fields with components along any of the three conventional directions, X, Y, and Z (see Fig. 3–9). Suppose a wave had a magnetic field along the Z-axis but no electric lines of force along this direction. The electric lines of force could extend in the X or the Y direction, or both. Since the wave travels in the Z-direction, to the magnetic field this is a longitudinal wave since it has a component in the Z-direction. However, since the electric field has no components in the Z-direction, but only in the X or Y directions, it can be called a transverse wave. This follows from the definition of transverse waves. Thus, there is a choice. With regard to the magnetic field, it is a longitudinal wave; with respect to the electric field, it is a transverse wave. The custom has been to label the wave after the transverse component. Hence in this case the notation would be TE, designating a transverse electric wave. Another name sometimes used is "H wave."

TM **Waves.** To reverse the situation, let electric lines of force extend in the direction of propagation, the Z-axis, but there be no variation of the magnetic field in this direction. The magnetic field will vary in the X-direction, the Y-direction, or both. In this case there would be a longitudinal wave with respect to the electric field and a transverse vibration with respect to the magnetic field. Since it is customary to label the wave after the transverse component, we get, for this wave, the name of TM wave, TM being an abbreviation for transverse magnetic. Another name that is sometimes used is "E wave." Having explained the two most important notations, a third and final type of wave, in reality a plane wave, might be mentioned. (See Fig. 3–8.) Here the electric and magnetic fields are at right angles to each other and both are perpendicular to the direction of propagation. This is truly a transverse wave, having no longitudinal components. The name given to this type of wave is a combination of the preceding two types and is TEM.

Thus far the nomenclature has been general, indicating the method of designating only a class of waves. There is still lacking a specific notation that will indicate a particular wave in any class. In order to bring this out more clearly, Fig. 3–25 shows three types of waves that are in the TE class. The simplest wave in this group is in Fig. 3–25A, where the dimension X is just wide enough to accommodate a half-wave of the electric field. In Fig. 3–25B, the frequency of the wave has been raised, so that now the same dimension X can accommodate a full wave. In Fig. 3–25C the frequency has again been increased and now there are three half-waves. This process can be continued as long as higher frequencies could be generated. Each wave is differentiated from the other by a small subscript m. Thus the lowest frequency wave (Fig. 3–25A) would be represented by setting an m equal to 1, Fig. 3–25B would have an m of 2, Fig. 3–25C would have an m of 3, etc. The nomenclature is now more specific than it was and takes the form TE_m.

But there is no reason why the dimension in the Y-direction should be ignored since it is perfectly possible to have the electric lines of force vary in that direction, too. In this case, use the subscript n and add 1 for each half-wave of variation in this direction. Thus the final notation is $TE_{m,n}$ and each different wave is known as a mode. Specifically, the wave in Fig. 3–25A is $TE_{1,0}$ mode, that in Fig. 3–25B the $TE_{2,0}$ mode, etc.

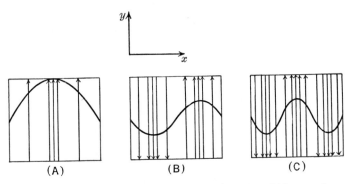

Fig. 3.25. The electric field of the $TE_{m,0}$ type of wave. (A) $m = 1$, so we have $TE_{1,0}$. (B) $m = 2$, so we have $TE_{2,0}$. (C) $m = 3$, so we have $TE_{3,0}$.

Zero is used for n because there is no variation of the electric field in the Y-dimension in the case shown; but waves like $TE_{1,1}$, $TE_{2,1}$, etc., are perfectly possible. They are not frequently mentioned because they are seldom used, but they can be generated. Whatever has been said concerning the subscripts n and m is equally applicable to the TM type of waves.

The various sections of Fig. 3–25 depict only the electric field distributions, but, as we have seen, associated with each of these is a magnetic field. (Refer to Figs. 3–11, 3–13, and 3–14.) For the first wave, $TE_{1,0}$, there is one half-wave of electric field variation across the guide (dimension X). The magnetic lines encircle the electric lines and, if we were looking into the mouth of the guide and could see them, they would appear as shown in Fig. 3–13. Another view, this time looking down on the top of the guide, would appear as shown in Fig. 3–11C. The lines of force of the electric field extend either straight up or down, according to their polarity. To distinguish between these polarities, dots and $\times$'s are used. They actually have no other significance. We could have used A's and

B's, or numbers, or any other two symbols. All they serve to signify is the fact that at one point the electric force is directed in one direction and at a subsequent point the force is directed in the opposite direction. Encircling the electric lines of force are the magnetic lines of force. They form complete loops. When the electric field is in one direction, the magnetic lines or loops have one polarity. When the electric field reverses, the magnetic field follows suit. In Figs. 3–11C and 3–13 this reversal is indicated by reversing the direction of the arrows on the magnetic loops.

Figs. 3–11 and 3–13 reveal quite clearly that none of the electric lines extends lengthwise along the guide. Hence, this is a *TE* wave. For a *TM* mode, the magnetic loops would extend across the guide (in the X and Y directions), but not lengthwise along the guide.

As we increase the number of half-wave variations placed across the guide, we also increase the complexity of the field pattern within the guide. Fig. 3–14 shows several views of the electric and magnetic fields of the $TE_{2,0}$ wave.

The longest wavelength that a guide can accommodate is known as its "dominant mode." In a rectangular guide, the $TE_{1,0}$ is the dominant mode. This mode does not depend on how the guide is excited but only on the geometrical size of the waveguide.

In actual practice, guides are generally used only with the lowest frequency signal they will transmit. This is done for several reasons. First, the lowest frequency signal is the one most easily generated. Second, it possesses the simplest field patterns, making it easier to attach auxiliary apparatus to the guide, such as flexible sections, corner bends, matching sections, etc., with a minimum of power loss. Waveguides, when run in other than straight directions, are subject to impedance mismatch and increased loss due to reflections. With the dominant mode, these mismatches and losses can be kept low more easily than if a higher mode, and consequently one possessing more complex fields, were used. Finally, with a simple mode, the possibility of mode jumping is minimized.

To illustrate this latter point, suppose a waveguide has the same X and Y dimensions (i.e., is square) and these are large enough to accommodate a half-wave of a certain frequency signal. The signal is introduced into the guide in the $TE_{1,0}$ mode, which means that the electric field extends from bottom to top. At the other end of the guide, a receiving antenna is inserted to receive the energy from this wave. During the passage of the wave down the guide, however, part of the energy of the wave changes polarization, and an electric field variation is also established along the Y-direction. This is perfectly possible since the wave is still transverse to the length of the guide along which the propagation occurs, and the Y-dimension is large enough to accommodate a half-wave of this signal. Thus, there is now a $TE_{0,1}$ wave together with the original $TE_{1,0}$ signal. The receiving antenna, however, will receive only that portion of the signal which is in the $TE_{1,0}$ mode, since maximum voltage is induced in an antenna when its polarization is the same as the polarization of the electric field in the arriving signal. That portion of the electric field which is horizontally polarized (the $TE_{0,1}$) would induce little or no voltage in the receiving antenna.

To prevent mode jumping with its attendant waste of power, only the simple modes are used, such as the $TE_{1,0}$, $TE_{2,0}$, etc., and the waveguide is designed to permit only this mode to be propagated through it. Thus, if it is desired to have only the $TE_{1,0}$ wave present in a guide, the X-dimension is made slightly wider than one-half wavelength of the $TE_{1,0}$ wave while the Y-dimension (the height) is kept less than one-half wavelength. Thus, the Y-dimension could not accommodate a half-wave of the signal and the signal is restricted to the desired $TE_{1,0}$ mode. It is interesting to note that, for any mode in which the number of half-wave standing waves along the Y-dimension is zero (such as the $TE_{1,0}$, $TE_{2,0}$, etc.), there is no lower limit for this height. It may be as small as desired. However, the attenuation imposed on a wave decreases as the X and Y dimensions are made longer and hence it is customary to make Y slightly less than one-half wavelength.

The $TE_{m,0}$ waves have a transverse electric field, which is at right angles to the direction of propagation of the waves. There may be reasons, however, for generating waves with the electric field longitudinal or in the direction of propagation. These waves are labeled TM waves. One reason for using a TM wave in place of a TE wave of like frequency may be due to attenuation. Perhaps one type of wave will have lower losses than the other. Or it may be that different signals are to be sent simultaneously, in which case both a TE and a TM wave could be transmitted and received separately, without interference to each other. The situation may, in a sense, be compared to the use of certain combinations of antennas over others at the low frequencies.

One would expect to find, following the foregoing line of reasoning, that the simplest TM wave would be the $TM_{1,0}$ or $TM_{0,1}$. Subscripts in the TM mode cannot be zero because magnetic lines of force must form continuous loops and, hence, when this field is transverse, there will be a half-wave (or more) variation not just in one direction (as in the $TE_{m,0}$ mode) but in both directions. If either the X or Y dimension of the guide is less than one-half wavelength, the TM mode cannot exist in a rectangular guide. However, it can exist in a cylindrical waveguide because of the difference in field arrangement.

It is interesting to note in connection with the generation of these fields that a straight antenna may be used to set up the electric field, which will in turn give rise to the accompanying magnetic fields. It is also possible to place a loop of wire properly in the guide so that the circulating currents in this conductor will set up the necessary magnetic fields. These will, in turn, likewise produce the electric forces. Either method may be employed, but, practically, the single straight antenna is used most frequently because it involves fewer mechanical difficulties.

Excitation of Waveguides—The TE Type of Wave. Excitation of waveguides was touched on briefly in a previous section when it was stated that an antenna was inserted into a waveguide and the electromagnetic energy radiated from it. Actually, each general pattern of wave (both *TE* and *TM*) and each specific wave require a different setup to produce the desired field patterns. However, a similarity between the various waves of the *TE* group will be readily evident and the same can be said for the *TM* group. The generator will be omitted in each case and only the placement of the concentric cable in the waveguide will be shown. It will be assumed that the connection of the cable to the UHF generator is understood.

The simplest wave of the *TE* group, the $TE_{1,0}$, can be generated by any of the methods shown in Fig. 3-26.

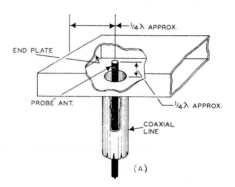

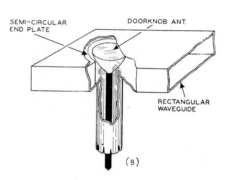

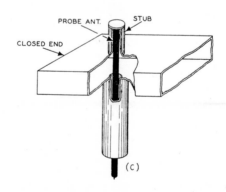

FIG. 3.26. Three methods of feeding energy to waveguides. (*Courtesy Radio Electronics*)

In the first illustration, Fig. 3–26A, the outer conductor of the coaxial line connects to the wall of the guide. The inner conductor, however, extends into the guide for a distance of approximately one-quarter wavelength.   The width of the guide is one half-wave and the inner conductor of the coaxial cable extends into the guide at its center.   In looking back at any of the previous illustrations in which the guide width was one half-wave, it will be seen that the electric field strength is maximum at this point.

One-quarter wavelength back along the guide from the antenna an end plate is inserted.   This returns any energy which reaches it from the antenna, the quarter-wave distance being chosen purposely so that this

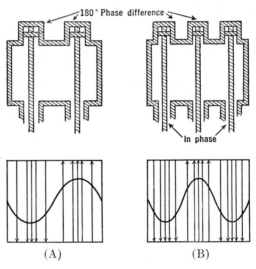

(A)   (B)

FIG. 3.27.   Methods of generating the $TE_{2,0}$ (A) and the $TE_{3,0}$ (B) types of waves.

reflected energy will reach the antenna in time to add to the energy traveling down the guide in the other (desired) direction.

In the second arrangement, Fig. 3–26B, the end of the probe has been flared out and rounded off to handle higher power and provide a more satisfactory match over a band of frequencies.   The straight end plate in the guide of Fig. 3–28A is replaced in this instance by a semi-circular end plate.

In the final illustration, Fig. 3–26C, the center conductor of the coaxial line extends up through the waveguide and terminates in a stub.   The stub length is adjusted until the energy transmitted by the antenna is maximum.   An end wall here serves the same purpose as in Fig. 3–26A.

The $TE_{2,0}$ wave can be produced by the arrangement shown in Fig. 3–27A.   Since the exciting rods are 180 degrees out of phase, the electric fields are in opposite directions on the left and on the right halves of the guide. The arrangement for a $TE_{3,0}$ wave is shown in Fig. 3–27B. Note that in all cases it is the central or inner conductor of the coaxial cable that extends into the waveguide and acts as the antenna.

TM Wave Excitation. To produce fields of the TM mode, the arrangement shown in Fig. 3–28A may be used. This is similar to the case of TE excitation except for the position of the antenna in the waveguide. For comparison, the method of generating a $TE_{1,0}$ wave is shown in Fig. 3–28B. In general, for the $TE_{m,n}$ type of wave, the antenna will be at right angles to the direction of propagation, while in the $TM_{m,n}$ case, the antennas are parallel to the direction of propagation. This is logical since

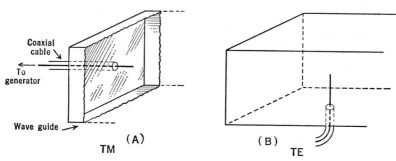

FIG. 3.28. A comparison of the general methods of exciting TE and TM types of waves.

the TE wave has no electric field in the forward direction while the TM wave has. It is only natural, then, that the placement of the radiators should also differ by 90 degrees.

Usually, provision is made whereby the length of the antenna in the waveguide can be adjusted to give best results. This is an important adjustment since the measured intensity of the transmitted wave may vary a great deal between the best condition and the worst. Another adjustment is to get the proper distance between the antenna and the near end of the waveguide. This end wall acts as a reflector or backboard. Correct alignment of the antenna can also greatly improve the transmitting efficiency. Although only transmission of the wave has been discussed so far, every radio man knows that a good transmitting antenna is also a good receiving antenna. Thus these adjustments are important for a receiving antenna as well. In the case of reception, however, the coaxial cable is connected to a crystal detector which rectifies the received current and makes it available for further use. These antennas, when used for reception, can be made very selective and will pick out one type of wave almost to the exclusion of all others. By having several types of transmitting antennas placed in various positions and by mounting receiving rods in similar positions at the other end of the guide, the guide may be used for multiple channel transmission.

Cylindrical Waveguides. Our attention, thus far, has been centered on the rectangular waveguide because it is easy to visualize the actions of the electromagnetic wave in them. However, there are many other

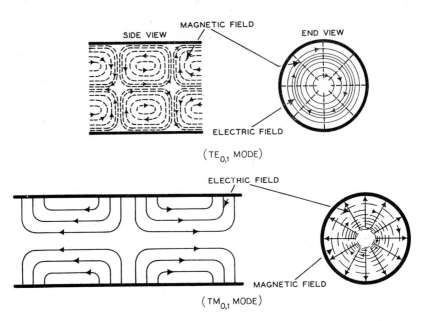

FIG. 3.29. The field patterns of the $TE_{0,1}$ and $TM_{0,1}$ modes in circular wave-guides. For the sake of simplicity, the side views show only the longitudinal field. The end view contains both fields.

forms of guides possible, most having little practical importance except the cylindrical waveguides. As with the rectangular forms, it is possible to use the two notations $TE_{m,n}$ and $TM_{m,n}$ to label the various types of waves that can be propagated down a cylindrical tube. Propagation is limited in this, as in a rectangular guide, to frequencies that are not too low for a particular diameter of the guide. The same conditions pertaining to electric and magnetic fields still hold true, even though the shape of these fields has changed because of the change in shape of the guide.

The notation applicable to cylindrical waveguides, while still retaining the form TE and TM, is altered in meaning for the two subscripts. The first subscript indicates the number of full-wave patterns of either the electric or magnetic fields which exist around a circular path concentric with the guide wall. The second subscript indicates the number of half-wave variations that can be counted in going from the center to the circumference of the guide along a diameter. Two illustrations of the fields in circular guides are shown in Fig. 3–29. In each instance the first subscript is zero because there is no variation in field as we travel around the circumference of the guide. This subscript will always be zero when the transverse field (either electric or magnetic) forms a complete series of circles about the center axis. In Fig. 3–29A, the electric field is transverse, producing circular electric lines of force. The field intensity is zero at the center, rises to a maximum at a point midway between the center and the circumference of the guide, and then decreases to zero again at the walls of the guide. There is one-half wave field variation in going from the center to the circumference of the guide and consequently the second subscript is 1.

The magnetic field with its circular lines of force will be at right angles to the circular electric lines and thus the two fields will entwine each other, somewhat like metallic links on a chain. A cross-sectional view and a side view of the fields of the $TE_{0,1}$ mode in a circular waveguide are shown in Fig. 3–29A and, by studying both of these closely, the reader will be able to form a fairly complete picture of the conditions existing within the guide. Fig. 3–29B illustrates the field pattern for the $TM_{0,1}$ mode.

Additional views (both cross-sectional and side) of other modes are shown in Figs. 3–30A, 3–30B, and 3–30C. In each instance note carefully which lines represent the magnetic fields and which represent the electric fields. When the modes change so that the first subscript is other than zero, there is a variation in the electric or magnetic field as we go around the circumference of the guide. Also, the transverse field is no longer circular about the center axis.

Three relatively simple modes, $TE_{1,1}$, $TE_{0,2}$, and $TM_{1,2}$ are shown in Fig. 3–30 and from a study of these it can be appreciated how quickly the field pattern complexity increases with rise in subscript number. The two most important modes used for transmission in circular waveguides are the $TE_{0,1}$ and the $TM_{0,1}$. More often than not, rectangular waveguides are used, despite the fact that they are harder to fabricate because it is more difficult to suppress mode jumping in circular waveguides than in rectangular guides.

For excitation of the $TM_{0,1}$ wave in cylindrical guides, it is possible to use the set-up pictured in Fig. 3–31. The $TE_{1,1}$ type depicted in Fig. 3–32 has only transverse components of the electric field. The critical or cut-off frequency is higher for the $TM_{0,1}$ wave than it is for the $TE_{1,1}$

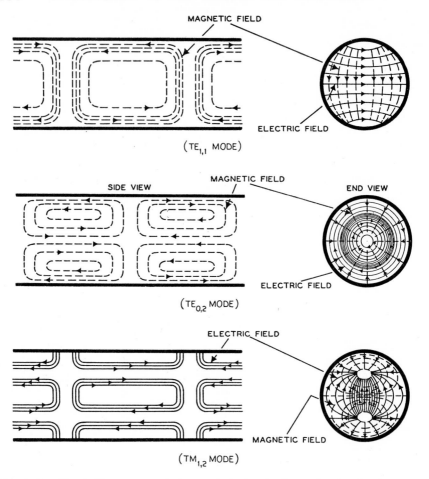

Fig. 3.30. The field patterns of three relatively simple modes in circular wave-guides.

wave, identical diameters being used in each case. This can be seen when the formulas are given:

$$f_{\text{cut-off}} = \frac{1.15 \times 10^{10}}{r(\text{cm})} \text{ cps}$$

for the $TM_{0,1}$ wave;

$$f_{\text{cut-off}} = \frac{8.79 \times 10^9}{r(\text{cm})} \text{ cps}$$

for the $TE_{1,1}$ wave. Because of the inverse relationship of frequency to radius, a higher cut-off frequency means a smaller opening of the cylinder. Remember again that the cut-off frequency represents the lowest frequency (or longest wavelength) that will be propagated down the tube without too much attenuation. Practically, it is possible to transmit below this frequency, but the range is rather limited. Theoretically, all higher wavelengths can be easily transmitted without much attenuation (using actual conductors). In practice, however, the upper frequencies begin to show

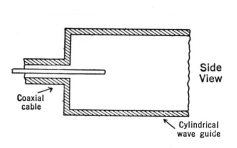

FIG. 3.31. Method of generating $TM_{0,1}$ wave in cylindrical waveguide.

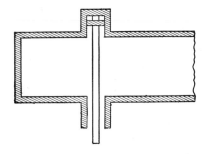

FIG. 3.32. Method of excitation of the $TE_{1,1}$ wave.

excessive attenuation because of increased skin effect. In between these two extremes a frequency can usually be found that will have least attenuation. Whether or not it is used will be determined by other factors that may assume greater importance than attenuation.

Practical Waveguides and Their Application. The most important application of waveguides is the transference of power from one point to another in ultra-high-frequency systems. The waveguide is essentially a transmission line which is designed specifically for the ultra-high frequencies. Its extensive use is due to its low attenuation, the principal losses arising from the interior skin effect and the dielectric, if a material other than air is used.

The electric and magnetic fields traveling through a waveguide are accompanied by a similar movement of electrons along the walls of the guide. Electric fields terminate on positive (or negative) charges induced in the walls and, as the fields travel down the guide, the charge distributions change in step. Since we are dealing here with frequencies well up in the megacycle region, the opposition of the conducting substance (in the form of skin effect) to these r-f currents is appreciable and the current literally flows on instead of in the conductors. How resistance rises with frequency is clearly indicated by the tabulation in Table 3–1. Five principal types of conductors or plated surfaces (brass, aluminum, gold, copper, and silver) used in waveguides are listed, together with the resistance and depth of current penetration at 100 mc, 1000 mc, 10,000 mc, and 100,000 mc. The resistance values are based on a metallic strip one centimeter wide and one meter long. It will be found that the average increase in resistance is proportional to the square root of the frequency. Thus, from 100 to 100,000 mc the frequency increase is a 1000-fold, whereas the resistance rise over the same range is approximately 30, which is close to the square root of 1000.

TABLE 3–1. THE VARIATION OF RESISTANCE WITH FREQUENCY
OF FIVE COMMON METALS.

(The resistances listed are for a strip of metal 1 cm wide and 1 meter long.)

Metal	100 Mc Ohms	1000 Mc Ohms	10,000 Mc Ohms	100,000 Mc Ohms
Brass	0.005	0.016	0.05	0.16
Aluminum	.0034	.011	.034	.11
Gold	.0032	.0103	.032	.103
Copper	.0026	.0083	.026	.083
Silver	.0025	.008	.025	.080

From the figures shown, silver would appear to be the best choice. Actually, tests and experience have shown that gold is better, because it possesses greater freedom from corrosion and better permanence of electrical characteristics. Silver tends to deteriorate faster, causing arc-over, and gradually develops surface pits. For low loss transmission, an absolutely smooth, clean surface is required. Any small changes in internal dimensions due to corrosion or dirt tend to act as a constriction, causing reflection and mismatching.

Most waveguides are made from gold-plated brass, silver-plated brass, or aluminum-plated brass. Sometimes, where weight considerations outweigh all others, aluminum waveguides are employed. Because of the minute depth of current penetration, plating the desired conductor over a cheaper base metal produces just as good results as employing the more expensive metal for the entire guide structure.

Other factors governing transmission loss in waveguides are the size of the guide and whether or not the guide has any bends. The matter of guide size has been covered previously, and it was noted that signal attenuation decreases with increase in the internal perimeter of the guide. Offsetting this is the fact that, as a guide is made large, it not only becomes bulky, but the possibility of mode jumping increases.

In transferring energy from the equipment to the antenna, it is generally impossible to maintain a straight run of waveguide, and guide bending becomes necessary. Any change in guide direction causes energy reflections and a consequent loss in power transfer. The losses, however, can be kept low if the bend is made as gradually as possible. As a rule, the radius of the bend is made equal to at least two wavelengths of the signal traveling along the guide. (See Fig. 3–33.)

Waveguide bends can provide not only a change in direction, but a change in polarization as well. (See Fig. 3–34.) Again, to maintain low loss of signal strength, the bend should not be completed in a distance less than 2 wavelengths.

The properties of waveguides and transmission lines are very similar and many transmission line applications have their counterparts—with the proper modifications—in waveguides. Thus, suppose it is desired to connect together two waveguides, each possessing different dimensions. We would not attach the two guide sections directly together any more than we would directly connect two different transmission lines. To hold the reflection loss to a minimum, a tapered section is interposed between the two

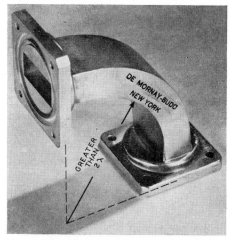

FIG. 3.33. To minimize energy loss due to reflection, waveguide bends should be made as gradual as possible.

guides as shown in Fig. 3–35. The change in guide characteristics thus is accomplished gradually and the loss due to reflection is held to a minimum.

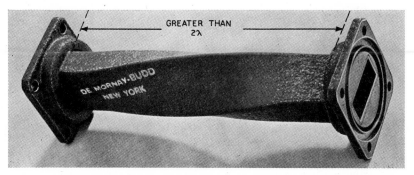

FIG. 3.34. A waveguide section possessing a 90° twist. (*Courtesy De Mornay-Budd, Inc.*)

The phenomenon of cut-off frequency makes waveguides essentially high-pass filters. All frequencies above the cut-off frequency are permitted to pass, whereas all lower frequencies are stopped.   This effect does not necessarily have to take place at the opening of the guide; it may occur anywhere along its length.   Thus, if a pipe of large diameter is tapered to one of smaller diameter, waves that could be propagated in the large pipe might be unable to continue in the smaller guide and thus would be attenuated and reflected.   In this manner, frequencies may be separated, an action that can be achieved only at lower frequencies by coils and capacitors. The analogy to filter circuits can be extended even further by combining sections of waveguides that have different filtering characteristics.

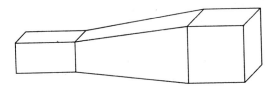

Fig. 3.35.   A transition from a waveguide of one size to a guide of another size may be achieved with a minimum loss of power by using a tapered connecting guide.

Another use is the cavity resonator. The transition of tuned circuits commences at the low frequencies with a coil and capacitor, becomes a section of a transmission line at the very high frequencies, and finally ends with the cavity resonator at the ultra-high frequencies. The function remains unchanged, but the method of accomplishing this does not.

Waveguides can also be transformed into efficient ultra-high-frequency antennas by flaring one end, thereby effecting a match between the characteristic impedance of the guide and the impedance of free space.   While the idea that free space possesses a certain impedance may seem strange, actually we have seen that the volume of air included between the ionosphere and the ground functioned as a gigantic guide.   And being a guide, although a gigantic one, it would possess a certain characteristic impedance. By flaring the end of the smaller guide, a partial matching of impedances is achieved, enabling a fairly efficient transfer of energy.   Waveguides, when used in this manner, are known as electromagnetic horns and possess directional characteristics comparable to antennas.   A more extended discussion of horns is given in the chapter on UHF antennas

Choke Joints.   The impedance inverting action of quarter-wave sections of transmission lines can be duplicated with waveguides.

Thus suppose that two sections of a guide must be constructed to allow for the effects of heat expansion.   If a single section were used, expansion due to heat might produce a bulge or other deformity in the guide, increasing signal attenuation.   To permit expansion without shape distortion, a choke coupling joint is used. (See Fig. 3–36.) The two sections of guide are mechanically connected together by means of a flange containing a circular slot a quarter-wave deep. The distance from the side of the waveguide to the slot is one-quarter wavelength (at the operating frequency

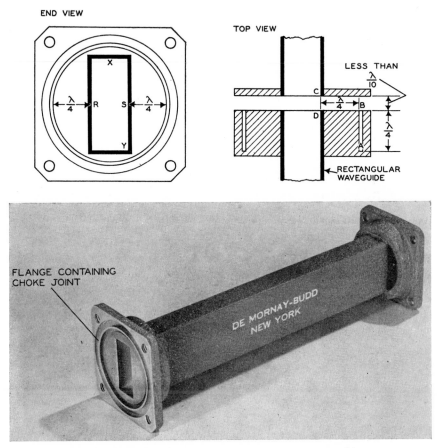

Fig. 3.36. A choke joint for a rectangular waveguide.

of the guide) and the slot itself is one-quarter wavelength deep. The total distance is thus one-half wavelength from the guide wall to the bottom of the slot. Since the bottom of the slot is short-circuited, a low impedance will be reflected, without change, to points C–D, and any energy traveling down the guide will not see any discontinuities here. Because the guide is rectangular and the connecting flange is circular, not all points on the guide wall will be a quarter-wave distant from the slot. In fact, this

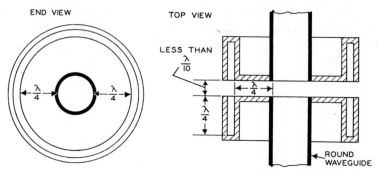

END VIEW   TOP VIEW

FIG. 3.37.   Choke joint for a circular waveguide.

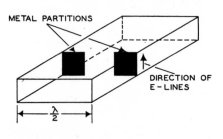

(A) INDUCTIVE REACTANCE

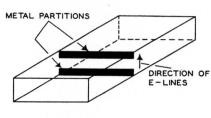

(B) CAPACITIVE REACTANCE

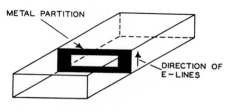

(C) REACTIVE OR RESISTIVE REACTANCE
(DETERMINED BY FREQ.)

FIG. 3.38.   The effect of various types of
partitions in waveguides.

will occur only at the center of the guide, points R and S of Fig. 3–36. However, this is the region of maximum electric and magnetic fields and hence requires the best matching. The matching is poorest at points X and Y, but the r-f energy here is low and so the loss is small.

In circular waveguides, the choke joint is equally effective for all points of the guide since all points are equidistant from the slot. (See Fig. 3–37.)

Guide Partitions. We can alter the properties of a waveguide either by changing its shape or by placing metal partitions in various positions within the guide. If a partition is placed parallel to the electric lines of force, currents will flow vertically in the partition and develop a local magnetic field. Hence the effect of the partition is inductive, and we can represent the circuit as shown in Fig. 3–38A. In this particular illustration, we are assuming that the energy traveling down the guide is in the $TE_{0.1}$ mode.

By the same token, if the metal partition is turned perpendicular to its previous position, an electric field is developed between the two sections of the partition. The field now is largely electric and the partitions act like shunt capacitances. (See Fig. 3–38B.) By combining both types of partitions, we can obtain either capacitive or inductive effects, depending upon the dimensions. By properly choosing the length and height of the partition, parallel resonance can be achieved and we obtain the same effect as placing a high shunt resistance across the line. (See Fig. 3–38C.) In this case, the passing wave is only slightly affected, passing through the opening with negligible attenuation.

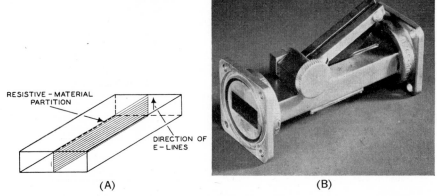

(A)   (B)

Fig. 3.39. A method of alternating a signal in a waveguide. (*Courtesy De Mornay-Budd, Inc.*)

Partitions similar to those just described are useful as filters, attenuating undesirable modes while permitting the desired wave to pass. The effect of any partition will depend upon the frequency of the wave and an inductive effect at one frequency may be capacitive at some other frequency.

To attenuate a signal passing through the waveguide, a lengthwise partition made of some resistive material, such as coated carbon, may be used. (See Fig. 3–39A.) The partition is placed lengthwise in the center of a guide through a slot so that it comes in contact with the maximum portion of the electric field. Energy is abstracted from this field because the electric lines of force set up current flow in the carbon. This is closely similar to the decrease in potential of a battery when resistance is connected across its terminals and current flows. An actual flap attenuator, as these are called, is shown in Fig. 3–39B. The attenuator strip is made of carbon-coated bakelite. The position of the flap, to which the attenuator strip is attached, can be varied, thus permitting the strip to be inserted to any desired depth. Varying amounts of attenuation are thereby available. A thumbscrew is provided in order that the flap may be fastened in any position.

Waveguides, in common with transmission lines and other electrical circuits, possess characteristic impedances. However, in waveguides, the value of this impedance depends upon the mode of the signal being transmitted down the guide. This can be seen from the accepted definition for

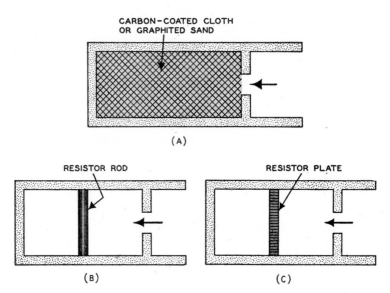

Fig. 3.40. Various methods of terminating waveguides. (A) Carbon-coated cloth or graphited sand; (B) resistor rod; (C) resistor plate.

characteristic impedance in guides, namely, the ratio of the value of the transverse magnetic field to the value of the transverse electric field for a given mode. Once this value has been determined, terminating a guide in a load of this value will cause all of the energy fed into the guide to be absorbed without reflection. Common types of loads used with guides are shown in Fig. 3–40. In the first illustration, Fig. 3–40A, the energy is absorbed by a mass of carbon-coated cloth. In Fig. 3–40B, the energy is dissipated in a small rod of resistive material placed upright in the guide at a point where the electric field intensity is high. Finally, in Fig. 3–40C, a flat resistor plate is placed crosswise in the guide.

Flexible Waveguides. It would be desirable if all waveguides extended in a straight line from source to load. However, in most instances, the mechanical limitations are such that bending and twisting of the guides must occur. Furthermore, in some high-frequency systems, the waveguide must be connected to devices which move mechanically (such as the scanning antennas in radar systems) or where a certain amount of vibration and shock must be absorbed. In these instances, guides possessing flexibility are more desirable than rigid guides.

Of the three types of flexible waveguides which have been used, the interlocked flexible guide has found the most extensive application. This guide is shown in cross section in Fig. 3–41 and in outward appearance in Fig. 3–42. It is constructed by winding a metal strip around a rectangular form, the edges of the strips overlapping each other and then folding the edges under until they interlock in the manner shown in Fig. 3–41. With this construction, the waveguide can be twisted, bent, and even stretched slightly, the latter due to the small amount of space between the interlocking edges. It is evident

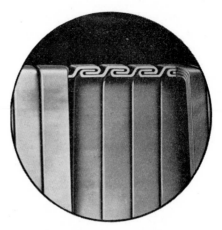

FIG. 3.41. A cut-away view showing construction of interlocked flexible waveguides. (*Courtesy Technicraft Laboratories*)

that the walls of the guide are not perfectly smooth and continuous, and a certain amount of energy reflection will occur. By careful construction, however, the energy lost can be kept quite small, resulting in voltage

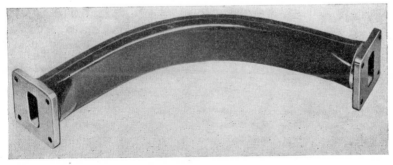

FIG. 3.42. A section of an interlocked flexible waveguide with a rubber protective jacket. (*Courtesy Technicraft Laboratories*)

standing-wave ratios of only 1.10, and only slightly greater attenuation than a rigid guide. The flexible sections are terminated by either flat or choke flanges in order to permit their attachment to rigid sections. In their most common form, these interlocked flexible guides are provided with molded rubber coverings which not only protect the guide from the elements, but also enable the section to withstand an internal pressure equal to 1½ atmospheres.

A second type of flexible waveguide consists of a rectangular, thin-walled metal tube constructed as shown in Fig. 3–43. Convolution or convoluting is used frequently to describe this assembly, and the word means a construction in which the surface is rolled or folded back on itself or coiled together. Because of its seamless type of construction, this guide is capable of withstanding sharp bends, extensive stretching, or compression. It can be damaged, however, by axial twisting. By covering the outside of the

Fig. 3.43.   A cut-away view showing construction of seamless, corrugated rectangular flexible guide. (*Courtesy Technicraft Laboratories*)

guide with a plastic cover, the guide can be made to withstand internal pressure exceeding 1½ atmospheres.

The metal used for making seamless guides is generally copper or bronze, plated with silver or gold. It is lightweight and used extensively for coupling to brittle or fragile substances. In spite of the fact that the inside surface of the guide is not smooth, the attenuation per foot is only slightly greater than that of a rigid guide. The voltage standing-wave ratio is quite low, being only 1.08.

The third type of flexible waveguide, known as the "vertebra-type," is shown in Fig. 3–44. It is constructed by combining a number of choke connectors, each spaced by a ribbed synthetic rubber jacket. The chokes, similar to those discussed previously, contain grooves which are one-quarter wavelength deep at the operating frequency of the guide. There is an additional quarter of a wavelength distance from the guide wall to the groove. Thus, we have one-half wavelength distance, at the end of which is a short. The short-circuit, reflected over one-half wavelength distance, presents an r-f short at the waveguide wall, and, to the energy traveling down the guide, there is no break in the electrical continuity of the side walls. A direct current, however, would not be able to pass from one section of the guide to the next.

End flanges are connected to the guide section to permit attachment to rigid waveguides. The particular construction of this guide permits it to be compressed, twisted, and elongated to a greater extent than either of the other two flexible guides. This guide, however, is heavier and bulkier than the others and is not used as extensively. Also, its frequency

FIG. 3.44. The components of the "vertebra-type" of flexible waveguide.
(*Courtesy Technicraft Laboratories*)

range of operation is more restricted because of the presence of the chokes. Chokes are most effective as short circuits (preventing radiation and loss) when the choke groove is exactly equal to one-quarter wavelength at the operating frequency. The shorting action becomes less effective as the signal deviates from this frequency.

QUESTIONS

1. What are the advantages of waveguides over transmission lines at the ultra-high frequencies? Explain.

2. What restrictions do waveguides impose on radio waves, restrictions that are not present on waves that travel in free space?

3. What is the importance of polarization of radio waves in waveguides?

4. What is the significance of electric and magnetic lines of force in waveguides? How are they shown?

5. Describe electromagnetic wave travel in guides.

6. What is meant by cut-off frequency and what is its significance with respect to waveguides?

7. Explain the relationship between the notation of these waves and longitudinal and transverse vibrations.

8. Draw an end view of a guide showing the electric field distribution for a $TE_{2,0}$ wave.

9. For the same guide, show the field distribution for a $TE_{1,0}$ wave.

10. For the excitation of TE waves, how should the antenna be placed in a guide? Why?

11. Explain the *TM* type of antenna.

12. How do the above two antennas differ (a) with respect to placement and (b) with regard to length?

13. How are the coordinates modified for cylindrical waveguides?

14. What factors determine the cut-off frequency of any guide?

15. Name several uses for waveguides.

16. In what respects are waveguides similar to transmission lines and in what respects do they differ?

17. Do the electric field distributions differ for cylindrical waveguides from those shown for rectangular guides? Illustrate.

18. Why are we justified in believing that waves do not travel in a straight line through a waveguide?

19. How do waves travel through waveguides? Explain briefly.

20. Explain the difference between group and phase velocity.

21. What metals are used in the construction of waveguides? What factors determine which metal is used in any particular guide?

22. What is a choke joint and when is it used?

23. Describe the construction of flexible waveguides.

24. When are flexible waveguides more desirable than rigid guides?

25. Compare the three types of flexible waveguides with respect to signal attenuation and application.

Chapter 4

CAVITY RESONATORS

Why Cavity Resonators? It has been noted in previous chapters that the trend in tuners was from using circuits with lumped L and C elements at the low frequencies to circuits with distributed L and C at the ultra-highs. At microwave frequencies conventional coils and capacitors are too small to be of any practical use. In addition, the Q of these circuits are quite low when compared to values which can be obtained with resonant lines. As the frequency is raised to 3000 mc (10 cm), even the lengths of tuned lines become too small to be practical to handle. For example, a quarter-wave line at a wavelength of 10 cm is only 2.5 cm, or roughly 1 in. long. That size cannot be handled with ease and would result in many of the same difficulties that have been experienced with conventional tuning coils and capacitors. The cavity resonator was designed to satisfy the requirements of UHF circuits.

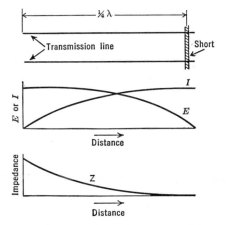

Fig. 4.1. The voltage, current, and impedance values on a short-circuited, ¼λ line.

Development of the Cavity Resonator. An explanation of the cavity resonator may be approached from two directions: first, by starting with transmission lines; and second, by way of waveguides. Both explanations will be given since they are actually related to each other.

Beginning with tuned transmission lines, consider the quarter-wave section shown in Fig. 4–1. If a generator is coupled to this line, the familiar

127

voltage and current distribution shown will be obtained. At the shorted end, the current will be a maximum and the voltage will be zero; at the open end, the reverse will exist, a low current and high voltage.

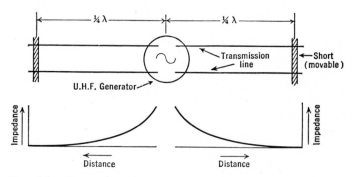

Fig. 4.2. Connecting two quarter-wave lines across a generator.

Now suppose that two quarter-wave lines are placed in parallel across the r-f generator. (See Fig. 4–2.) This line, too, will be excited in the same manner as the first line. If we continue to add more and more lines in parallel across the generator, Fig. 4–3A, we finally form a metal container

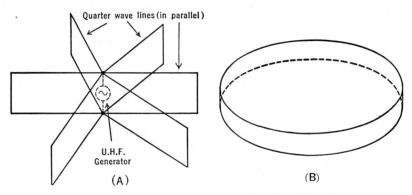

Fig. 4.3. By carrying the addition of shorted transmission lines to the limit, we would obtain, finally, the cavity resonator shown in Fig. 4.3B.

having a shape as shown in Fig. 4–3B. The generator could remain at the center, exciting the infinite number of units that have now been blended into one. The final product is a cavity resonator. It is interesting to note that, in adding quarter-wave lines in parallel, the total capacitance changes only slightly, but a major reduction in inductance occurs. Both components, exist, however, not in lumped form, as in low-frequency tuners, but in distributed form, as in transmission lines.

Excitation of a cavity resonator need not be made by actually connecting an r-f generator directly across the center of the unit as illustrated in Fig. 4–3A. It may be accomplished by inserting loops or probes into the cavity, or even by drilling holes at the center and then sending bunches of electrons through the space.

From the foregoing analysis, it can be reasoned that the cavity resonator is composed of an infinite number of quarter-wave tuning lines combined in parallel. Since a quarter-wave line exhibits the characteristics of a resonant circuit, the same behavior can be expected of cavity resonators. Keep in mind the voltage distribution along a quarter-wave line as shown in Fig. 4–1. It will help to relate the cavity resonator, as explained above, to the cavity resonator which will be derived from waveguides.

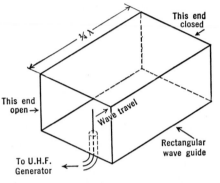

FIG. 4.4. Demonstrating resonance in a closed waveguide. This is quite similar (in principle) to the whistles small boys often use.

The easiest way to begin is to examine the section of waveguide shown in Fig. 4–4. One end of the waveguide has been blocked and the other end left open. A small antenna sends waves down the guide. The waves will travel unmolested until the closed end is reached. Upon striking this solid wall, a reflection of energy will take place, and waves will now be traveling in two directions similar to the action that occurs on a transmission line. In order to have the reflected waves arrive back at the opening so as to reinforce the electric field set up at this point, the distance from the open to the closed end is made one-quarter wavelength long. Standing electric and magnetic fields are now set up in a manner similar to the quarter-wave tuning line.

To complete the unit, place a similar section of a closed waveguide on the other side of the transmitting antenna, as shown in Fig. 4–5. Waves from the antenna will travel in both directions away from the antenna and both will be reflected when they strike the two closed ends. If the lengths of both guides are equal and correctly adjusted, the standing waves set up will reinforce at the antenna and the continuous pattern, shown in Fig. 4–6, will be obtained. The unit is now a cavity resonator which will resonate best at certain frequencies. The standing fields developed in this device are similar to the standing waves of currents and voltages established on tuned transmission lines.

The two methods of deriving cavity resonators show a marked resemblance to each other, and it should become apparent to the reader that, although it was not specifically mentioned in the chapter on Waveguides, the waveguide may be considered as being composed of an infinite number

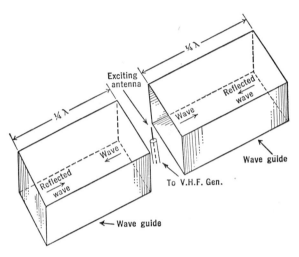

FIG. 4.5. The cavity resonator (entire unit) derived from two quarter-wave waveguides.

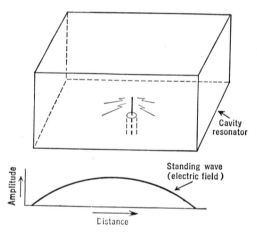

FIG. 4.6. The complete resonator with exciting antenna.

of parallel transmission lines. In transmission lines, we are concerned primarily with currents and voltages because these quantities are measured easily with familiar instruments. In waveguides it is simpler to deal with magnetic and electric fields. The relationship between fields on one hand and currents and voltages on the other is clearly indicated by electric theory. The mathematical knowledge required to understand the development, however, is considerably beyond what has been assumed for this book.

Sizes of Cavity Resonators. A cavity resonator must be at least one-half wavelength long at the frequency it is to operate in order to act as a tuning unit. This fact can be understood from the development process, for it will be remembered that the distance from the generator to the point of reflection was one-quarter wavelength. From the generator to the other point of reflection is another quarter wavelength distance, giving a total of one-half wavelength from one end of the unit to the other. Furthermore, if a one-half wavelength cavity resonator will operate, a resonator that is any whole number multiple of one-half wavelength, such as a full wavelength, one and one-half, etc., will also be suitable. This is true, also, of ordinary transmitting antennas where a half-wave antenna, a full-wave antenna, or any full multiple of a half-wave antenna will work. The basic principle remains the same. In all instances, the length of the resonator must be an integral (whole number) multiple of the fundamental half-wave unit. Any wave sent out, say, from the antenna, must be reflected and returned in such a manner that the maximum amplitude of the standing wave is obtained. This will occur for a certain distance or multiples of this distance. If this distance is not maintained, the forward and backward (or reflected) waves will no longer combine to aid each other, and the standing wave will be weakened, resulting in inefficient operation of the line or resonator as a tuning unit. The situation is analogous to the reduction in output signal that occurs in a receiver when the set is detuned. Varying the length of a cavity resonator is one way of tuning it.

Electric and Magnetic Fields in Resonators. A knowledge of the distribution of the r-f voltage across an ordinary coil is important when coupling it to other circuits. Likewise, the distribution of currents and voltages along transmission lines must be known if adequate use is to be made of the lines. However, in cavity resonators, it is not currents and voltages that we are concerned with, but magnetic and electric fields. Energy is introduced or coupled into the resonators by means of such fields, and energy is transferred out in the same way. A study of the electric and magnetic field distribution in a cavity resonator is not difficult if the facts mentioned in Chapter 3 are recalled. There, various field intensities were shown and described for waveguides and, as just noted, a cavity resonator may be considered as essentially derived from a waveguide.

Consider the small rectangular cavity resonator shown in Fig. 4–7. Any electric wave set up must be so arranged that its intensity is zero at any side wall. This condition, it will be recalled, was also necessary in waveguides. In order to satisfy this rule, a wave will be established across dimension X (the width of this rectangular box) so that it is maximum in the middle, tapering gradually down to zero at the sides. This is shown in Fig. 4–7 and represents a half-wave.

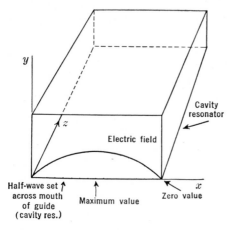

FIG. 4.7. Fitting a half-wave across the width of a cavity resonator so that it conforms to Maxwell's equations.

There is also an electric field distribution along the length of the rectangular cavity to consider. This is dimension Z in Fig. 4–7. Since the cavity is three-dimensional, the electric field will vary not only along the X-axis, as described above, but it will also change as it moves down the length of the enclosure. As the wave travels in the Z-direction, it must eventually reach the end wall of the cavity resonator where, again, the electric field must be zero. This is shown separately in Fig. 4–8, where the length of the resonator has been adjusted for one-half wavelength. In a complete picture,

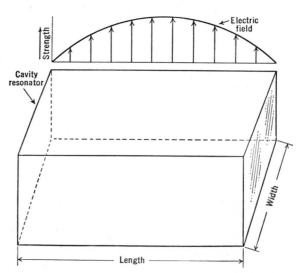

FIG. 4.8. Adjusting the length of a cavity resonator in order that the electric field (and consequently the magnetic) has the correct variation from point to point.

there would be a half-wave distribution in electric field intensity along dimension X (Fig. 4–7) and a half-wave distribution along dimension Z (Fig. 4–8).

The dimensions of either the length or the width may extend beyond one-half wavelength. Thus, in Fig. 4–9, the width is kept at one-half wavelength, but the length has been increased to a full wave and a half. No matter how long or wide these resonators may be, even with different shapes, the precautions laid down in previous chapters regarding the distributions of electric and magnetic fields are still valid.

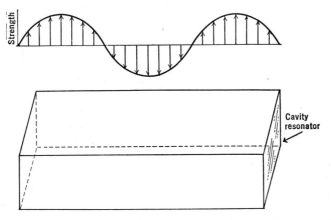

FIG. 4.9. The length is now 1½ wavelengths long. The equations are still obeyed, allowing the cavity to be used as a resonator (width constant).

The foregoing explanation has dealt exclusively with electric fields, but, of course, magnetic fields are present, too. These have been omitted purposely in order to simplify the discussion and to avoid a complicated three-dimensional diagram which is not easily comprehended. As in waveguides, or with electromagnetic waves in space, the r-f energy oscillates between the magnetic and electric fields. One instant it is in the electric field; the next it has smoothly been transferred to the magnetic field. The rate at which the changes occur is the same as the frequency of the wave itself. It is through this interchange of energy that the wave sustains itself and moves forward. Whether the energy is in a cavity resonator, a waveguide, or in ordinary space, the same things happen in essentially the same manner. The only difference is the way the energy is distributed, and this is determined by the shape of the containing space.

Exciting Cavity Resonators. To combine a cavity resonator with the elements of a tube, the arrangement in Fig. 4–10 is utilized. Cavity resonators are attached between plate and grid and between grid and cathode of a lighthouse tube. The connections between the tube and the resonators are accomplished with multiple-spring contact fingers. These possess little inductance, permitting the tube and the resonators to be intimately connected in such a manner that there is actually little distinction between the tuned circuit and the electronic system. The resonator cavities supply essentially the inductance, whereas the major portion of the capacitance exists between the plate, grid, and cathode elements. Note

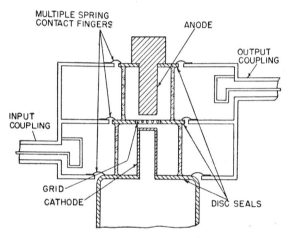

Fig. 4.10. Combining a cavity resonator with a lighthouse tube.

carefully that the interelectrode elements of the lighthouse tube are as much a part of the cavity resonator tuning system as the walls of the cavities themselves.

Energy from some external source, perhaps an antenna, is introduced into the grid-to-cathode resonator by means of a single-turn loop. The currents flowing in the loop introduce magnetic energy into the resonator which, in turn, establishes the electromagnetic fields throughout the cavity. The input loop is positioned purposely near the walls of the resonator since this is the region where the magnetic intensity is strong in a resonator. The electric field, on the other hand, is strongest near the elements of the lighthouse tube.

This method of introducing (or abstracting) energy into a cavity resonator may be compared with inductive coupling between coils at the low frequencies. Placing one coil close to another coil will, as shown in Fig. 4–11, act to transfer energy via the magnetic lines of force from the circuit on the left to the circuit on the right. Moving the coils closer together will provide a greater transfer of energy. Increasing the distance between them will have the opposite effect.

In a cavity resonator, the inserted loop represents the left-hand coil
of Fig. 4–11. The other coil represents the inductance of the cavity
resonator. To affect close coupling between them, the loop must be
positioned at a point where the magnetic field in the resonator is high.

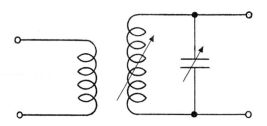

FIG. 4.11.   Inductive coupling at the low frequencies.

This occurs near the walls. If looser coupling is desired, the inserted
loop would be moved away from the walls of the resonator. To increase
the amount of energy fed into the cavity, we could use a loop having
several turns of wire instead of the single turn shown in Fig. 4–10. However, the space within the resonator
is limited and the inserted loop does
alter to some extent the operation
and properties of the cavity. Hence,
a single turn is most frequently employed. A diagram of a magnetic
probe that may be made from a
coaxial cable is shown in Fig. 4–12.

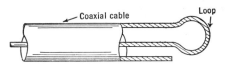

FIG. 4.12.   High-frequency inductive
coupler.

It is not necessary to restrict the methods of introducing or abstracting
energy from cavity resonators to magnetic means. Capacitive coupling
may also be used. Thus, inserting a probe into the electric field within
a resonator may be compared to the capacitive coupling used in low-
frequency circuits. (See Fig. 4–13.) In order that maximum energy may
be transferred, the wire from the capacitor C is placed at a point on the
coil where the r-f voltage is high. Moving the tap up or down will either
increase or decrease the amount of energy taken off. To apply this to a
cavity resonator, it is first necessary to find where the electric field is
concentrated, this being analogous to a point of high r-f voltage. From
what has been stated previously, a high intensity electric field would not
be found near any of the conducting walls, but rather toward the center
of the cavity resonator. To illustrate, refer to Figs. 4–7 and 4–8 where
the electric field distribution along the width and length of a cavity resonator
is shown.

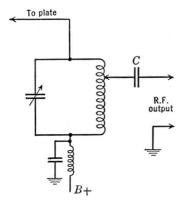

FIG. 4.13. Low-frequency method of obtaining output energy by capacitive coupling.

A suitable probe to pick up the ultra-high-frequency energy is shown in Fig. 4–14. Two views are given: one (A) showing the small antenna separately; and the other (B), where it actually connects to the cavity resonator. To construct this type of probe, fashion a coaxial transmission line with the inner conductor extending a little beyond the outer cylindrical conductor. The hole in the cavity resonator through which this cable passes is usually threaded to enable the outer conductor of the coaxial line to be screwed firmly into place and at the same time to make contact with the inner surface of the cavity chamber. The inner coaxial rod then extends into the chamber and comes in contact with the electrical field. The electrons in the center rod will be acted on by the electric field and thus energy will be transferred from the resonator. The other end of the connecting coaxial line may be attached either to a suitable waveguide or to an antenna.

In the low-frequency capacitive coupling method shown in Fig. 4–13, less energy is transferred to the output circuit when the tap is moved down the coil. To accomplish the same results in a cavity resonator, the probe is moved to a region where the electric field is less intense, perhaps by moving the probe closer to one of the walls and away from the center.

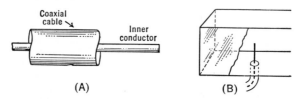

(A)   (B)

FIG. 4.14. (A) Extended inner conductor acts as capacitive coupler to electric field in cavity resonators and waveguides. (B) Actual position in resonator.

In most cavity resonators, capacitive coupling using the probe shown in Fig. 4–14 is not ordinarily employed because of the inconvenience of inserting such a probe near the tube elements where the electric field is most intense. It is easier to employ magnetic coupling, and this is the method most frequently found.

There is still another method of electrically introducing energy into resonators, and this is by the use of electrons. Consider the rectangular cavity resonator shown in Fig. 4–15. This chamber is similar to the cavity resonators previously described except that the sides have been altered slightly. At the center of two opposite sides a series of holes have been drilled to permit a stream of electrons to pass through the resonator. Every time an electron approaches side 1, there is a movement or displacement of electrons away from this side, repelled by the charge on the approaching electron. As this electron passes through the first set of holes, the induced charge may be considered as moving with it.

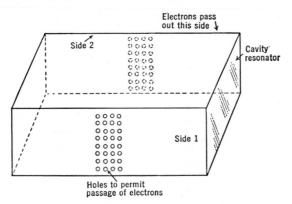

Fig. 4.15. Excitation of a cavity resonator by groups of electrons passing through holes drilled in the sides of the cavity.

However, the positive charge is confined to the surface of the metal. When the electron leaves the resonator through side 2, the electric charge that it induced may be considered as released and the charge returns to its equilibrium position. Thus there is a flow of current in one direction when the electron passes through and a flow in the opposite direction when the electron leaves the enclosure. This may be compared to a pendulum that is pushed aside every time something passes it and then returns to its former position when the disturbance has gone. In each case oscillations will occur, which is the desired result. If the exciting electrons swing through the cavity resonator at definite intervals, then the oscillations set up in the resonator will continue, just as in an ordinary oscillating circuit. Needless to say, the frequency mentioned in the last statement must be related to the resonant frequency of the cavity resonator.

A similar action of establishing and maintaining oscillations in a tuned circuit is encountered in low-frequency oscillators and class-C amplifiers. Current through the tubes in these circuits flows in spurts, each timed to surge into the tuned circuit at the proper moment to keep the currents flowing steadily back and forth between capacitor and coil.

In the lighthouse tube, Fig. 4–10, the electrons traveling from cathode to plate receive their r-f energy from the electric field variations that are set up by the grid-to-cathode resonator. These same electrons, in turn, transfer this energy to the output resonator when they pass through the interelectrode space existing between grid and plate of the lighthouse tube. If we were to place either of these input or output resonators alongside the rectangular resonator of Fig. 4–15, a difference would be immediately discernible. (See Fig. 4–16.) The distance that an electron must travel through the resonator used with the lighthouse tube is considerably less than the distance it travels through the rectangular resonator of Fig. 4–15.

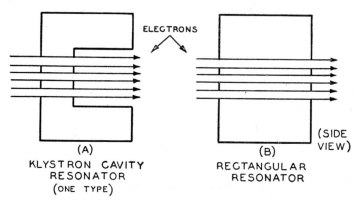

Fig. 4.16.   To reduce the undesirable effects of a long electron transit time, the resonator must be narrowed at those points where the electrons pass through.

There is a good reason for this: namely, electron transit time. An electron requires a definite time to travel from one side of the resonator to the other, and it is desirable that this time be very short in comparison with the period of the r-f voltage on the grids. If this is not so, the electron, while in the space between the sides of the resonator, will be acted upon by changing values of the r-f voltage and its velocity may be altered in the wrong direction.

To make certain that the electron spends only a short time within the cavity resonator, the side walls at the center of the resonator are moved closer together. On either side of this section, however, the walls flare out again. There are additional shapes which the cavity resonator can assume, some of which are shown in Fig. 4–17. In each case that portion of the resonator through which the electrons pass is made narrow, and comparatively little time is spent by the electrons in going from one side to the other.

Excitation of resonators by electrons actually belongs under the category of capacitive coupling since the electrons are introduced into the cavity at a point of high capacitance and it is the electric field of the electrons that serves as the exciting agent. (The capacitance between the grids of the resonator due to their close spacing represents most of the capacitance of the tuning unit. The electric field here is very strong.) The same transfer of energy could have been obtained if the probe in Fig. 4–14 had been inserted at the same point.

Q of Cavity Resonators. One of the reasons why ordinary coils and capacitors are not used at the ultra-high frequencies is due to the low value of the Q or selectivity (and efficiency) of these tuning units at the higher

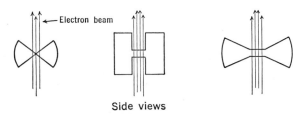

Side views

FIG. 4.17. Three additional shapes for cavity resonators.

frequencies. This was explained in a previous chapter. It might be interesting however, to determine how the Q of a cavity resonator is obtained, since nowhere in its make-up is there any lumped inductance. The usual equation for Q at low frequencies is given by

$$Q = \frac{\text{inductive reactance}}{\text{resistance (r-f)}}$$

$$Q = \frac{\omega L}{R}$$

The resistance is not the d-c resistance read on an ohmmeter but the r-f resistance actually offered by the circuit at the frequency of operation. This increases with frequency for one or more of the following reasons:

1. Skin effect, which causes the current to be concentrated near the surface of the conductor as the frequency goes up.

2. Dielectric losses and leakage. At the high frequencies, insulators often act as partial conductors. We are referring here to those substances that act as insulators at the low frequencies but lose this property at the very high frequencies.

3. Eddy currents in the conductors.

It is possible to express Q in slightly different terms without altering the value obtained. This follows from the fact that the energy put into the coil is divided into two parts: that which is stored in the magnetic field and that which is lost because of the resistance of the coil. It can be shown that the following ratio

$$2\pi \; \frac{\text{Energy stored per cycle}}{\text{Energy dissipated per cycle}}$$

is also equal to Q. From this we can deduce that a coil which has a high Q is more efficient than one which has a low Q.

To apply the foregoing formula to a cavity resonator, it is necessary to know where the energy is stored and where it is lost. The first question is easy to answer since any energy contained in a cavity resonator can be found in the electric and magnetic fields. As previously noted, the

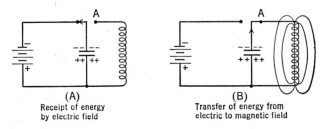

(A)
Receipt of energy
by electric field

(B)
Transfer of energy from
electric to magnetic field

Fig. 4.18.   Low-frequency resonant circuit showing how energy alternates between electric and magnetic fields.

energy is alternately stored in each. The comparison, at this point, between the old and the new is excellent and can be brought out by a very simple example. Consider the circuit of a coil and capacitor shown in Fig. 4–18. By means of a switch it is possible to charge the capacitor to the same voltage as the battery. If the switch is opened, the capacitor retains its charge. The energy may be considered as residing in the electric field between the plates. Move the switch to position A and the electrons will flow from the capacitor to the coil and build up a magnetic field around the coil. Eventually, all the energy that was formely lodged in the capacitor is now found in the magnetic field around the coil. However, as soon as the current stops flowing, the magnetic field will collapse and force the electrons to continue to the other capacitor plate. The capacitor is now charged, but in the opposite direction. The process repeats itself, only now the electrons flow in the opposite direction. Thus it can be seen that here, too, at a frequency determined by the size of the coil and capacitor the energy changes from the electric to the magnetic field, just as it is in a cavity resonator.

There is only one place in a cavity resonator where energy is lost and this is in the confining walls. The fields in a resonator continually move back and forth, striking the various sides and causing currents to flow. This represents an energy loss since the walls are not perfect conductors with zero resistance. The situation might be compared with the resistance in an ordinary coil and its connecting wires.

With the energy shown to be stored in the volume or hollow portion of the resonator and the loss occurring at the various sides or surfaces of the resonator, the ratio

$$\frac{\text{Volume of resonator}}{\text{Surface area of resonator}}$$

should be proportional to the Q of the resonator. Thus a higher Q will be obtained if the Volume to Surface Ratio is large, which is the objective striven for in the designing of these units. Fundamentally, the definition and purpose of Q remain the same.

With the conclusion of the discussion on the Q of a cavity resonator, this chapter is brought to a close. Only the basic theory has been covered and applied essentially to a simple rectangular resonator. There are innumerable shapes that resonators may assume, each operating in the same basic manner but possessing different field distributions. To date, the mathematical theory has been applied only to a few of these complex shapes, so that the experimental process of "cut-and-try" is used extensively when designing resonators for ultra-high-frequency oscillators. The application of cavity resonators is best considered with the tubes and circuits with which it is normally associated and hence will not be given here.

QUESTIONS

1. Which are more flexible with regard to frequency changing: cavity resonators or transmission lines? Why?

2. How may we derive a cavity resonator from a transmission line?

3. How can a cavity resonator be formed from a waveguide?

4. What is the shortest length of a resonator for any one frequency? Why can it not be shorter?

5. In a cavity resonator, what would correspond to a large current? A large voltage?

6. How are cavity resonators excited? (Two methods.)

7. Explain the reason for the narrow section of the klystron cavity resonator.

8. Describe how energy from a resonator may be removed by inductive coupling.

9. Do the same as in question 8 for the case of capacitive coupling.

10. What modifications are necessary in the ordinary definition of Q when it is applied to cavity resonators?

11. How can the above definition of Q help us design a resonator for best results?

12. What type of probe is used for capacitive coupling? Inductive coupling?

13. Describe how an electron or group of electrons can excite a resonator.

Chapter 5

HIGH-FREQUENCY OSCILLATORS

In most of the preceding discussion we have been concerned primarily with components and their modification for high-frequency use rather than with circuits. Let us now turn our attention to complete circuits—notably oscillators—and observe how high-frequency signals are generated. This will not only provide us with an insight into high-frequency operation but also introduce such important tubes as the magnetron, the klystron, the resnatron, and the traveling-wave tube.

One of the most popular oscillators used at relatively high frequencies is the ultraudion circuit shown in Fig. 5–1. While the circuit, in this form, may appear strange to some readers, a simple rearrangement of components will reveal that the ultraudion is really a modified Colpitts in which use is made of the internal plate-to-cathode and grid-to-cathode capacitances of the tube. To alter the frequency of the circuit, the inductance may be varied according to one of the tuning methods previously described. Conventional inductances are utilized until the frequency becomes so high that the coil is nothing but a single loop of wire (generally around 200 to 300 mc). Thereafter, either transmission-

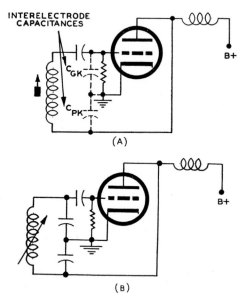

Fig. 5.1. (A) Ultraudion oscillator. (B) Colpitts circuit from which it is derived.

line tuners or butterfly circuits may be used. For the sake of simplicity, the following discussion will revolve around transmission-line tuners, but at any frequency up to 1000 mc, butterfly tuners may be substituted. Above this frequency, coaxial-line tuners or cavity resonators are generally used.

An ultraudion oscillator, using parallel transmission lines, is shown in Fig. 5–2A. The parallel lines are one-quarter wavelength long at the

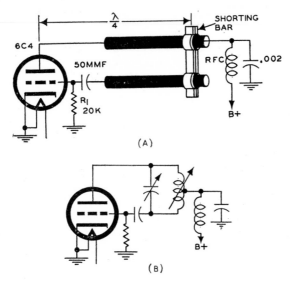

Fig. 5.2. A high-frequency ultraudion oscillator using a transmission-line tuner. (B) Low-frequency equivalent circuit.

frequency that it is desired to operate the oscillator. B+ voltage is fed to the plate of the tube through the transmission line, with a blocking capacitor inserted between the grid terminal and the line to prevent this B+ from reaching the grid of the tube. The grid-leak bias is developed across the grid resistor, R_1. The low-frequency equivalent circuit of this oscillator is shown in Fig. 5–2B.

In Fig. 5–2 and in other diagrams, the resonant lines are shown actually as being less than one-quarter wavelength long, the remainder of the inductance being obtained from the connecting leads to the tube elements plus the inductance of the elements. Thus, while we speak loosely of quarter-wave tuning lines, it should be understood that inductances external to the line reduce this length somewhat.

In order for this oscillator to function properly, the cathode should be at ground potential. In a low-frequency oscillator this is accomplished by simply connecting the cathode terminal to the chassis. As the frequency is increased, however, the inductance in the cathode lead begins to assume impedance values which can no longer be considered negligible, and the plate currents, flowing through this impedance, place the cathode at

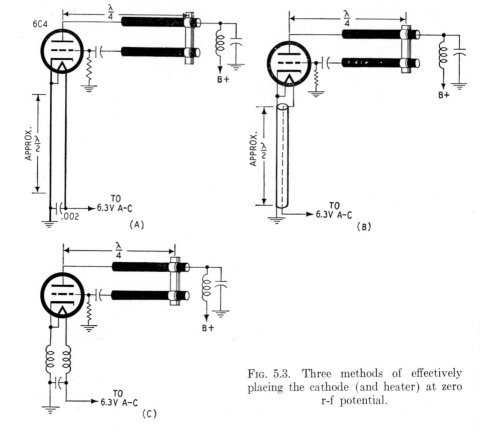

FIG. 5.3. Three methods of effectively placing the cathode (and heater) at zero r-f potential.

other than zero potential. The result is a decrease in output power and operating efficiency.

In order to place the cathode at ground potential, it is necessary to neutralize its inductance. This can be done in two ways, both more or less equivalent. We can use a section of a transmission line which, when added to the inductance existing in the cathode, develops a standing half wave from the far end of the transmission line to the cathode element within the tube. (See Fig. 5–3A.) If now we place the end of the line at r-f ground potential, the cathode at the other end of this line, being one-half wavelength away, will likewise be at r-f ground potential. The cathode terminal is connected to one heater terminal, and both of these are attached to one conductor of the transmission line. The other heater connects to the other conductor of the line. At the other end of the line, one conductor is grounded directly, whereas the other conductor requires a by-pass capacitor. This is needed to prevent the heater voltage from being short-circuited to ground. Note that, in this arrangement, both heater and cathode elements are at r-f ground potential. This is desirable since it minimizes the possibility of the a-c heater voltage modulating the output of the oscillator.

In place of a parallel-wire line, we can substitute a coaxial section. (See Fig. 5-3B.) In most instances this is preferable because it shields the lines carrying the 60-cycle a-c heater voltage.

If the operating frequency of the oscillator is not too high, a half-wave line can be simulated by adding enough additional inductance to have a half-wave develop between each end of this inductance. If, now, we ground the far end of the inductance, then the filament end automatically will be placed at r-f ground potential. (See Fig. 5-3C.) If the proper amount of added inductance is used, just as good results will be obtained with this method as with the preceding transmission line. However, as the operating frequency increases, it becomes more and more difficult to obtain the proper amount of inductance because a small length of wire, more or less, throws the system out of balance. When this point is reached, use of transmission lines is recommended.

Output from the oscillator may be obtained by balanced (Fig. 5-4A) or unbalanced (Fig. 5-4B) capacitive coupling, or inductively by means of a loop (Fig. 5-4C). Whichever method is used depends primarily on the type of circuit to follow.

A 140-250 mc oscillator using parallel rods to form a quarter-wave transmission line tuner is shown in Fig. 5-5. The shorting bar is moved back and forth by a screw drive. B+ voltage is fed to the plate cap by a wire running through the center of the plate tuning rod. The B+ is prevented from reaching the grid by a blocking capacitor inserted between the plate of the tube and the tuner.

In the previous illustrations, parallel-wire or parallel-rod tuning lines were indicated. These lines are exposed, and therefore we can expect to find that some energy is radiated directly. As the operating frequency is increased to about 300-350 mc, the amount of energy which is radiated becomes great enough to decrease the efficiency of the circuit appreciably. To avoid this, we can employ coaxial tuners. In these lines all of the energy is confined between the inner and outer conductors, while the outer shell of the line is at zero r-f potential at all points on its surface.

A single-tube, coaxial-line oscillator is shown in Fig. 5-6A. The grid

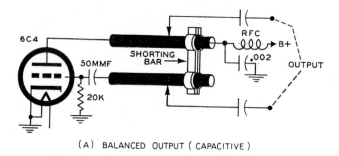

(A) BALANCED OUTPUT (CAPACITIVE)

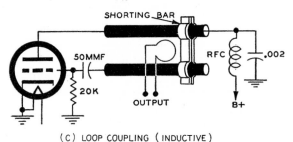

(B) UNBALANCED OUTPUT (CAPACITIVE)

(C) LOOP COUPLING (INDUCTIVE)

Fig. 5.4.   Three methods of obtaining energy from an oscillator.

of the tube connects to the inner conductor, and the plate is placed at r-f ground potential with a small by-pass capacitor. (The grounded end of the plate by-pass capacitor could have been connected to the outer surface of the coaxial line since this is also at r-f ground potential.) The cathode and one side of the heater are attached to the inner conductor of the line at a point below the grid connection. The other heater wire passes down through the hollow center of the inner conductor to the heater power supply. The overall length of the coaxial line, from the short-circuited end to the open-circuited end, is one-quarter wavelength long. To change the resonant frequency of the oscillator, a movable shorting disk attached to a plunger can be used.

The equivalent circuit of this oscillator, Fig. 5–6C, reveals it to be a Hartley oscillator. With coaxial lines, the Hartley oscillator is easier to construct, physically, than the ultraudion and hence is used more fre-

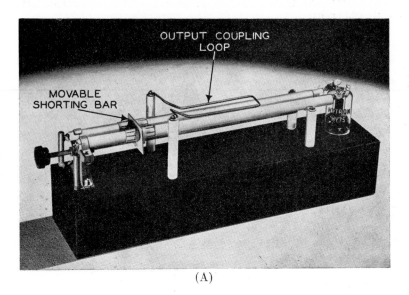

(A)

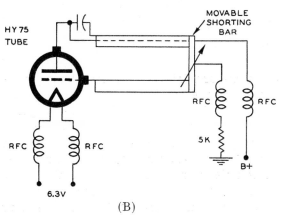

(B)

FIG. 5.5. A 140–250 mc oscillator using parallel tuning rods. (A) Actual appearance. (*Courtesy Hytron*) (B) Schematic diagram.

quently. The physical size and shape of the UHF tuning elements exert a greater influence over the type of circuit to be used than is true of similar components at the low frequencies.

Output from the coaxial-line tuner can be obtained by attaching a wire directly to the inner conductor and extending the wire out through a small opening in the outer conductor. This would be direct or capacitive coupling, if a capacitor is inserted in this lead. Inductive coupling can be achieved by placing a half-turn of wire near the inner conductor, as shown in Fig. 5–6B.

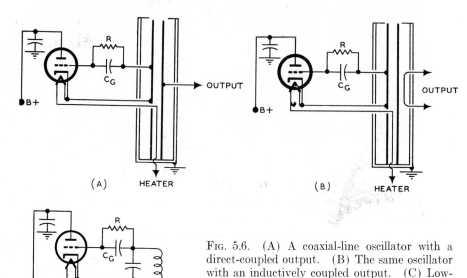

FIG. 5.6. (A) A coaxial-line oscillator with a direct-coupled output. (B) The same oscillator with an inductively coupled output. (C) Low-frequency equivalent circuit of oscillator (no output connections shown).

Tube capacitance and internal lead inductance, at frequencies in the range of 300 mc or above, can form a significant part of the total circuit inductance and capacitance. This reduces the length of line which is needed externally in order to reach the operating frequency. A small external line, in turn, presents little inductance to which we can couple a loop to obtain a useful output. What we desire is as much external tuning line as possible in order that a large coupling surface be available. One way to achieve this is to place the tube at the center of a one-half wavelength line, as shown in Fig. 5–7A. This arrangement may be regarded as equivalent to two quarter-wave tuning lines (similar to the lines we have used previously) placed in parallel with each other. Coupling inductances in parallel causes the total inductance to decrease and this permits us to employ a longer length of line for the same value of tube capacitance in order to tune to the same frequency again.

Another way of looking at this arrangement is to consider that only half of the tube capacitance is associated with each line, which again permits us to lengthen each line in order that the resonant frequency return to its previous value. Whatever the method of reasoning, the end result is the same—that is, a lengthening of the line.

The effectiveness of the arrangement in Fig. 5–7A can be demonstrated by considering the equivalent tuning circuit in Fig. 5–7B. At some instant the currents in the wires will be flowing toward the center; at some other instant, the currents will be flowing away from the center. For the region

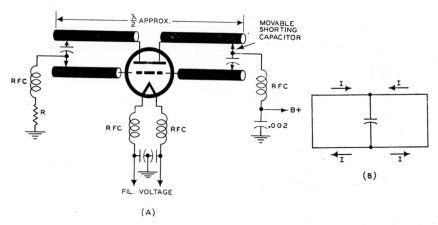

Fig. 5.7. (A) An oscillator which utilizes specially constructed tubes possessing two terminals, each, for the grid and plate elements. Longer tuning elements are possible with such tubes. For (B), see text.

close to the center, the magnetic effects of the oppositely flowing currents will nullify each other, and all voltages of self-induction in this area will be neutralized. With this neutralization, we remove the effect of the inductance of the connecting wires (at the center). Hence, by placing the tube and the tuning capacitor at this point, we effectively minimize the inductance contained in these components. This permits us to add even more inductance to the tuning lines—which is very desirable. Special high-frequency tubes have been built which contain two external connections to the grid and two external connections to the plate. The leads (for each electron) come out from opposite sides of the glass envelope, permitting them to be used precisely as indicated in Fig. 5–7A.

Still further reduction in tube capacitance can be effected by connecting two tubes in push-pull, as shown in Fig. 5–8. With this arrangement, each of the interelectrode capacitances of the tubes are in series with each other, and since equal capacitors in series produce a final capacitance which is half that of one capacitor, we again achieve a reduction.

To the reader accustomed to dealing with conventional circuits, all this preoccupation with what appears to be minute inductances and capacitances may appear to be a needless exaggeration—yet nothing could be further from the truth. The point to remember always is that these components, while they may appear to be small in comparison to the inductances and capacitances employed in everyday A–M sets, are not small in comparison to the inductances and capacitances which are used in the high-frequency circuits. Hence, they cannot be ignored.

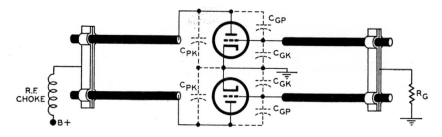

FIG. 5.8.   A push-pull oscillator.

Coaxial Oscillator Circuits.   To reach the region of 1000 mc and above with conventionally operated tubes, considerable use has been made of disk-seal tubes in combination with coaxial line tuners. Unlike the oscillators previously indicated in this chapter, these tubes are combined more intimately with the coaxial line. The first illustration of this type of construction was shown in Chapter 1, Fig. 1–36. The oscillator there consisted of two tunable sections of a coaxial line separated by the grid plane of the tube. One tuning section is between grid and cathode; the other, between grid and plate.

Instead of placing the two tuning circuits end to end, a more compact arrangement can be obtained by folding the grid-cathode coaxial line over the plate-to-grid section. This is shown in Fig. 5–9A. There are now three concentric cylinders. Through the innermost cylinder the positive d-c potential is fed to the plate of the tube. The space between this and the second cylinder contains the circular tuning plunger and the output loop. This is the resonant grid-to-plate circuit. The second tuner exists between the second and third (or outermost) cylinders. This is the resonant grid-to-cathode circuit and it, too, contains a circular plunger for tuning purposes. A d-c connection for grid bias is made by connecting a 20,000-ohm resistor between the grid spring contact and the outer coaxial cylinder. This cylinder connects to the lighthouse tube base shell and this, in turn, is grounded.

To obtain sufficient feedback to maintain oscillations over the full range of the oscillator, a small screw in the plate-to-grid cavity extends through the grid cylinder (without making contact with the cylinder) and into the resonant space between the grid and cathode.

A careful distinction must be maintained in these oscillators between the r-f and d-c paths. A direct metallic connection between two points

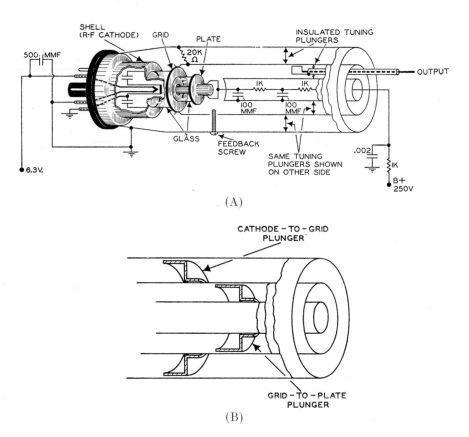

FIG. 5.9. (A) A coaxial oscillator using a lighthouse tube. The illustration is partly in pictorial and partly in schematic form. (B) Tuning plungers which do not provide a d-c path between cylinders.

will provide a low-resistance d-c path between these points. It may not, and generally will not, represent a low impedance path to r-f currents. Thus, consider the tuning plungers which are placed between concentric cylinders in the oscillator of Fig. 5–9A. Whether or not these plungers make direct metallic contact to the cylinder walls will depend upon the d-c currents and voltages present here. If, for example, the plate cylinder made direct d-c contact to the anode of the lighthouse tube, it would obviously not be desirable to have the d-c plate voltage reach the grid of the tube. Hence, this plunger should not provide a d-c path between these two cylinders. This may be accomplished by making the plunger one-quarter wavelength long at the frequency of operation and leaving a small air space between the plungers and the cylinder walls. (See Fig. 5–9B.) The air space breaks the d-c path between cylinders while presenting a low r-f impedance across the air gap at the inside edge of the plunger. This low r-f impedance is due to the quarter-wave distance between the two ends of the plunger and the fact that the far end of this air space is open.

If it is structurally more desirable to have the plungers come into contact with the cylinder walls, then the plate cylinder can be capacitively coupled to the anode cap of the tube. D-c plate voltage can still be applied as shown in Fig. 5–9A.

Whatever has been said regarding the grid and plate cylinders can also be applied to the grid and cathode circuit. In most applications of this oscillator, the outer shell is grounded. This does not affect the r-f field existing between the grid and cathode cylinders. However, if the grid has a negative d-c bias, the tuning plunger in this circuit should not provide a d-c path between grid and cathode cylinders.

Most illustrations of coaxial oscillators are flat or two-dimensional drawings. The cylinders, on the other hand, are circular and three-dimensional. To indicate that a tuning plunger is continuous throughout the space between two cylinders (as in Figs. 5–8 and 5–9) it must be shown on both sides of the diagram, at the same level.

The Re-entrant Oscillator. Each of the two preceding types of coaxial oscillators contained a separate plunger for each tuned circuit which required separate adjustment whenever the frequency was changed. A more desirable arrangement, from the standpoint of tuning, is the re-entrant oscillator shown in Fig. 5–10. This contains only one tuning control, has a simpler mechanical arrangement, and is capable of fairly constant power output over a considerable frequency range. The resonant circuit between plate and grid consists of an open-ended cylinder which clamps on to the grid ring of the tube. Plate connection is made by a rod which extends down through the center of the coaxial cylinder. The outer shell of the cylinder connects to the cathode base of the lighthouse tube. The grid cylinder and the plate rod form one resonant circuit, while the grid cylinder and the outer shell of the coaxial line form the other resonant circuit. Coupling between the two tuned circuits is achieved through the open end of the grid cylinder.

The plunger in this oscillator does not determine the frequency generated. It is merely adjusted for maximum output. Tuning can be accomplished in several ways. One method is to make the grid cylinder telescopic and change its length. In a second method, spring contact fingers are placed at the end of the plate rod to grip the plate cap firmly. A screw-drive mechanism, similar to the arrangement used for micrometer calipers, then moves the plate rod along the plate cap. The position of the plunger or choke must also be adjusted as the cavity is tuned. By proper design

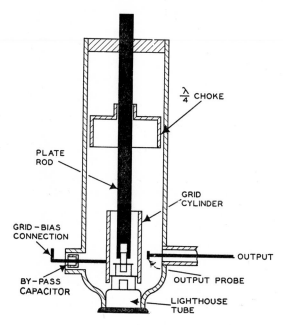

FIG. 5.10. A re-entrant coaxial oscillator. (*Courtesy I.R.E.*)

this may be done by connecting the choke to the plate rod and moving both simultaneously. (See Fig. 5–11.) In still another method, a movable tuner is placed over the plate rod. The tuner on the plate rod is first put as close to the plate of the tube as possible and the plunger adjusted for optimum operation. Then the plate tuner and the plunger are locked rigidly together and both moved at the same time for tuning. (See Fig. 5–12.)

Positive Grid Oscillators. All of the oscillators discussed thus far in this chapter have employed conventionally operated tubes in which the grid is negative and the plate is positive. By ingenious mechanical and electrical construction, the frequencies obtainable from these circuits extend as high as 3000 mc. Note, however, that we still have the effects of electron transit time to contend with and, at about 3000 mc, even a disk-seal tube possesses very poor efficiency. If extensive use is to be made of the frequency spectrum lying beyond 3000 mc, an approach from some other direction is indicated. As far back as 1920, an attempt was made to get away from using tubes in their conventional manner. Although the circuit which was developed, known as the Barkhausen and Kurz oscillator, is of little practical

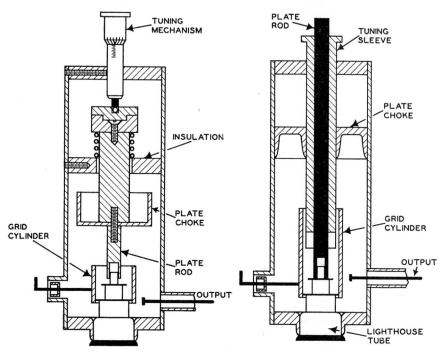

FIG. 5.11. A method of tuning the re-entrant oscillator by moving the plate rod along the anode cap of the lighthouse tube. (*Courtesy I.R.E.*)

FIG. 5.12. Another tuning method for the re-entrant oscillator using a sleeve that slides over the plate rod. (*Courtesy I.R.E.*)

use today, it does illustrate how electron transit can be made an ally instead of an enemy.

Barkhausen and Kurz discovered that by placing a large positive voltage on the grid and either a zero or slightly negative voltage on the plate, oscillations were produced when a tuned circuit was placed externally between the plate and grid. Over a limited range of grid and plate voltages, it was found that the frequency of oscillation was independent of the tuned circuit attached to the tube and was dependent only on the transit time of the electrons within the tube which gave rise to these oscillations. Of course, greater output was obtained when the frequency of oscillation of the electrons was equal to the resonant frequency of the tuned circuit. The important point, however, was that even if the resonant frequency of the tuning system did change, it did not affect the frequency of the electrons in the tube. Wavelengths generated by Barkhausen and Kurz varied from 200 cm to 43 cm (approx. 150 mc to 700 mc) and were found related to the grid potential by the formula

$$\lambda^2 E_g = K$$

where E_g is the grid voltage,

   K is a constant of the circuit,

   λ is the wavelength generated.

In 1922, Gill and Morrell, working with an oscillator similar to the B–K oscillator, found that for the range from 60 mc to 150 mc the generated frequencies were not independent of the external circuit but varied slightly with it. The formula for the frequencies of oscillation put forth by Gill and Morrell was

$$\frac{\lambda^2 I_g}{E_g^{1/2}} = K$$

which reduces to the B–K formula if the grid current, I_g, varies as the 3/2 power of E_g. In the Barkhausen-Kurz unit the frequency of oscillation does not change by changing the tuning circuit attached to the tube; in the Gill-Morrell oscillator the circuit will not work correctly unless the electron oscillations in the tube are properly related to the period of the tuned circuit. It is apparent that the two oscillators are interrelated, and it was discovered that the Gill-Morrell oscillator will smoothly and gradually work into the B–K unit as the frequency is changed by changing the operating voltages. Electron transit time, which causes the conventional type of oscillator to fail at the high frequencies, is the operating principle of both these generators. Most of the oscillators to be dealt with in the next two chapters possess arrangements whereby transit time is used to advantage rather than as a liability. It is the old dodge of joining an opponent if he cannot be beaten.

How These Oscillators Function. The generation of oscillations in a positive grid oscillator (shown in Fig. 5–13) can be explained best if the motion of the electrons during two conditions is studied: (1) when there is a constant difference of potential between plate and grid and (2) when the grid has an r-f or alternating voltage applied to it with respect to the cathode. The period of this alternating voltage should be close to the time required by an electron to reach a point near the plate where the reversal of direction occurs.

Turning our attention to the *first condition,* we find that an electron emitted by the cathode is accelerated forward by the grid (which has a positive voltage on it) and, if it misses the grid wires, will continue on toward the plate. The electron, however, now is moving away from a highly positive grid and toward a slightly negative plate. Its velocity will therefore decrease until the electron is brought to a halt somewhere near the plate. It will be attracted again by the positive grid potential and so be forced to speed toward it. If the grid is missed, the cathode will probably receive the electron. This represents one complete cycle and the net gain or loss of energy by the electron is zero. The electron gained energy when it was speeded up by the positive grid voltage, and it lost energy when it drew away from the grid and was slowed down. In the entire process there are two intervals when it is slowed down and two times when it is speeded up. The net result—no energy loss or gain. This point will be referred to again in the next few paragraphs.

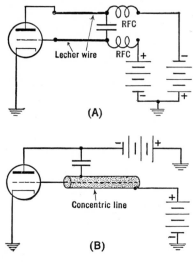

Fig. 5.13. The Barkhausen-Kurz oscillator with two different tuning arrangements. The inner and outer conductors of the concentric line are shorted together only at battery end.

Under the *second condition,* a small r-f voltage is superimposed on the direct potential of the grid. The period for a complete cycle of this alternating voltage is equal to the travel time of the electron from the cathode to the vicinity of the plate. In order to visualize the following discussion, refer to Fig. 5–14, where the position of the electron is indicated at various instants during the r-f grid voltage cycle.

Consider, first, time t_1, when the electron is leaving the cathode and the voltage on the grid is increasing. Because of the increased voltage, the electron will receive more acceleration than it normally would have without the superimposed r-f voltage. At time t_2, the electron is just passing the plane of the grid and, since the grid is now going less positive than normal, due to the reversal of the r-f voltage, the electron traveling toward the plate will receive less deceleration and probably strike the anode. The electron, it can be seen, has gained more energy during this trip than the electron traveling in the same direction under the first condition (see above), and this energy must be supplied by the alternating voltage on the grid. If the electron should not gain sufficient additional energy to strike the plate, then at time t_4 it will return past the grid and at t_5 will strike the cathode with excess energy. Whether or not the electron strikes the plate during its first trip depends on the grid-to-plate distance and the operating voltages of the tube. In any event, if the electron starts out at the time mentioned, it will absorb energy and be useless as far as the generation of oscillations is concerned. Electrons are desired which release energy, not absorb it.

Consider now an electron which leaves the cathode when the r-f voltage on the grid is going negative. (See Fig. 5–15.) Since the r-f voltage is considerably smaller than the positive d-c voltage here, negative values of r-f voltage will only lower the positive d-c potential. It will not remove this voltage. The electron, traveling forward under the attractive force of this reduced d-c voltage, will be accelerated less than if no r-f voltage had been present. At time t'_2, the electron has reached the plane of the grid and is advancing toward the plate. The grid now is assuming a

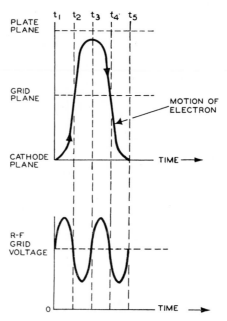

Fig. 5.14. The motion of an electron which absorbs energy in a B–K oscillator.

voltage more positive than its normal d-c value and the electron will receive a greater deceleration, preventing it from approaching as close to the plate as it would have with constant grid voltage. On the return cycle, time t'_4 will again find the electron at the grid and time t'_5 will find it coming to a halt some distance from the cathode. The fact that the electron came to rest at a point farther from the plate than it normally would with constant grid voltage indicates that it had lost energy. The recipient of this energy was the source of alternating voltage on the grid.

Some readers may wonder why the electron will strike the anode on one trip and come to a halt some distance from it on another trip. The answer is that, when the electron is going away from a grid which is more positive than normal, this electron, being negative in nature and so attracted to a positive grid, will suffer a greater deceleration than formerly and so go farther before coming to a stop. In each case, the electron will be decelerated, but by different amounts.

Now return to the last electron considered, the one that started out from the cathode when the a-c grid voltage was going negative. It was seen that this electron did not reach the plate or the cathode again because it gave up energy to the grid on each trip. An electron loses energy, or gives it up (so to speak), when it is working against the grid voltage. The electron that has lost energy will continue to make trips back and forth between the cathode and plate, each time losing a little energy and so

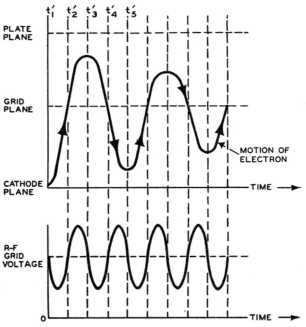

Fig. 5.15. The motion of an electron which gives up energy in the B–K oscillator.

moving shorter distances from the grid. It is possible for an electron to oscillate about the grid in this manner for a considerable time, but this is generally not desirable for two reasons:

1. As the distance that the electron travels decreases, less and less energy is delivered by the electron to the grid.

2. Eventually the electron may even start absorbing energy which would work against the above process. In order to guard against this tendency, the grid is so designed that it will, on the average, capture the electron by the time the phase has shifted sufficiently to cause absorption of energy.

Although two separate and special cases have been employed to describe the action of the B–K oscillator, it can be shown that all electrons leaving the cathode when the alternating voltage on the grid is going positive will absorb energy and either strike the plate and be lost or return and strike the cathode and meet the same fate. On the other hand, all electrons leaving the cathode when the a-c grid voltage is going negative will lose energy and so vibrate back and forth in the interelectrode space until they are caught by the grid. Since equal numbers of electrons leave the cathode when the grid is going positive as when it is going negative, and since the electrons that gain energy are taken out of action after one cycle, at most, while the other electrons (those that lose energy) remain in the space for several cycles, it can be seen that the alternating voltage source of the grid gains more energy than it loses. This is important and differs from the first case described where there was only a constant voltage on the grid. Here, there was no resultant gain or loss of energy. It is this gain by the alternating source of the grid that sustains oscillations.

What is the source of the energy that the electron gives up? The d-c positive voltage on the grid is accelerating the electrons and imparting energy to them. When the electrons are slowed down they return part of this energy to the r-f grid voltage source. Hence the d-c grid voltage is being changed, via the electron, into the r-f grid voltage. Does this seem strange? It shouldn't, because this changing of d-c to r-f energy is true in all oscillators. The only difference occurs in the method whereby the energy transference occurs, but the end result is the same.

This point of energy transfer, via the electron, is so important that it deserves a more detailed explanation. The idea will arise again in the other oscillators and cavity resonators to be discussed, where energy will be obtained from the electrons that are moving through the tube or vibrating in the interelectrode space.

When an electron leaves the cathode it is speeded up by the large positive potential on one of the other elements, the grid or plate. Thus the electron is given energy which may be in addition to what it might have by virtue of the fact that it was emitted from the cathode with some small initial velocity. Thus the first phase of this process sees the electron receiving energy obtained from a d-c source. The next step in this process is to utilize this energy for the continuance of the oscillations in the tuning circuits.

The electron, as it travels toward an element, either the plate or the grid, will cause the electrons in these elements to be displaced. This is due to the natural repellent effect electrons have on each other. If a large number of electrons are traveling toward the element, there will be a correspondingly large displacement of the element's electrons. When the traveling electrons in the interelectrode space move away from an element, say the grid, the electrons that were displaced will return to their previous positions.

But suppose that the traveling electrons pass this element at frequent intervals. Then the element's electrons will be forced to move back and forth with the same frequency. This vibratory motion is our oscillation. If a tuning circuit is connected between the elements, we will have an oscillator.

The moving electrons must be kept continually in motion; otherwise the entire process will cease. The large d-c potentials accomplish this. Hence, we say that the d-c energy is converted to r-f energy. The moving electrons lose some of the d-c energy when they force the element's electrons to move from their present positions. The loss in energy is evidenced by a reduction in the speed of the interelectrode electrons.

Carry these ideas over to the preceding explanation of the B–K oscillator. Here, when the electron leaves the cathode, it is accelerated by the large positive d-c potential on the grid. On approaching the grid, the moving electron causes a displacement of the grid electrons. This effect decreases as the electron moves past the grid and speeds toward the plate. Near the plate, the electron is slowed down and finally stopped. Again the large positive d-c potential on the grid attracts it and again the electron is accelerated as it travels toward the grid.

Approaching the grid, the moving electron causes another displacement of grid electrons. Then the electron passes through the grid wires and is brought to a stop near the cathode. By constantly passing the grid at periodic intervals, this electron and all its companions will cause oscillations to be built up in any tuned circuit connected between the grid and plate. The entire process is dynamic, with the moving electrons losing members, gaining others, but, on the whole, keeping the net oscillations constant.

The reason for the negative voltage on the plate now becomes obvious. If it were positive, the electrons would flow to it and no vibration of electrons about the grid would occur. With the plate slightly negative, the electrons are forced back to the grid and from this motion, oscillations occur. The frequency of the oscillations is, of course, dependent on how fast the electrons move back and forth. Thus, the B–K oscillator is said to depend upon the electron transit time.

Another point that can now be cleared up relates to the starting of oscillations in the B–K oscillator. In the previous explanation, an alternating voltage is assumed on the grid. Actually, however, when the circuit is first connected, no such a-c voltage exists on the grid. How then does this process start? By closing the power switch, a slight disturbance will tend to set this oscillator in action, and the motion of the electrons in the tube due to this sudden disturbance helps build up the r-f grid voltage. This method of starting an oscillator is just the same as in the Hartley or Colpitts oscillators. Here, too, the closing of the power supply switch gives rise to a disturbance in the circuit and this builds up the oscillations.

After a very short time a state of equilibrium is reached, and the oscillations become steady.

Efficiency of Operation. The Barkhausen-Kurz oscillator can be used to generate oscillations in the range from 60 to 700 mc. The efficiency of this device is low, with typical values of from 1 to 3 per cent, because most of the electrons leaving the cathode are caught by the grid, therefore resulting in a low ratio of r-f grid current to direct grid current. In addition, a tremendous amount of energy must be dissipated at the grid. As the frequency is raised, the elements must be brought closer together and higher voltages must be used. These are two conflicting considerations since higher voltages mean more heat dissipation, which would ruin the closely spaced electrodes. Although the practical application of these oscillators is limited where very short wavelengths are concerned (30 cm and less), they represent the first attempt to cope with the difficulties of transit time in ultra-high-frequency generation.

QUESTIONS

1. Draw the low-frequency circuit of a Hartley and a Colpitts oscillator.

2. How is the ultraudion oscillator related to the Colpitts? Illustrate your answer by means of diagrams.

3. Draw the circuit of a high-frequency ultraudion oscillator using a transmission-line tuner. In what respects, other than the resonant circuit does this unit differ from a low-frequency ultraudion oscillator?

4. Why must special attention be given to the cathode circuit in some high-frequency oscillators?

5. Illustrate the modifications that must be made in the cathode leg of these high-frequency oscillators.

6. Show how energy is coupled out of an oscillator using transmission line tuning.

7. When are coaxial-line oscillators more desirable than parallel-wire oscillators? When might the reverse be true?

8. Why is it sometimes advantageous to place a tube at the center of a half-wave line rather than at the end of a quarter-wave line?

9. Draw the circuit of an oscillator in which the tube is located at the center of a half-wave tuning line.

10. Indicate (and illustrate) why a push-pull oscillator might be even more desirable than the circuit drawn in question 9.

11. How is feedback achieved in coaxial line oscillators employing disk-seal tubes?

12. Name two methods whereby it is possible to break a d-c path in a high-frequency circuit without, at the same time, breaking the r-f path.

13. How are coaxial oscillators using disk-seal tubes tuned?

14. What advantages do re-entrant type coaxial oscillators possess over other coaxial oscillators?

15. Describe several methods used to tune re-entrant coaxial circuits.

16. How does the Barkhausen and Kurz arrangement of a tube differ from the conventional applications?

17. Describe the operation of a B–K oscillator when there is a constant potential on the elements.

18. Do the same as in question 17, but assume an alternating potential on the grid.

19. Where do the electrons obtain the energy they give to the grid circuit of a B–K oscillator?

20. What are the disadvantages of a B–K oscillator?

21. Draw the diagram of a B–K oscillator.

Chapter 6

THE MAGNETRON OSCILLATOR

Comparison to Other Oscillators. Throughout the preceding chapters, examples have been given of improved components for UHF operation. The limitations at UHF of conventional vacuum tubes, tuners, and amplifiers have been cited as reasons why changes in the design of the components were necessary. The magnetron is a good illustration of how the need for a stable, high-frequency, high-power oscillator that could not be obtained in the usual manner led to the design of an oscillator completely different in physical appearance from most conventional oscillators.

However different the physical appearance of the magnetron may be, electronically it follows most of the principles characteristic of conventional oscillators. That similarity gives us a basis for understanding how magnetrons function. Let us review and compare the old and the new.

The first item that an oscillator must have is an oscillatory circuit. At the lower frequencies this is provided by a coil and capacitor. At the higher frequencies, this combination gave way first to transmission lines and then to cavity resonators. Since magnetrons operate high in the microwave region, their tuning circuits are almost always cavity resonators. Fig. 6–1 shows the type of cavity resonator used with present magnetrons.

Second, there must be provided a means for starting the oscillations and, the oscillations (r-f) once having started, a means of reinforcing them to make up for losses due to resistance and energy withdrawal from the resonant circuit. In all oscillators, the initial starting is provided by the disturbance created when the power is turned on. The oscillations thus created are then maintained by suitably converting the applied d-c power into r-f power. In the low-frequency oscillator, an inductive or capacitive coupling between a vacuum tube and the oscillatory circuit is used to feed energy back from the vacuum tube to the oscillatory circuit. In the magnetron, the feedback of energy from the d-c anode potential to the r-f fields takes place in the space between the anode and cathode (or

163

filament) shown in Fig. 6–1 by an interaction of the electrons with an r-f field.

Third, oscillators need a device to regulate the feedback both in amplitude and phase. Conventional oscillators use a combination of grid capacitors and resistors, together with adjusting the anode potential to regulate the feedback. In the magnetron this regulation is achieved largely by designing the cavity and by adjusting the anode potential to a critical ratio of d-c anode voltage to the strength of a magnetic field.

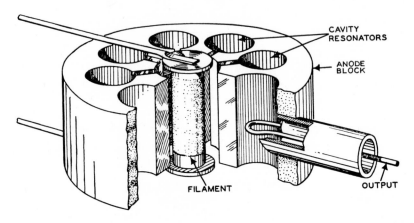

FIG. 6.1. A cut-away view showing the principal components of a multicavity resonator. (*Courtesy Bell System Technical Journal*)

There is a feature about the magnetron not common to more conventional oscillators, and that is the presence of a strong, permanent magnetic field within the space surrounding the cathode. An open view of a complete multicavity magnetron is shown in Fig. 6–2. Note carefully the relative positions of the cathode, anode, and cavities because an understanding of the action of the magnetron depends upon their relationship.

How a Magnetron Works. To start, several actions within the magnetron will be discussed individually first and then as combinations of the actions to form a functioning magnetron.

Physically, the modern traveling-wave magnetron appears as shown in Fig. 6–1. At the center is a circular filament or cathode from which electrons are obtained when the cathode is suitably heated. Surrounding the cathode is a circular anode wall into which a number of cavity resonators have been machined. Energy is coupled out of the magnetron by means of a loop feeding a coaxial transmission line.

Now, assume that you are looking down on this magnetron (Fig. 6–3A) with the hot cathode surrounded by a space charge. Fig. 6–3B shows the space charge concentrated in the vicinity of the cathode. If, now, we apply a positive voltage between anode and cathode (with the anode positive with respect to the cathode), then electrons will be drawn from the cathode to the anode. (See Fig. 6–3C.) This is an action which is completely familiar from conventional vacuum tube behavior.

FIG. 6.2. An internal view of a 700 A–D magnetron (40 kw, 700 mc) showing the cavity resonator system of six hole and slot circuits, the cathode, the cathode end disks and support leads, and the output coupling loop and lead. (*Courtesy Bell Telephone Laboratory*)

For the moment, concentrate on just one such electron. As it travels toward the anode, it will gradually speed up, acquiring energy from the d-c electric field of the anode. The energy build-up continues until the electron crashes against the anode, thereby dissipating all its acquired energy in heat. The heat developed in this process is an undesirable by-product which cannot be avoided. However, the important point for the reader to remember is the fact that the electron obtains energy from the d-c electric field as it moves.

Next, to this magnetron let us add a magnetic field whose lines of force are parallel to the cathode. (See Fig. 6–4.) What will the path of the electron be under these circumstances? To obtain the answer, it is first necessary to recall that an electron in motion is itself surrounded by a magnetic field. When the electron is more or less motionless near the cathode, the magnetic field is weak; but as the electron moves, the magnetic field builds up.

When we add an external magnetic field to the magnetron, it will interact with the magnetic field set up by the electron. Under these

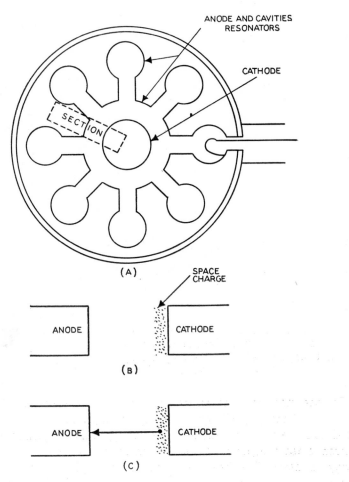

FIG. 6.3.   Action of d-c electrostatic field in a traveling-wave magnetron.

circumstances, the moment an electron leaves the cathode it will find itself being acted on by the added magnetic field. The force arising from this interaction will be at right angles to both the added magnetic field and to the line of motion of the electron, causing the electron to move in more or less of a curved or spiral path. If the magnetic field is weak, the electron path will be only slightly curved (*A* in Fig. 6–5), and the electron will still reach the anode and give up whatever energy it gained in going from cathode to anode.

As the magnetic field strength is gradually increased, the electron path will tend to curve more and more until, at a certain value of magnetic

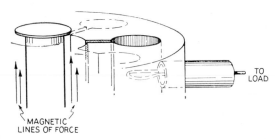

FIG. 6.4. Magnetic lines of force are introduced between cathode and anode of magnetron.

field, the electron will just barely graze the anode wall and then be brought back to the cathode. (See curve B of Fig. 6–5.) The field strength at which this occurs is called the critical magnetic field strength (written B_c).

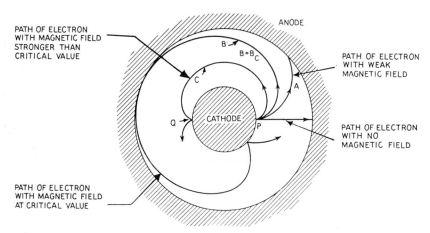

FIG. 6.5. Electron paths in magnetron under varying magnetic field conditions.

If the magnetic field strength is increased beyond this critical value, the electron will never reach the anode. (See curve C of Fig. 6–5.) It will start out for the anode from point P, but the force produced by the magnetic field will be so great that the electron will be quickly brought back to the cathode, perhaps at point Q. It reaches point Q with little or no velocity, and it no sooner comes to rest when the positive anode voltage once more attracts it.   Again the electron starts for the plate, again it travels through its circular path, ending up now at some new point on the cathode.   The same sequence continues to recur, with the electron hopping its way around the cathode cylinder and never reaching the plate.

Thus, for a given potential difference between anode and cathode, the distance an electron travels from the cathode depends upon the strength of the magnetic field present between the two electrodes.   We can achieve a similar variation in electron motion by altering the positive anode voltage. An increased voltage will cause the electron to move in a larger circle; a lowered voltage will reduce the circle radius.

In the magnetron the problem is to adjust the magnetic field strength and anode potential so that electrons will curve properly to obtain the desired oscillation and efficiency of operation.   This will be dealt with presently.

There is but one more point to review and that is the r-f oscillations of cavity resonators in relationship to magnetic fields and electron movement.   Suppose that the application of a high d-c potential to the anode shock-excites the circuits into setting up weak oscillations in the cavities. If the electron's path is such that, in curving toward the anode the energy released by the electron adds to the energy of the r-f field, oscillations will be built up and sustained.   On the other hand, some electrons in curving take energy away from the r-f field.   These must be eliminated as quickly as possible.   The problem then is to control the movement of electrons so that more energy is added to the r-f field than is taken from it.   Just how this is done is explained below.

Three Types of Magnetrons.   There are three types of magnetrons: the negative resistance or dynatron type, the transit-time or cyclotron type, and the traveling-wave magnetron.   All three have been useful, but because of limitations of the first two, they are not manufactured today. Only the traveling-wave magnetron finds wide applications.   Hence it will be the only one discussed here.

In the traveling-wave multicavity magnetron, shown in Fig. 6–1, oscillations are established in the various cavity resonators by the interaction of electrons rotating in the space between the cathode and anode and the r-f fields set up in each of the cavity resonators.   The actual velocities and curvature of the electrons are determined by the value of d-c voltage used and the strength of the magnetic field, and this velocity may be set at any desired value.   Maximum output at any frequency is obtained when the d-c voltage and the strength of the magnetic field are adjusted so that the electrons transfer energy to the cavity resonators at the proper time, thereby building up large oscillations in the cavity resonators.   At other values of voltage and magnetic field strength, the motion of the electrons will not be such as to aid and reinforce any oscillations set up in the cavity resonators, and the output energy will either be zero or considerably smaller than the maximum obtainable under the proper operating conditions.

A positive d-c voltage is connected between the cathode and anode block, and an axial magnetic field is provided by an external magnet. Electrons emitted by the cathode are attracted to the highly positive anode block. The moment the electrons start traveling toward the anode, however, they interact with the axial magnetic field, which forces them to travel in the circular path previously described. These electrons, traveling toward the anode, shock-excite the cavity resonators in the same manner that a conventional oscillator is shock-excited into oscillations when power is suddenly applied and electrons flow through the tube. As a result of this shock excitation, the cavity resonators will oscillate at their resonant frequencies

Now, the cavity resonators in the anode block represent a series of tuned resonant circuits, all coupled to each other. The r-f fields set up in the cavity resonators when they are excited either may be in phase with each other or differ by certain values up to 180 degrees. When all the resonators are in phase with each other, the voltage variations appearing across the mouth of each cavity resonator rise and fall in step with each other. In the more usual case, some phase difference exists between adjacent cavity resonators. As an illustration, consider similar points in each of the cavity resonators, such as points A_1, A_2, A_3, A_4, A_5, A_6, A_7, and A_8, in the eight cavity resonators shown in Fig. 6–6A. When the r-f potential of A_1 is zero, that of A_2 is at 45° in the r-f cycle, A_3 is at 90°, A_4 is at 135°, A_5 is at 180°, A_6 is at 225°, A_7 is at 270°, and A_8 is at 315°. Thus each point is going through a different portion of the r-f cycle at this particular moment, with the phase varying gradually around the circle. At the next moment, the phase of each point changes, with perhaps A_8 reaching 360° (which is the same as 0°), A_1 becoming 45°, A_2 going to 90°, etc. This phase variation moves around the cavity resonators at r-f velocity, producing the equivalent of a rotating r-f field. The electrons emitted by the cathode react with this traveling r-f field, forming clusters or clouds (of electrons) which rotate in step or synchronism with the traveling r-f field while, at the same time, spiraling outward from the cathode to the positive anode block. An electron which leaves the cathode at a time when it absorbs energy from the r-f fields set up by the cavity resonators is quickly returned to the cathode. On the other hand, an electron which leaves the cathode at a time when it gives up energy to

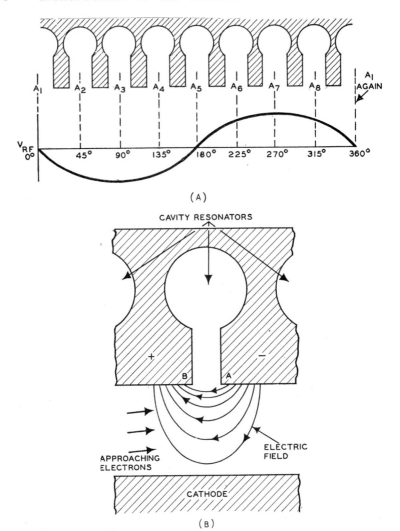

FIG. 6.6.   (A) An eight-cavity magnetron with a phase difference of 45° between successive resonators.   For ease in presentation, the cavity resonators are shown in a straight line, although they would actually appear as shown in Fig. 6.1.   (B) Electrons approaching the mouth of a cavity resonator in time to transfer energy to the resonator.

the resonators remains in the interaction space for several complete spirals and then reaches the anode wall and is removed from the circuit, with other electrons moving in from the cathode to take its place.

In order to maintain oscillations, the emitted electrons must give up energy to the cavity resonators. This will occur if the electrons approach the mouth of a cavity resonator when the r-f voltage existing across the mouth of the resonator is at its maximum negative value. As an illustration, consider the situation shown in Fig. 6–6B. Electrons, attracted by the positive d-c potential applied between the plate wall and the cathode, are approaching the mouth of the cavity resonator when maximum r-f negative voltage exists across its mouth. Side A of the cavity resonator mouth contains a large accumulation of electrons. The r-f potential presented by side A to the oncoming electrons is negative and, since the electrons are also negative, the two will repel each other. The closer the electrons get to side A, the greater their repelling action, thus giving the electrons accumulated on side A an added push to move back to side B around the inner surface of the cavity resonator.

This action is similar to that obtained when striking a pendulum just as it comes to the end of its swing. If we did not hit it, the pendulum would still swing back but, because of air resistance and other friction, would traverse a smaller arc during each successive swing, finally coming to rest. However, by striking it, we impart enough additional energy to help it overcome these resistances and permit it to swing over a full arc. A similar situation prevails in the magnetron oscillatory circuit. If no interspace electrons came along at the proper times to help move the accumulation of electrons from A to B in the tuning circuit, the oscillations would rapidly die out.

The oncoming electrons are slowed down a little (that is, lose some of their energy) each time they pass a cavity resonator gap and, after one or two revolutions around the eight cavity resonators, they fall onto the anode block and are returned through the external circuit to the cathode.

Electrons which perform in the manner just outlined are known as favorable electrons since they aid in the continuation of oscillations. However, the cathode is emitting electrons all the time, and so it will happen that electrons will be emitted when the conditions existing across the resonator mouth are exactly opposite to that shown in Fig. 6–6B. That is, side A will be relatively positive to side B. An electron leaving the cathode at this moment will be speeded up (rather than slowed down) because of the added attracting force of the positive r-f potential at side A combining with the normal anode d-c voltage. This speeding up of the electron will result in a greater interaction between its magnetic field and that existing in the magnetron, causing the electron to curve more and quickly bringing it back to the cathode. (See Fig. 6–7A.) This can be compared to the path followed by the favorable electrons, Fig. 6–7B.

Since the unfavorable electrons (those that absorb energy from the cavity resonators) are quickly removed from the interaction space, only the favorable electrons remain to spiral about in this space. In the multicavity magnetron just described, there is only one point, at any instant of time, where energy should be transferred from the spiraling electrons to the cavity resonator system. For maximum operating efficiency, all of the favorable electrons in the interaction space should be bunched together, and this is actually the way they appear. (See Fig. 6–8.)

In the preceding discussion, we noted the operation of a multicavity magnetron in which a phase difference of 360 degrees was proportioned

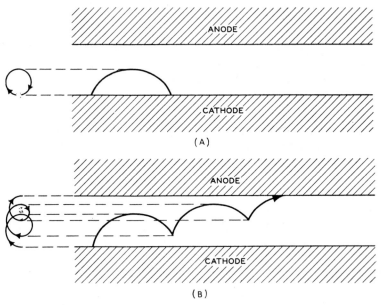

FIG. 6.7. (A) Path of an electron which absorbs energy from the r-f field. (B) Path of an electron which gives up energy to the r-f field. Note: The anode and cathode elements are shown as straight for the sake of simplicity. Actually, of course, they are circular. (*Courtesy Bell System Technical Journal*)

among each of the eight cavity resonators. This is known as one *mode* of operation. A magnetron may have a number of different modes of operation, each representing various resonant frequencies of the cavity resonators which can be generated by the electrons whirling about in the interaction region. Note, then, that the factors governing the frequencies that can be generated depend upon the resonant frequency of the cavity resonators and the velocity at which the electrons whirl about between the cathode and the plate block containing the resonators. The latter factor, in turn, is determined by the values of the applied d-c voltage and the external magnetic field.

Of particular interest is a mode of operation known as the π (pi) mode, so called because there is a phase difference of 180 degrees (π radians) between the electrical oscillations of successive cavity resonators. This mode is important because it is capable of high output and good efficiency. In many of the other modes which are possible, the output is low and hence of no practical importance.

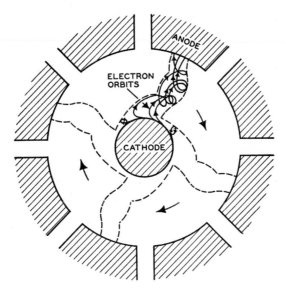

Fig. 6.8.   The orbits of favorable electrons traveling from cathode to anode while, at the same time, whirling around at r-f velocity.

To represent the conditions in the π mode at different instants of time, it is helpful to employ a diagram such as shown in Fig. 6–9. Each of the eight resonators is shown in a straight line, although their actual physical placement within the magnetron would be circular. On the first line beneath the resonators there is shown the r-f voltage distribution at some instant of time which we will call T. The voltage or potential is constant across the face of the anode wall but varies linearly from a negative to a positive value (or vice-versa) in the gap between. Thus, at the time T shown, the r-f voltage is positive on the resonator wall labeled #1, and it varies from a positive to a negative value across the gap between walls #1 and #2. In the gap between walls #2 and #3, the potential distribution is 180 degrees out of phase with the potential variation in the preceding gap. This is characteristic of the π mode.

To indicate graphically the progress of a group of electrons, we can use a dotted line. At time T, this group of electrons is traveling across the gap between walls #1 and #2. Note that it is traveling toward face #2 which is approaching its maximum negative value. Thus, as the electrons pass the gap near face #2, they repel the accumulated electrons here back to face #1.

The space electrons now travel past gap #1 and move on to the next gap, between faces #2 and #3, arriving here just when the potential difference across this gap is the same as it was across the previous gap an instant before. The time now is $T + \frac{2}{4}T$ seconds later. Since the same potential conditions exist here, the same action will occur, with the bunched electrons repelling the accumulated electrons at face #3 and thereby aiding them to move back to face #2. Each time the traveling electrons do this, they are moving closer to the anode wall, transferring energy to the electrons oscillating in the cavity resonators. The traveling electrons continue to lose energy until they strike the anode wall and are removed from the circuit. However, the process is a continuously dynamic one, with electrons being emitted from the cathode in a steady stream and other electrons reaching the anode wall at the same rate. The energy to travel this distance is supplied by the d-c accelerating potential established between the cathode and the wall by an externally applied power source.

Returning to Fig. 6–9, we see that the bunched electrons continue traveling, reaching the gap between wall faces #3 and #4 at time $T + \frac{4}{4}T$. The dotted line, followed down to the bottom of the chart, shows the electron travel for one complete encirclement of all of the cavity resonators. In the diagram, Fig. 6–9, four complete r-f cycles occur in the time required for the electrons to encircle the cavity resonators once. Note that by employing *other* values of d-c voltage and magnetic field strength, it is possible to have the electrons travel at lower velocities and still maintain the same mode of operation. Thus, in Fig. 6–9, the dotted line indicated by the number 12 illustrates how a group of electrons can travel once around the interaction space while 12 r-f cycles are generated by the cavity resonators. The electrons are traveling one-third as fast as those in the previous illustration. Shown also are other dotted lines for which bunched electrons travel once around the magnetron while 20 and 28 r-f cycles, respectively, occur.

If we were to open a magnetron containing eight cavity resonators, and operating in the "π" mode, it would be found to contain four spokes whirling about at r-f velocity. Each spoke would contain all of the favorable electrons since each spoke passes a cavity resonator gap when the r-f field potential possesses the correct polarity. Electrons leaving the cathode and not entering one of these four spokes will absorb energy from the field and quickly return to the cathode. The spiral paths of the favorable electrons as they travel from cathode to anode are shown in Fig. 6–10.

In a previous illustration, Fig. 6–8, only one rotating spoke was shown because there existed only one point, at any instant of time, at which maximum energy transfer could occur. In the "π" mode of operation, examination of Fig. 6–9 will reveal that maximum energy transfer can occur at any one of four points, at any given instant of time. Thus, for

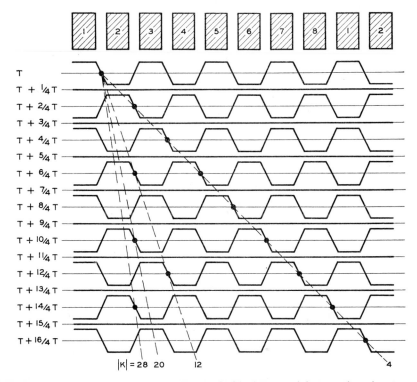

FIG. 6.9. A plot showing the π mode anode block potential at various instants of time. The dotted lines represent favorable electrons. See text.

example, at time T, a spoke passing either gap #1, gap #3, gap #5, or gap #7, will transfer energy to the oscillating r-f field. This is so because, at time T, the electrical conditions are identical at each of these points. During the next instant, the spokes passing across gaps #2, #4, #6, and #8 will transfer maximum energy to the r-f field. Thus, at any time, electrons can be at one of four different points and still be considered as "favorable" electrons. Hence, the existence of four rotating spokes of electrons.

As a general rule, the *maximum* number of electron spokes that can exist in a magnetron is limited to $N/2$, where N is the number of cavity resonators. Thus, whether the electrons traverse once around the magnetron while 4 r-f cycles are being generated, or once while 12, 20, or 28 r-f cycles are being generated, there are still only four points, at any instant, where the energy transfer can go from the electrons to the resonators. Hence, the maximum number of spokes can be four.

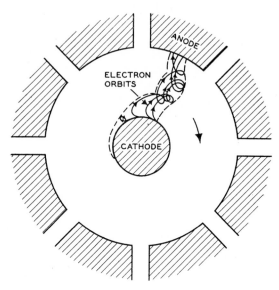

Fig. 6.10. In the "π" mode, a maximum of four spokes is possible. Favorable electrons must fall into one of these spokes. (*Courtesy Bell System Technical Journal*)

It is interesting to note that the resonant frequency of the mode is actually the lowest or cut-off frequency that can be generated by the magnetron. When the phase difference between successive gaps becomes greater than 180 degrees, oscillations cease altogether.

Modes of Operation. Now that we have gained some concept of the operation of a multicavity magnetron, we can examine the cavity resonators more closely. Each resonator can be considered as a parallel resonant circuit which is inductively coupled to the resonators on either side of it. If there are eight cavity resonators, there are essentially eight parallel resonant circuits which are inductively coupled to each other. It has been found that if two tuned circuits, each having the same resonant frequency when used separately, are coupled together, the combination will oscillate simultaneously at two slightly different frequencies. Stated in other words, this coupled system is said to have two modes of operation. The reason the system can oscillate at two different frequencies arises from the mutual inductance existing between the two circuits. This mutual inductance either can add to the self-inductance existing in the tuned circuit, in which case the resonant frequency is reduced, or it can substract from the self-inductance of the tuned circuit, raising the resonant frequency.

In ordinary low-frequency circuits it is well known that if two tuned circuits are very loosely coupled, their frequency response curve has a single peak. As the coupling between the circuits is increased, two peaks are observed in the response curve, the frequency separation of the peaks increasing as the coupling becomes tighter. This action could be inferred from the preceding paragraph, because with increased coupling, the effect of the mutual inductance increases. When more mutual inductance is added to a circuit, its frequency decreases; when a greater mutual inductance subtracts from the self-inductance of a circuit, the resonant frequency increases. Thus, the two peaks, representing the two resonant frequencies of the coupled system, are widely separated.

When there are eight resonant cavities in the magnetron, there will be eight different resonant frequencies, each separated slightly from each other. The exact frequency separation of each of these eight frequencies will depend upon the coupling between the resonators. If the coupling is loose, the eight frequencies will be closely bunched together. Under these conditions it will be found that the magnetron will oscillate at some or all of these frequencies, dividing its energy in a complex fashion between them. In order to achieve maximum efficiency, the magnetron should resonate at one frequency only, with little or no power being expended in any of the other modes or frequencies of which the cavity resonators are capable. Now, in order to have the magnetron oscillate in only one mode, the coupling between the cavity resonators must be increased, thereby separating the various resonant frequencies as far as possible from each other. The d-c voltage applied to the magnetron and the magnetic field is then adjusted so that the magnetron oscillates only in the desired mode. Since the other modes are relatively far apart, there is little chance that "mode-jumping" will occur.

Magnetron Strapping. Two methods are currently employed for increasing the coupling between cavity resonators. One method, known as strapping, is shown in Fig. 6–11. In this arrangement, the anode segments are connected together by means of wire straps in such a way as to fix the phase relationship between the resonators. In Fig. 6–11A, alternate anode segments are connected together, forcing the voltages of alternate anodes to keep in step with each other. In the π mode, it will be remembered, alternate resonators were in phase with each other. By using straps to connect these alternate resonators, any tendency for them to change phase is reduced, thereby solidly establishing this phase relationship and forcing the magnetron to remain in one mode of operation. The straps add a capacitive and an inductive effect to the cavity resonators, the exact amount of each being determined by the manner in which they are connected. The straps may either be mounted directly above the cavity

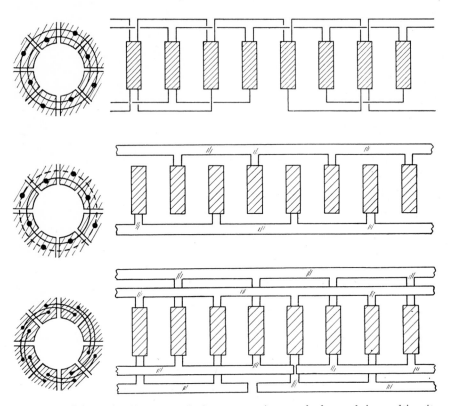

FIG. 6.11. Schematic diagrams of three strapping methods used in multicavity magnetrons. At the left of each illustration is a top view and, at the right, a rolled-out view.

resonators, in which case they are exposed to the electrons traveling in the interaction space, or the straps may be set in grooves, thereby being shielded.

Two other methods of strapping are shown in Fig. 6–11. A cut-away view of a magnetron having straps is shown in Fig. 6–12.

The second system of separating mode frequencies is to employ the so-called "rising-sun" resonator system. (See Fig. 6–13.) This method achieves mode frequency separation by using cavity resonators having widely separated resonant frequencies. When these resonators are closely coupled, as they are in the magnetron, the π mode frequency lies between

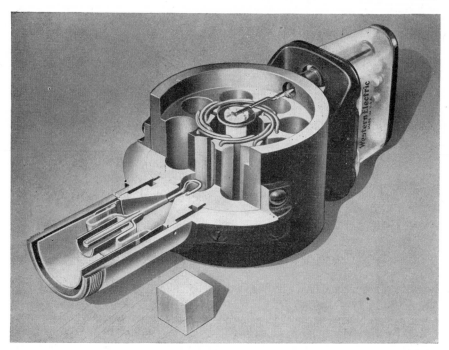

FIG. 6.12. A cut-away view of a 5J23 magnetron (275 kw, at 1050 mc) showing the strapping between resonators and the coaxial output circuit. A one-inch cube is included for size reference. (*Courtesy Bell System Technical Journal*)

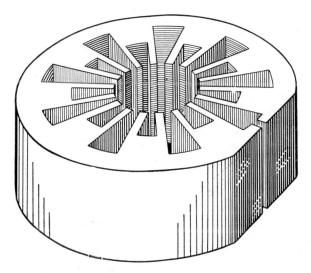

FIG. 6.13. A "rising-sun" resonator system.

the two resonant frequencies of the cavity resonators and is well separated from either of these. The "rising-sun" resonator is particularly useful in extremely high-frequency magnetrons where the space is small and straps would be difficult to install.

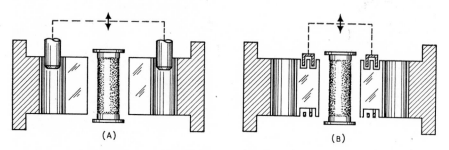

(A)   (B)

Fig. 6.14.   (A) Varying the inductance of a cavity resonator by means of tuning pins.   (B) Varying the capacitance of a cavity resonator.

Magnetron Tuning.   The first magnetrons that appeared commercially possessed a single frequency that could not be altered. Some method of tuning was desirable, however, and this has been accomplished, as in conventional circuits, by changing the circuit inductance or the circuit capacitance. To vary the resonator inductance, a pin, known as a tuning pin, is inserted in each of the resonator cavities by some form of mechanical assembly. (See Fig. 6–14A.) These tuning pins are composed of some nonmagnetic substance and, as they move deeper into the cavity, they reduce the volume available for the magnetic flux, thereby reducing the inductance and causing the frequency to increase. This method of frequency variation is identical in operation, although not in execution, to that employed in eddy-current tuning. Tuning ranges as great as ±7% of the mean frequency have been accomplished in this manner.

Frequency tuning by means of capacitance variation can be achieved by the method shown in Fig. 6–14B. A ring, shaped like a cookie cutter, is moved in or out of grooves cut into the anode block. Usually this ring is placed on the side of the anode block opposite to that containing the straps, if these are employed. The deeper the ring moves into the groove, the higher the magnetron frequency. A cut-away view of a magnetron employing capacitive tuning is shown in Fig. 6–15. The tuner consists of two concentric rings which are moved up and down in the grooves in the segments of the anode structure. The resonator system is strapped on the end not seen in the figure. The complete magnetron is shown as No. 2 in Fig. 6–16B.

In design of magnetrons, it has been found that it is easier to vary

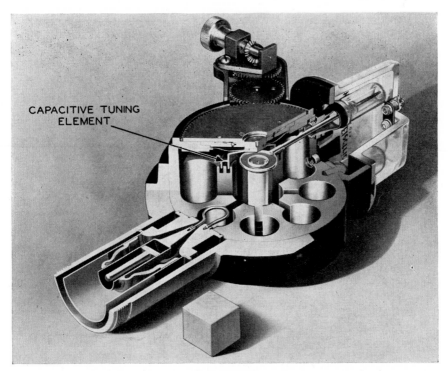

CAPACITIVE TUNING ELEMENT

Fig. 6.15. A cut-away view of a 4J51 tunable magnetron. The tuning member consists of two concentric rings which are moved up and down in the grooves in the segments of the anode structure. The resonator system is strapped on the end not seen in the illustration. (*Courtesy Bell System Technical Journal*)

the inductance for the high frequencies and the capacitance at the low frequencies.

Four fixed frequency magnetrons are shown in Fig. 6–16A and four tunable magnetrons are shown in Fig. 6–16B. Note that some of the units have attached magnets, while others do not; some use coaxial output circuits while others use waveguides.

Magnetron Cathodes. Magnetrons are generally employed as pulsed oscillators, the pulse duration being 1 microsecond long and recurring at the rate of 1000 times a second. During this pulsing interval, the cathode of the magnetron may be required to deliver as much as 100 amperes of current. If we compare this with the 30 or 40 milliamperes obtainable from a receiver power tube, we see that a very special type of structure is needed in the magnetron. There are several different types of cathode structures in use, one of the most common consisting of a double carbonate mixture placed on a cylindrical mesh form made with nickel wire. A

Fig. 6.16B. Four tunable magnetron oscillators. They are: (1) the 4J42 magnetron (660 to 730 mc); (2) the 4J51 magnetron (900 to 970 mc); (3) the 5J26 magnetron (1220 to 1350 mc); and (4) the 2J51 magnetron (8500 to 9600 mc). (Courtesy Bell System Technical Journal)

Fig. 6.16A. Four fixed frequency magnetron oscillators. They are: (1) the 3J21 magnetron (24,000 mc); (2) the 4J52 magnetron (9375 mc); (3) the 720A–E magnetron (2800 mc); and (4) the 4J21–30 magnetron (1280 mc). (Courtesy Bell System Technical Journal)

heater wire is then placed inside the cathode structure, as shown in the cut-away view of Fig. 6–17.

The method by which the enormous pulsed currents of 100 amperes is obtained is not completely understood. When the cathode current is measured under conditions of no oscillation, it is found to be less than 1 per cent of the current which is obtained during the pulsing periods when the magnetron is oscillating vigorously. From this it has been concluded

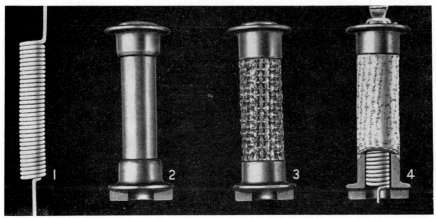

FIG. 6.17. Construction of a magnetron cathode. Shown are: (1) the heater element; (2) the nickel cathode blank; (3) the cathode blank with nickel wire mesh; (4) cathode with oxide coating applied, cut away to show heater element in place. (*Courtesy Bell System Technical Journal*)

that conditions must exist during the oscillatory periods which are responsible for the tremendous surge of energy. Possible explanations for this behavior are as follows:

1. The unfavorable electrons which are returned to the cathode arrive with such force that they knock out other electrons which join the interaction electrons. Of these secondary electrons, some are returned to the cathode, causing further secondary emission. This process is cumulative, resulting in a high cathode current.

2. Another contributing factor is the effect of the large electric fields present in the tube. These fields, acting at the cathode, tend to reduce the forces which hold the electrons to the cathode-emitting material. Under these conditions, the large electric fields are able to draw more electrons from the cathode than would be possible in their absence.

3. Ionic conduction or electrolytic action in the coating may also contribute toward a lowered holding force on the electrons and permit them to be drawn away more easily.

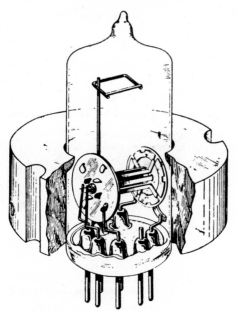

It is believed that each of these factors helps provide the tremendous currents obtained from the cathode during the pulsing interval.

Tunable Miniature Magnetron.* All of the foregoing magnetrons were designed for high power output. Recently General Electric engineers have come up with a miniature magnetron which, it is claimed, will operate over the range from 0 to 1000 mc and deliver a continuous power output of one-half watt or less.

The tube, shown in Fig. 6–18, can be mounted on a standard 7-pin miniature base. The anode structure consists of eight vanes

FIG. 6.18. A cut-away view of the General Electric miniature magnetron. (*Courtesy Electronics Magazine*)

fastened alternately to two end rings; that is, four vanes connect to one end ring and four to the other. The vanes are nonmagnetic in order not to be affected by the magnetic field applied to the tube. A field strength of 500 to 600 gauss is required.

To utilize the tube as an oscillator, it is connected as shown in Fig. 6–19. A push-pull arrangement is employed, and as the voltage is raised from zero upward, oscillations at the resonant frequency of the circuit will occur. The manner in which oscillations are produced depends upon the operating voltage and the frequency of the resonant circuit. For frequencies from a few cycles to about 100 mc, the tube operates as a

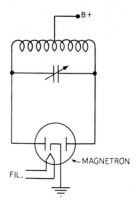

FIG. 6.19. The magnetron of Fig. 6.18, connected as an oscillator. The external magnetic field required for operation is not shown.

negative-resistance magnetron. The positive anode voltages and the magnetic field strength are adjusted to values at which the negative resistance produced between the two end rings (to which the alternate vanes are connected) is sufficient to offset the positive circuit resistance. Under these

* "Tunable Miniature Magnetron," by Wilbur, Peters, and Chalberg, *Electronics,* January 1952.

conditions, oscillations are sustained in any tuned circuit connected to the tube. The frequency of oscillations is determined by the circuit resonant frequency.

A necessary condition for oscillations in this mode is that the d-c voltage be strong enough so that the time it takes electrons to pass from one vane to the next is small in comparison to the period of one cycle of the voltage being generated. In fact, the highest frequency possible is determined when the period of one-half of an r-f cycle becomes comparable to the time it takes an electron to pass from one vane to the next.

Above 100 mc, the magnetron swings over to the traveling-wave mode of operation. Now, the electrons need travel only fast enough (when passing from one vane to the next) to keep in step with the changing r-f voltage. This permits the tube to operate with a lower d-c voltage and results in a consequent increase in efficiency. There is, however, a minimum starting voltage for each frequency in this mode.

Tuning circuits of almost any variety may be used with this magnetron. Possible applications of this tube range all the way from UHF receivers to signal generators and low-powered transmitters.

QUESTIONS

1. Magnetrons and conventional oscillators have many characteristics in common. Indicate what these are.

2. How does the magnetron differ from the previously mentioned tubes?

3. Name the three types of magnetrons which have been used for the high frequencies. Which is in general use today?

4. Name the various electrical and mechanical components of a traveling-wave magnetron.

5. Describe what happens when an electron in a traveling-wave magnetron travels from cathode to anode. Compare this action in three steps: (1) when the magnetic field is quite weak, (2) when the magnetic field is at the so-called critical value, and (3) when a powerful magnetic field is present.

6. What type of tuned circuits are used in magnetrons? Describe their operation briefly.

7. How are the oscillations in these tuned circuits initiated? How are they subsequently sustained?

8. Distinguish between favorable and unfavorable electrons in magnetrons.

9. Describe what happens to each of the foregoing electrons in the operation of a magnetron.

10. Describe briefly the overall operation of a traveling-wave magnetron.

11. What is meant by a mode of operation? Which mode is most frequently employed? Describe the electrical conditions which exist within the magnetron for this mode.

12. What is the purpose of strapping? Indicate several commonly used strapping methods.

13. Why was the "rising-sun" resonator developed? How does it achieve its purpose?

14. How can the frequency of a traveling-wave magnetron be changed? Describe one method in detail.

Chapter 7

THE KLYSTRON OSCILLATOR

Introduction. The magnetron is an efficient generator of high-frequency voltages, but it requires an external magnetic field and does not lend itself readily to simple forms of modulation for the transmission of intelligence. Another high-frequency tube, known as the klystron, does not use an external magnetic field, is relatively small physically, and may be operated with fairly low voltages. The klystron possesses the added advantage of lending itself readily to frequency modulation, and in this capacity has been employed extensively in studio-to-transmitter equipment for A–M, F–M and television broadcast stations.

The klystron tube was developed originally by the Varian Brothers in 1939 and operates on a principle of velocity modulation which is completely different from the operation of any of the conventional tubes. In the latter tubes, the electrons emitted by a cathode pass through a mesh grid which regulates or controls the number of electrons which can pass the grid at any instant of time. In this way we are actually regulating the density of the electrons traveling between cathode and plate, and hence we call this method "current density modulation." In klystron tubes, grids act upon the electrons emitted by the cathode also, but their purpose is not to alter the number of passing electrons but to vary the velocities of these electrons and by means of this velocity variation, to cause the tube to function either as an amplifier, oscillator, detector, or frequency multiplier.

Action in a Klystron. The internal structure of a klystron tube is shown in Fig. 7–1. A stream of electrons, produced by a cathode and focused into a sharply defined beam with the aid of the first grid G_1, is accelerated toward G_2 and G_3 by a positive voltage V. The grids G_2 and G_3 are placed very close together so that the electrons spend only a relatively short time between them. Superimposed on the high d-c voltage V is a small r-f voltage V_1. (For the moment we will disregard where such a voltage may be obtained.) If an electron reaches the grids when the r-f voltage between them is zero, it will pass on unaffected. However, any electron reaching the grids when V_1 is going positive will receive a greater acceleration than if the r-f voltage were not present. Similarly, when the r-f voltage is going negative, each oncoming electron will be subjected to less positive voltage V than usual, and its velocity will be reduced. In this way, the electrons will tend to have different velocities, dependent upon the time in the r-f cycle at which they pass the two grids.

At this point, the electron beam may be said to be velocity-modulated because we have altered the velocity of the electrons as they passed through grids G_2 and G_3. This particular fact is, of itself, not significant. However, if we let the electrons travel long enough, then those electrons which were acceler-

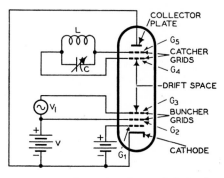

FIG. 7.1. The arrangement of electrodes within a klystron tube.

ated in going through grids G_2 and G_3 will eventually catch up with those electrons that passed through G_2 and G_3 shortly before this and were slowed down. The result will be bunches or clusters of electrons. At the center of the clusters will be found those electrons that passed G_2 and G_3 with their velocities unchanged.

Another way of visualizing this bunching process is to consider three electrons: the first, which passed through G_2 and G_3 when the alternating voltage V_1 was still negative (around 340 degrees of its cycle); the second, which passed through when V_1 was zero; and the third, when V_1 was just starting to go positive. The first electron was slowed down, the second passed through with its velocity unchanged, and the third electron had its velocity increased. At some time after they passed G_2 and G_3, these three electrons will meet to form a bunch.

A graphic illustration of this bunching process is shown in Fig. 7–2. Each column represents a picture of the electron distribution throughout the tube at a different instant of time. The input grids are G_2 and G_3; the output grids represent two other grids located some distance from G_2 and G_3.

The earliest moment is at the left, with time successively increasing as we proceed to the right. At a point slightly below the center of the first column, a bunch of electrons is just beginning to form. Each successive column to the right then reveals how the bunches gradually assume a more definite shape until, by the time the electrons reach grids G_4 and G_5, the formation of the bunch is complete.

Thus, the electron beam that started out by being velocity-modulated ends up as a density-modulated beam. This density modulation effect is desirable because, in this form, energy can be extracted from the beam.

The space between grids G_2, G_3 and grids G_4, G_5 is known as a drift space and is kept completely free of any electric or magnetic fields. At the end of the drift space, there are two grids G_4 and G_5, and these are connected to a tuned resonant circuit (in the klystron, a cavity resonator). This circuit will be set into oscillation if the bunches of electrons pass through at intervals equal to the natural period of the circuit. These grids (G_4 and G_5) are called the catcher grids since it is their express purpose

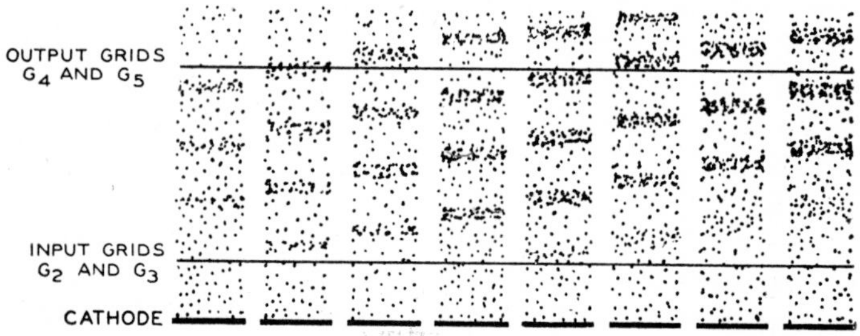

Fig. 7.2. The electron distribution in a klystron indicated at eight different moments. By following the electrons as they progress down the drift tube, the formation of the bunches can be seen.

to intercept and absorb the r-f energy that was imparted to the electrons as they passed through G_2 and G_3 (which are known as the buncher grids). Energy will be delivered to the catcher grids only if the electron bunches pass through when the field between these grids is a retarding field. The energy transfer should occur in one direction, that is, from the electron beam to the catcher grids, or when the electron beam is decelerated.

The action of the electron bunches in causing the cavity resonator, of which G_4 and G_5 are the two grids, to develop and maintain an r-f voltage is closely similar to the action of the plate current pulses in a low-frequency r-f amplifier. These plate current pulses, occurring at regular intervals, will shock-excite any tuned resonant coil and capacitor circuit inserted in the plate circuit of this tube. By the same token, the bunches of electrons, passing by G_4 and G_5 at regular intervals, will shock-excite the cavity resonator, causing it to develop an r-f voltage.

There are several requirements which the catcher grids must satisfy in order to work most efficiently:

1. The grids should not be placed too far from G_2 and G_3. There is a critical spacing that gives the best results in bunching the electrons.

2. The resonant circuit of the catcher should be tuned to the correct frequency.

3. The strength and phase of the oscillations in these grids should be such as to absorb from the electron bunches as much of the high-frequency energy as possible. After the beam has given up its high-frequency power to the catcher, it expends its direct-current power on a collecting electrode which then returns these electrons to the cathode, thus completing the circuit. Throughout the entire process the total current remains constant and is referred to as the conduction current.

The spectre of transit time, which casts its shadow so ominously over conventional tubes at UHF, is actually employed to advantage in the klystron. Instead of drawing the electrons as rapidly as possible from cathode to anode, they are purposely permitted to drift along until the desired bunching action has been achieved. For this, a special drift space is provided, and time (within limits) rather than speed determines how efficiently the tube operates.

That the klystron is not completely free of transit-time problems is due to the buncher and catcher grids. These project into the electron path, and the time that electrons spend in traversing each set must be short compared to the time of one cycle of the applied signal. Failure to observe this precaution will result in loading of the associated resonators and reduced operating efficiency. Fortunately, the grids are in regions where the electron velocity is high, and so it is much easier to avoid transit-time difficulties here than in conventionally operated tubes.

Summary of Process. The action in a klystron may be summarized as follows:

1. The electron stream must first be velocity-modulated.

2. The velocity-modulated beam must then be converted into a density-modulated beam by means of the field-free drift space.

3. Finally, the high-frequency power must be removed from this beam by means of a suitable circuit. In klystrons, the circuit consists of a cavity resonator. However, even an ordinary transmission line arrangement would work.

Thus the klystron tube uses all the electrons to transfer power from the buncher to the catcher grids. The first set of grids changes the velocity of the electrons and the drift space allows them to form into bunches. These electron clusters, as they pass the catcher grids, deliver energy to

these grids and thereby produce oscillating current in the cavity resonator
attached to them. If the bunches of electrons pass by the catcher grids
at the proper time, the oscillations will be strong, and strong electric and

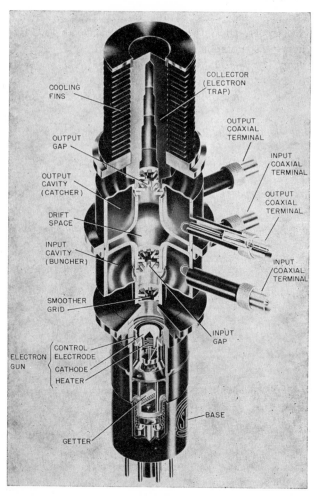

FIG. 7.3. A cut-away view of a 3K30/410–R klystron. (*Courtesy Sperry
Gyroscope Co., Inc.*)

magnetic fields will form inside the resonator. By inserting a loop through
a small hole on one side of the resonator, energy can be transferred to
various other points.

It is interesting to note from Fig. 7–2 that not all of the electrons
traveling through the drift space form into bunches. Some of the electrons
drift along separately, passing the catcher grids at times other than the

most desirable time. These electrons absorb energy instead of giving it and thereby lower the operating efficiency of the tube.

A cut-away view of a type 3K30/410R klystron (Fig. 7–3) reveals its internal construction. The input gap represents the space between grids G_2 and G_3 of Fig. 7–1. Connected to these grids is the buncher (or input) cavity resonator. The output gap is formed by grids G_4 and G_5, and connected to them is the catcher (or output) cavity resonator. Several coaxial cables are coupled to the resonators by means of small loops to

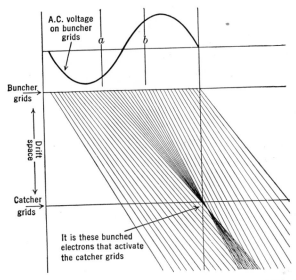

FIG. 7.4. Applegate diagram of klystron showing (by means of lines) the paths of the electrons from buncher to catcher grids.

feed energy into the circuit or transfer it out. In the buncher cavity, energy is received from the input coaxial line. The voltage and current variations of the line establish electric and magnetic fields within the resonator, and the r-f voltages, appearing across the buncher grids, cause the electron beam to become velocity-modulated. (This is the way the voltage V_1 in Fig. 7–1 is produced. The energy may come from the output resonator, in which case we have an oscillator, or from another klystron.) At the catcher resonator, the r-f energy contained in the beam is absorbed, developing strong fields within this cavity. The small loops of the output coaxial lines, coupled to the magnetic fields, transfer this energy to an antenna or whatever other load is designed to receive it.

Applegate Diagram. A more accurate presentation than Fig. 7–2 of what occurs within the klystron can be obtained by the use of a diagram such as Fig. 7–4. This is known as an Applegate diagram and shows, by means of lines, the paths of the various electrons in their travel from buncher to catcher grids. The lines start at the top of the diagram, at the buncher grids. All electrons are assumed to enter these grids from the cathode with the same velocity. In passing through the buncher grids the electrons are acted upon by the r-f voltages shown at the top of diagram. The horizontal axis, the one that goes across the page, indicates time. Starting at the extreme left-hand side of the diagram, the first electrons reaching the buncher grids when the r-f grid voltage is zero will pass through unaffected. The flight of these electrons is indicated by following the first few lines as they proceed through the drift space until they reach the catcher grids. These lines are tilted to the right to indicate that electrons arrive at the catcher grids at a later time. The smaller the tilt, the more swiftly the electrons travel; the greater the tilt, the longer it takes the electrons to reach the catcher grids. In the Applegate diagram, the tilt of the lines is varied according to the velocity of the electrons. By following all the lines, it can be seen that most of the electrons leaving when the r-f voltage is passing from negative to positive will tend to form bunches by the time they reach the catcher.

The diagram indicates that, for best results, the catcher grids must be placed at a certain distance from the bunching grids. This distance depends upon the large d-c accelerating voltage and upon the r-f voltage on grids G_2 and G_3. Since the distance between the two sets of grids is fixed, the voltages must be adjusted to produce the proper amount of bunching. This factor will soon be considered in much greater detail. The operating potential of a klystron tube influences its operation to a considerably greater degree than is true in conventional tubes.

Complete Klystron Oscillator. In order to convert the foregoing klystron into an oscillator, we would proceed as we would with any conventional amplifier, that is, we would couple energy from the output circuit back to the input. In a klystron this is accomplished simply by connecting a section of transmission line between the input (buncher) and output (catcher) resonators. Fig. 7–5A shows a typical set-up, complete with all the necessary components; in Fig. 7–5B, the connecting coaxial line can be plainly seen.

Phase Relations in Klystron Oscillator. As is customary in all oscillators, energy must be fed back from the plate to the grid in correct phase. Because of the structure of the tube itself, there is a considerable phase shift arising from the long interval the electrons spend in the drift tube space. Signals that act at the buncher grids show up some time later at the catcher grids. In amplifiers this is of little significance, but in designing oscillators, phase shift is very important and must be given careful consideration. In order to see where the various phase shifts

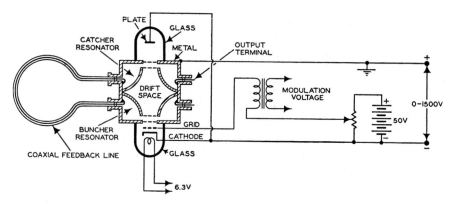

FIG. 7.5A. A complete klystron oscillator circuit showing the tube and associated operating voltages.

FIG. 7.5B. Sperry type 2K30/410–R klystron connected as an oscillator. (*Courtesy Sperry Gyroscope Co., Inc.*)

arise, it might be instructive to follow the energy transfer from the input grids to the output circuit and through the connecting coaxial cable back to the buncher grids again.

The first phase shift that is encountered in going from the buncher grids to the catcher grids occurs in the drift space. The time that an electron spends in traveling this relatively long distance depends upon the following factors:

1. The distance between the centers of the buncher and catcher grids.
2. The d-c accelerating voltage.
3. Finally, the change in velocity brought about by the r-f voltage on the input grids, G_2 and G_3.

The time that the electron requires to cover this distance will usually be equal to several cycles of the r-f voltage on the buncher grids. This is the reason that the drift tube space is said to be relatively long. Its actual length is only a few centimeters but, in comparison to the time it takes the r-f voltage to complete one cycle, it is long. These relative values must be kept constantly in mind, otherwise erroneous ideas may be formed. Mathematically it can be shown that the actual phase shift introduced by the drift space is proportional to each of the following quantities:

$$f, D, V$$

where f is the frequency of input wave,
$\quad D$ is the length of drift space,
$\quad V$ is the direct accelerating voltage.

A second large phase shift occurs in the coaxial cable connecting the two cavity resonators and can be denoted by θ_2. Finally, there is an additional phase shift of 90 degrees due to the relationship of the buncher to the catcher. It has been mentioned that the electrons reach the catcher in groups. From the Applegate diagram it can be seen that these bunches are made up of electrons that passed through the buncher when it was going from negative to positive, for example, that section of the r-f wave between lines a and b (Fig. 7–3). Now, these two lines are equally placed with respect to the point where the sine waves cut the zero line. Thus it can be said that the center of the bunches arriving at the catcher consists of those electrons that passed through the buncher grids when the r-f voltage was zero. But when these bunches are passing the catcher, the catcher grids must have maximum retarding voltage in order to obtain the most energy from the passing electrons. Thus, maximum voltage at the catcher is associated with zero r-f voltage at the buncher. This leads to a 90-degree phase shift because there is a 90-degree difference between zero and maximum on a sine wave.

All these phase shifts must equal $2 \pi n$, where n is any whole number. When this condition is satisfied, the energy fed back will be in correct phase to aid the oscillations and keep the circuit in operation. This is known as positive feedback in contrast to negative feedback. With the latter, the energy is returned 180 degrees out of phase. Of all the foregoing factors that determine the total phase shift, only the voltage is readily variable. Thus, to have the tube oscillate at a desired frequency, the correct voltage must be determined. This may be either computed mathematically or obtained experimentally by varying the acceleration voltage until the circuit breaks into oscillation.

Regulated Power Supply. In order to maintain a constant accelerating voltage (once the proper value has been determined), a regulated power supply of the type shown in Fig. 7–6 is used. For those readers who have never encountered a unit of this type, the following brief explanation is given. The regulating circuit is essentially a degenerative amplifier. Tube

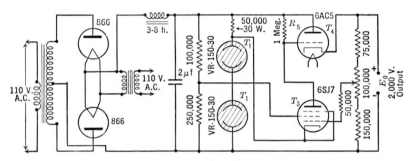

FIG. 7.6. High voltage power supply, compensated for changes of input voltage and load current by using a two-stage inverse-feedback circuit.

T_3 and resistor R_5 form this amplifier and it is their function to amplify any voltage variations applied to the grid of T_3. Assume that the circuit is stable and then, for one reason or another, there is a tendency for the output voltage E_0 to increase. The increase of E_0 will cause the control grid of T_3 to go in a more positive direction and the plate current will increase. Since this plate current must flow through resistor R_5, a greatly amplified voltage will appear across this resistor and drive the grid of T_4 more negative. This will increase the internal resistance of T_4 and reduce the power supply current flowing through it. The load current will thus decrease, and E_0 will be brought back to its normal value. When E_0 decreases, the action is reversed.

The function of the voltage regulating tube T_1 is to maintain the cathode of T_3 at a constant potential with reference to the negative side of the line. T_1 may be one or more regulator tubes of the VR–150–30 variety, depending upon how much voltage is needed for the bias. The 100,000-ohm and the 250,000-ohm resistors in series provide the correct screen potential for T_3. The 50,000-ohm, 30-watt resistor in series with the two voltage regulating tubes is designed to limit the current through these tubes. This type of stabilizing unit is used extensively in installations where good regulation is desired. Although the current-carrying capacity is rather small, appreciable power can be obtained by using several tubes in place of the one tube T_4.

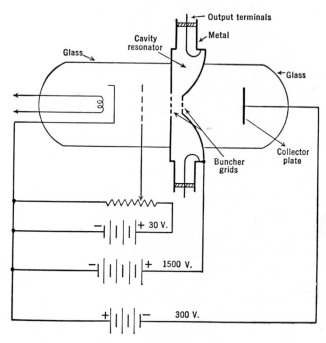

FIG. 7.7. A reflex klystron oscillator with single resonator as buncher and catcher.

Reflex Klystron Oscillators. Oscillations in a two-resonator klystron are maintained by feeding back energy from the output to the input. It is possible, however, to obtain oscillations by the use of a single cavity resonator. Such oscillators, known as reflex oscillators, have been developed and are used extensively—probably more so than two-resonator oscillators.

The internal construction of a reflex klystron oscillator is shown in Fig. 7–7. Up to the first cavity resonator the construction of this tube is similar to the previous two-resonator klystron. Beyond the resonator there is a long drift space at the end of which is a collector plate. If the voltage on this plate were positive, electrons streaming down the drift space would impinge on the plate and be removed from the circuit. Under these conditions the circuit would not oscillate. However, by applying a negative voltage to this plate, the electrons moving through the drift space are slowed down, stopped, and then repelled back to the buncher grids. It is this return trip that permits this tube to be used as an oscillator, as the following discussion will indicate.

If we assume an r-f voltage existing in the single cavity resonator, then electrons leaving the cathode and accelerated by a positive voltage applied to the resonator and the walls of the klystron will be either speeded up or slowed down as they pass through the resonator grids, depending upon which portion of the r-f cycle they encounter. If the r-f voltage is increasing in value, the electrons will be accelerated more than if the r-f voltage had not been present. By the same token, if the electrons pass through when the r-f voltage is going negative, some of the positive d-c accelerating voltage will be offset and the electrons will not receive as much acceleration. Finally, the electron velocities will be unaffected if the electrons pass through the buncher grids when the r-f voltage is zero.

The action, thus far, is similar in all respects to the two-resonator klystron. Now, the electrons, leaving the resonator grids behind, travel toward the plate, gradually being slowed down by the negative retarding potential of the plate. At some point before, but not at, the plate the electrons are completely halted and, because of the repelling force of the plate voltage and the attracting force of the positive grids, are accelerated back to the cathode. The reversing point for each electron will depend upon the time it initially passed through the buncher grids. Those electrons whose velocities were increased will approach closer to the negative plate than those electrons whose velocities were decreased. At some intermediate point there will be those electrons whose velocities were unaltered because they passed through the resonator grids when the r-f voltage was zero. If the operating potentials are properly chosen, the repelling force on these three groups of electrons will cause them to come together and form a bunch on the return trip, arriving back at the resonator grids at a time when the r-f voltage, as they feel it, impels them to slow down. The result will be a transference of energy from the bunched electrons to the resonator in sufficient quantity to maintain oscillations.

The foregoing operation of a klystron oscillator can be illustrated graphically by means of the Applegate diagram shown in Fig. 7–8. At the bottom of the illustration, there is shown the r-f voltage variations existing at the resonator grids. At the top of the diagram, the paths of three electrons passing through the resonator grids at different instants in the r-f cycle are indicated. Electron 1, leaving at time T_1, when the r-f voltage is positive, comes closest to the reflector plate. Electron 2, leaving at time T_2, when the r-f voltage is passing through zero, does not come quite as close to the negative reflector plate. Electron 3, passing the resonator gap when the r-f voltage is negative, will come to rest at a point farthest from the reflector plate. The electrons now will start the return trip back to the resonator grids, arriving there at time T_4, in a bunch. At this moment, the resonator gap voltage should be maximum negative, providing the greatest decelerating or slowing down force for the

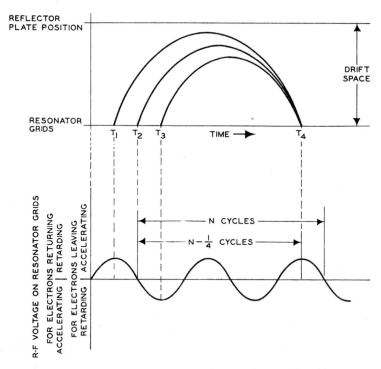

FIG. 7.8. A simplified Applegate diagram for a reflex klystron.

three electrons and consequently obtaining the maximum energy from them.

This latter point may appear confusing in Fig. 7–8, since at time T_4 the r-f voltage on the resonator grids is shown as maximum positive. However, this voltage is drawn for electrons approaching the resonator grids from the cathode. Since the bunched electrons that we have been considering are approaching the resonator grids from the opposite direction, what they see is a maximally negative voltage.

The illustration in Fig. 7–8 is a simplified Applegate diagram for a reflex klystron oscillator. Actually, the bunching action for all the electrons passing the resonator grids is not quite so complete, and some electrons return back to the resonator grids from the reflector plate at times when they absorb energy from the resonator instead of giving it energy.

Those electrons that give up energy are collected by the metal walls of the klystron and returned to the cathode. Electrons that absorb energy pass through the resonator grids and are brought to a halt somewhere near the cathode. Then, they reverse direction and join other electrons just starting to travel toward the resonator grids. Finally, some electrons are captured by the grid structure itself.

It may be instructive to examine the bunching process further to determine what conditions must exist for oscillations to occur. A favorable group of electrons—which is a group that will give up energy to the cavity resonator on the return trip—must arrive back at the resonator when the r-f voltage here is at its maximum negative value to electrons approaching it from the rear. As we have just indicated, this means a maximum positive r-f voltage for electrons approaching it from the front. Now, the previous analysis has indicated, using Fig. 7–3, that the bunch is formed about these electrons which pass through the resonator grids when the r-f voltage is zero. This occurred at time T_2 in Fig. 7–8. The earliest moment after this that these electrons can return to the resonator grids and release energy is $\frac{3}{4}$ of a cycle later, when the r-f voltage (for these electrons) will be maximum negative.

It is possible for electron bunches to spend $1\frac{3}{4}$, $2\frac{3}{4}$, $3\frac{3}{4}$, etc., cycles traveling from resonator to reflector and back and still maintain oscillations. Precisely how much time the electrons spend in traveling this distance will depend primarily upon two factors: the values of the negative reflector voltage and the positive accelerating voltage. If either of these voltages is varied, it will be found that, for certain values of voltages, the tube will oscillate and for other values it will not. Thus, if we hold the accelerating voltage fixed and vary the reflector voltages, we obtain results such as shown in Fig. 7–9. As the negative reflector voltage is increased from zero (in a negative direction), the unit will begin to oscillate and the power output will increase to a maximum. Continued increase in repeller voltage, however, will result in zero power output, indicating that the electrons do not return to resonator grids at the proper time to sustain oscillations.

By further increasing the negative voltage, a second point will be found where oscillations will again occur. The process can be continued until the electrons return to the resonator grids in the fastest time of $\frac{3}{4}$ of a cycle at the operating frequency of the klystron. Further increase in negative voltage will not produce any oscillations. Increasing the reflector voltage decreases the distance which the electrons travel, causing them to bunch and return to the resonator grids earlier.

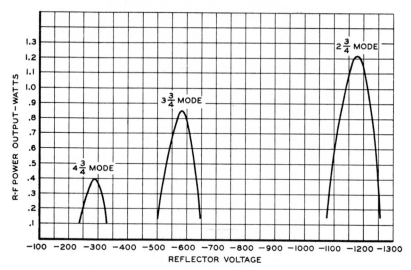

FIG. 7.9. The power output of a reflex klystron oscillator (here, a type SRC–8) is a function of the reflector voltage.

A similar situation prevails if the reflector voltage is maintained fixed and the beam or accelerating voltage is varied. It is also possible to vary both reflector and accelerating voltages in order to have one compensate for the other.

Several popular reflex klystrons are shown in Fig. 7–10.

FIG. 7.10A. Cut-away view of the reflex klystron (type SRC–8). (*Courtesy Sperry Gyroscope Co., Inc.*)

FIG. 7.10B. The complete physical appearance of the SRC–8. (*Courtesy Sperry Gyroscope Co., Inc.*)

The Klystron as an Amplifier. We have seen how the klystron can be employed as a fairly efficient oscillator, generating frequencies well up in the microwave region. By driving the buncher with an external source of power, and obtaining the output energy from the catcher resonator,

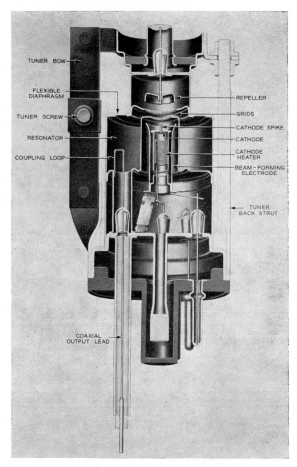

FIG. 7.10C. A cut-away view of a 2K29 reflex klystron. (*Courtesy Bell System Technical Journal*)

it is readily possible to employ the two-resonator klystron as an amplifier. The input r-f voltage velocity modulates the electrons streaming past the buncher grids. These electrons are allowed to form bunches in the drift space which, when passing the catcher grids, transfer their energy in part to the catcher cavity resonator. An output loop then couples this energy to whatever circuit is designed to receive it.

The equivalent circuit of a conventional tuned amplifier is shown in Fig. 7–11. The signal developed by the input resonant circuit, e_s, is applied between grid and cathode of the tube (here shown as a pentode). The

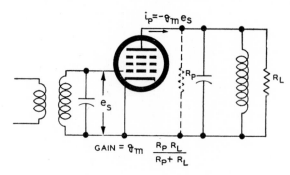

FIG. 7.11.   The equivalent circuit of a conventional tuned amplifier.

plate current due to e_s is $i = -g_m e_s$ which flows through the tube resistance (R_p) and the load (R_L). (For the purpose of computing gain, the negative sign may be disregarded.) It can be shown that the gain of this circuit is given by

$$\text{Gain} = \frac{R_p R_L}{R_p + R_L} g_m$$

Using the same type of notation, we can indicate the equivalent circuit of a klystron amplifier in the manner shown in Fig. 7–12. A tuned L

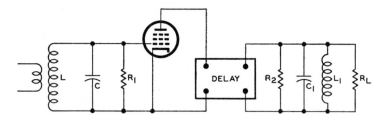

FIG. 7.12.   The equivalent circuit of a klystron amplifier.

and C circuit receives the input signal by means of inductive coupling. After some delay in the drift space, this same signal appears in the output circuit, formed by the catcher resonator and indicated in Fig. 7–12 by the parallel resonant circuit L_1 and C_1. To indicate the output load, a resistor R_L is inserted across L_1 and C_1. Finally, losses in the cavity resonators are taken care of by placing resistances across each of the tuned circuits (R_1 and R_2) which will absorb an amount of power equal to these losses.

Comparison of Figs. 7–11 and 7–12 reveals a very definite similarity between the two equivalent circuits, and so it comes as no surprise when the equation for the voltage gain of a klystron amplifier is given by

$$\text{Gain} = \frac{E_{\text{in}}}{E_{\text{out}}} = g_m \frac{R_2 R_L}{R_2 + R_L}$$

which is similar in form to the gain equation of a conventional tuned amplifier, at resonance.

While the analogy between conventional amplifiers and klystron amplifiers aids in understanding the operation of the latter, there are significant differences between the two. Power output in the klystron is dependent upon the amount of input power, upon the beam voltage, and upon the tuning of the input cavity resonator. While it is true that similar dependence exists in a conventional amplifier, the relationship is entirely different in the klystron, as the following discussion will reveal.

Fig. 7–13 is a graph showing the variation of power output with power input. Maximum power output is obtained when the driving power, which is applied to the buncher grids, is approximately 2 watts. (The values used here are for the 410R klystron.) Increasing the input power does not serve to increase the output power, but rather causes it to decrease to a minimum when the driving

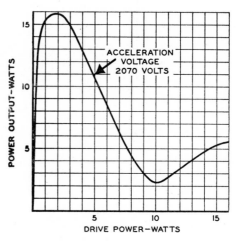

FIG. 7.13. The variation in power output of a klystron amplifier with variation in driving power. The graph indicated here is for a Sperry-Gyroscope type 410-R klystron.

power reaches 7½ to 8 watts. Continued increase in input power will again cause the output power to rise, reaching a second maximum at about 17 watts input power. The second maximum is considerably lower than the first maximum. Further increase in driving power will produce alternate maxima and minima, each successive peak being smaller than its predecessor. Eventually, no matter how much power is put into the tube, little or nothing is obtained at the output.

The conditions shown in Fig. 7–13 exist for a fixed beam (or accelerating) voltage. Increasing this voltage will cause the power output to rise. (See Fig. 7–14.) In this illustration, the driving power is maintained constant and the beam voltage is increased. The result is a general increase in power with beam voltage rise.

In each of the foregoing two illustrations, any decrease in output power was the result of overbunching. This is a condition whereby the electrons in the bunch spread out, permitting some of them to pass the catcher grids at times when the maximum amount of energy is not transferred to this

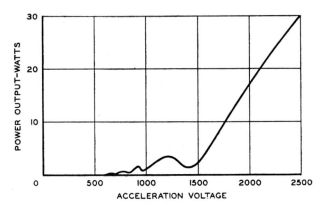

FIG. 7.14. The variation in power output with beam-accelerating voltage in a klystron amplifier.

resonator. The voltage at the catcher grids is changing at the r-f rate of the signal, and in order for these grids to obtain the maximum amount of energy from the passing electrons, as many electrons as possible must pass the grids when the field here is at its most negative value. Any influence which speeds up or retards the electrons so that they arrive sooner or later than this moment causes the power output to be other than maximum. When equal numbers of electrons pass the catcher grids during each half-cycle of an r-f wave, the total power gained becomes zero.

The curves in Figs. 7–15 and 7–16 illustrate how the output power varies with input cavity tuning. In the first illustration, Fig. 7–15, the driving power is not great enough at any point within tuning range of the input resonator to produce overbunching of the electron stream. Consequently, as the input voltage is increased by tuning the cavity resonator closer to resonance, the output voltage follows suit.

In the second illustration, the input voltage has been increased to such an extent that, when the cavity resonator approaches resonance, the voltage across the buncher grids is strong enough to cause overbunching. The result is a decrease in output voltage. However, on either side of

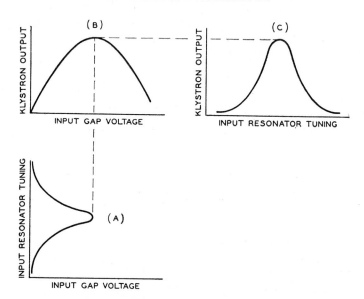

Fig. 7.15. The variation in klystron output with variation in input tuning. At no point within the tuning range does the input voltage become strong enough to produce overbunching.

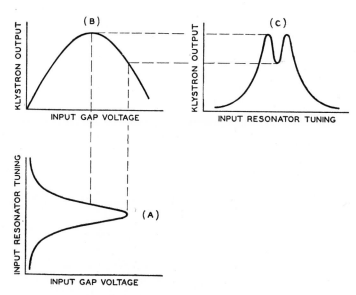

Fig. 7.16. A double-humped output curve is obtained when the input voltage, near resonance, is strong enough to cause overbunching.

resonance, the voltage developed in the resonator is lowered to a value just below that at which overbunching occurs, and now optimum output voltage is obtained. Thus, as we tune through resonance under these conditions, we obtain the double-humped curve of Fig. 7–16.

Typical efficiences for klystron amplifier tubes range about 15 per cent, although the theoretical efficiency is actually 58 per cent. With design improvement, the 15 per cent efficiency could be increased. Klystron amplifiers have not found extensive application in UHF receiving equipment primarily because of their large internal noise due to fluctuations in current. Power gains as high as 20 can be obtained from single-stage amplifiers.

The electrons traveling between the buncher and catcher grids tend to form groups or bunches of electrons. It might at first be thought that, if the bunched electrons arrived at the catcher grids in a single peak, maximum output would be obtained. This is not so. More power can be obtained when the electrons are permitted to diverge or spread out slightly. By permitting the electrons to diverge slightly, more electrons are contained in the bunch and fewer electrons arrive when the catcher grids are releasing energy rather than absorbing it. However, if the divergence is too great, power output decreases sharply. Fig. 7–17 shows the bunched beam current at the catcher grids, during one cycle, for maximum output.

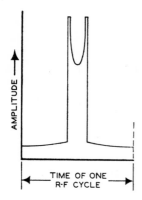

Fig. 7.17. The manner in which the electrons passing the catcher grids vary, in number, over one r-f cycle.

Klystron Frequency Multiplies. The beam current pulse, it will be noted, contains fairly steep sides. This means that its harmonic content is high. Consequently, if the catcher resonator is tuned to some harmonic frequency of the signal applied to the buncher grids, the output will consist principally of the harmonic frequency. (See Fig. 7–18.) So great is the harmonic content of the bunched electron beam that the overall efficiency of a klystron frequency multiplier for harmonics up to the third is not appreciably less than when the unit is operating as a straight amplifier. Good output for even the tenth harmonic is readily obtainable.

A significant difference between klystron amplifiers and frequency multipliers is the fact that, as the value of the desired harmonic increases, the beam accelerating voltage should be changed to produce a single beam current peak in order to obtain maximum output. In the amplifier, maximum output is obtained when the beam is allowed to spread out slightly and two closely spaced peaks appear.

Multiple-Resonator Klystrons. In all of the preceding discussion we have been concerned with klystrons containing either one or two cavity resonators. There is no reason, however, why three, or more, cavity resonators could not be included in the klystron, each separated by a certain drift space. As a matter of fact, klystrons are built with as many as six cavity resonators. In the following discussion, attention will be centered on three-cavity klystrons in order to indicate the method of operation of these multiple-resonators units.

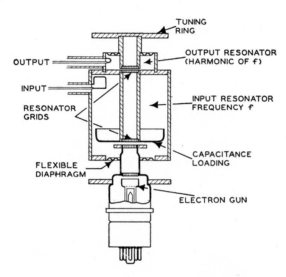

FIG. 7.18. The internal construction of a klystron frequency multiplier.

The internal construction of a klystron containing three cavity resonators is shown in Fig. 7–19A and in actual appearance in Fig. 7–19B. If we consider the first two resonators only, the unit is a conventional klystron amplifier of the type previously discussed. By adding a third cavity resonator beyond the second resonator, we add, in effect, another amplifier to the previous two-resonator amplifier and thus a three-resonator klystron is known as a cascade amplifier.

In the two-resonator klystron amplifier, the voltage on the input resonator grids is adjusted to provide enough bunching of the electron beam to produce maximum output at the second resonator. When three resonators are employed, the voltage variations required on the first set of grids is decreased appreciably. This means that the beam will be bunched only slightly by the time it reaches the second set of grids. The voltage induced in the second cavity resonator will be greater than

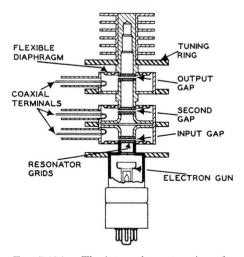

FLEXIBLE DIAPHRAGM

TUNING RING

OUTPUT GAP

COAXIAL TERMINALS

SECOND GAP

INPUT GAP

RESONATOR GRIDS

ELECTRON GUN

FIG. 7.19A. The internal construction of a three-resonator klystron.

the voltage appearing at the first set of grids by an amount equal to the voltage gain of an ordinary two-resonator klystron amplifier. The second set of grids will now affect the electron beam, further bunching the electrons so that when the beam finally reaches the third or final set of grids, it will possess the proper bunching form to induce maximum voltage in this cavity resonator. Thus, by using three resonators, we can obtain the same output as that available from a two-resonator klystron but with considerably less driving power at the first set of grids. In the two-resonator klystron previously discussed, an input driving power of 1 watt was needed to develop an output power of 15 watts. With a typical three-resonator klystron, only 6 milliwatts of driving power would be needed at the first set of grids to produce the same 15 watts at the third resonator. The power gain has thus been increased considerably.

FIG. 7.19B. A 2K35 klystron cascade amplifier. (*Courtesy Sperry Gyroscope Co., Inc.*)

The bunching action within the cascaded amplifier is best illustrated by an Applegate diagram, similar to the one shown in Fig. 7–4. Such a diagram is indicated in Fig. 7–20. The small r-f voltage at the first set of grids produces some, but not much, bunching of the beam by the time this reaches the second resonator. Here, the induced voltage is great

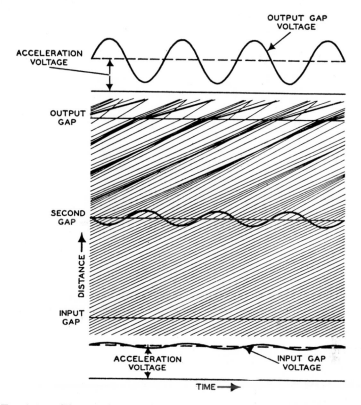

FIG. 7.20.   The Applegate diagram for a klystron cascade amplifier.

enough to cause the beam to possess the proper degree of bunching at the final resonator grids.

One advantage that is obtained by using two bunching resonators is the fact that, when the electrons reach the final set of grids, there are more electrons contained in the bunches and fewer electrons arriving between bunches. This results in more energy being transferred to the grids and less energy being lost in the interval between bunches. The increase in efficiency is approximately 30 to 35 per cent greater than that obtainable from a two-resonator klystron.

In operating a cascaded-amplifier klystron, care must be taken not to apply too much driving power to the first set of grids. The output power will increase sharply with input power until the beam becomes over-bunched; beyond this point, the output power will decrease rapidly to

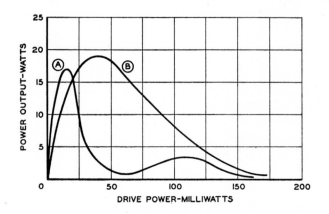

FIG. 7.21. The output power of a cascade amplifier is dependent upon the frequency to which the second resonator is set. The two curves represent the variation in power output at two slightly different frequencies.

approximately zero. A second maximum, at greatly reduced output, is obtained if the input power is increased still further. This is shown by curve *A* of Fig. 7–21. If, however, the second resonator is detuned slightly, the voltage developed here is reduced, overbunching does not occur, and

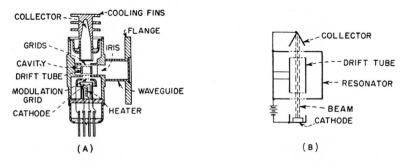

FIG. 7.22. A floating drift-tube klystron. (A) Outline of tube; (B) diagrammatic representation of tube. (*Courtesy Electronics Magazine*)

the output remains high. This is shown by curve *B* in Fig. 7–21. By applying more power to the input resonator, we can obtain more power output—if the second resonator is slightly detuned. Note that the overall

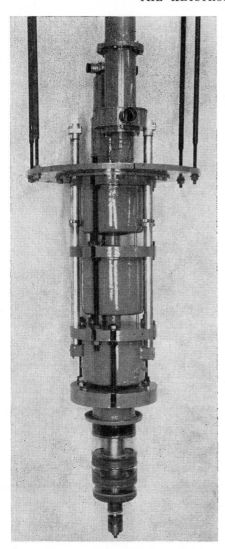

FIG. 7.23. A high-power UHF-TV klystron developed by Varian Associates to specifications provided by General Electric.

power *gain* is now less, because, although we obtain more output, we need more power to drive the tube. However, if more power is available at the input, then this method is feasible.

Floating Drift-tube Klystron. A tube which combines many of the good features of reflex and two-resonator klystrons is the floating drift-tube klystron. In this tube, Fig. 7–22, a drift tube is so suspended in a resonator that the grids at the first gap bunch the electrons while the grids at the second gap absorb energy from the beam. There is only one resonator cavity, as in the reflex klystron, but there are two sets of grids, as in the two-resonator klystron. Although this tube was first built before the war, it is only recently that attempts have been made to perfect its design.

High-Power Klystrons. For a long time after the development of the klystron, its application consisted chiefly as a local oscillator in receiving systems or as a generator of low-powered signals in transmitters. There was no fundamental reason, however, why high-powered klystrons could not be built and within the last few years much progress has been made in this direction.

As an illustration, the klystron* shown in Fig. 7–23 can deliver 5 kilowatts output at any frequency between 500 and 1200 mc. It is further capable of a power gain of 250 and possesses a band width of 5.6 mc between the 1-db points. It was designed for and is now being used in a UHF television transmitter.

* "High-Power UHF-TV Klystron," by the Engineering Staff of Varian Associates. *Electronics,* October 1951.

The klystron possesses three cavities (Fig. 7–24) and therefore operates in the same manner as the cascade klystron amplifiers previously described. Note that the resonator grids have been eliminated, although the cavity resonator operation remains unaltered. Removal of the grids reduces the amount of noise generated and also aids in raising the maximum power limit of the tube. The collector is water-cooled to remove the considerable amount of heat dissipated at this electrode.

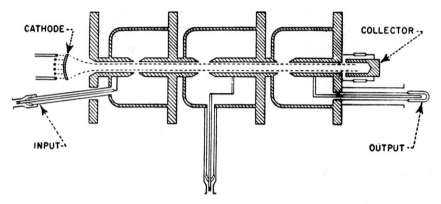

FIG. 7.24. A drawing of the internal structure of the three-cavity high-power klystron amplifier. (*Courtesy Electronics Magazine*)

To produce a high-beam electron stream, the cathode structure was completely redesigned to a form known as a bombarded cathode. A tungsten coil of wire was mounted behind a tantalum cathode and heated by passing a current through it. The electrons given off by the tungsten wire are then made to strike the back side of the cathode by the application of a direct voltage between the heater and the cathode. In the absence of this voltage, the electrons given off by the heater would not be capable of developing enough heat in the cathode by bombardment to cause the cathode to emit. Useful life of the bombarded cathode is 10,000 hours. At the end of this period, the cathode structure may be removed and another one substituted in its place. The rest of the tube structure has an unlimited life span.

The electron beams developed in these tubes are high-density beams and they tend to broaden out before they reach the collector. To prevent this, a magnetic field of approximately 200 gauss is directed axially through the tube (along the beam path). Electrons diverging from the beam axis interact with this field and the net result is that the beam is kept focused throughout its path of travel. The magnetic field for the tube shown in Fig. 7–23 is produced by coils placed around the outside of the resonators.

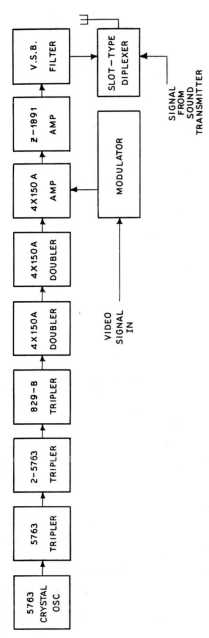

Fig. 7.25. A block diagram of the video section of a 5-kw UHF television transmitter. Z–1891 is the klystron tube. (*Courtesy Electronics Magazine*)

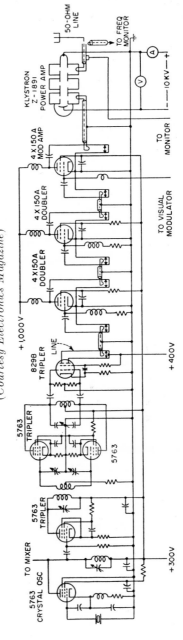

Fig. 7.26. Some of the actual circuitry employed in the various multipliers and amplifiers of the system shown in Fig. 7.25. (*Courtesy Electronics Magazine*)

Application of this klystron as the final amplifier in a 5-kw UHF television transmitter is shown in Fig. 7–25. A crystal oscillator with a fundamental frequency between 4.4 and 8.2 mc develops the initial signal which is then fed through three triplers and two doublers where a 108-fold multiplication occurs. This raises the initial crystal frequency to whatever value is desired in the UHF-TV band, 475 to 890 mc. Modulation of the carrier takes place in a 4X150A amplifier, after which the signal is fed to the klystron for its final power amplification. Beyond the klystron, the signal is fed through appropriate filters and a combining network (called a diplexer) to the television broadcasting antenna.

The actual circuitry employed in the various multipliers and amplifiers is shown in Fig. 7–26.

The sound portion of the television broadcast is developed by a somewhat similar arrangement of stages. However, the final frequency of the sound carrier must be 4.5 mc higher than the frequency of the video carrier. After the sound signal has been properly modulated and brought to full power, it is combined with the video carrier signal in the diplexer unit and then both signals are radiated from the same antenna.

KLYSTRON TUNERS

Klystrons are used solely in conjunction with cavity resonators, and the resonant frequency of oscillation or operation of the klystron is governed primarily by the resonant frequency of the resonator. The latter, as indicated in the chapter devoted to cavity resonators, is dependent upon the volume, surface area, and shape of the resonator. At the moment we are concerned with methods frequently employed in varying the resonant frequency of these resonators when they are used in conjunction with klystron tubes.

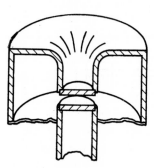

Fig. 7.27. illustrates the shape of the cavity resonator most frequently used. This shape is known as a re-entrant type of cavity resonator, the name "re-entrant" being used to describe the shape of an object which has one or more of its sides directed inward. The resonator shown has one side folded inward, forming a narrow gap at the innermost point. Small sections of the resonator walls on each side of this gap are then removed and two grid structures inserted in their place. The electrons traveling forward from the cathode pass through these grids across the gap and receive their velocity modulation. The capacity formed by the gap represents

FIG. 7.27. The re-entrant type of cavity resonator frequently used in klystron tubes.

most of the capacitance of the cavity resonator, while the magnetic field established throughout the rest of the resonator cavity constitutes the inductance of this resonant circuit. Variation of frequency then can be accomplished by increasing or decreasing one or both of these components, a procedure which is analogous to the change in frequency in the conventional *L-C* circuit.

Capacitance variation, which is the most frequently employed method of obtaining frequency variation, is accomplished by changing the gap spacing. Inductance variation, which is frequently employed when the cavity resonator is detachable from the tube, is accomplished by altering the volume of the resonator. In the most prevalent form, one or more small plugs are screwed into the cavity resonator. As the plugs penetrate deeper into the resonator, they decrease the effective volume of the magnetic field. This lowers the inductance of the tuner and raises its resonant frequency. By the same token, withdrawing part of the plug increases the volume and raises the inductance.

Klystron tuners may either be constructed as integral parts of the tube, as illustrated in Figs. 7–3, 7–10 and 7–19, or may come as separate assemblies which are mechanically attached to the tube. Such is the case, for example, with the klystron tube shown in Fig. 7–28. The tube contains a cathode, a beam-forming grid, the two resonator grids, and the repeller plate. The resonator grids are mounted on copper disks, one of which has a cup-like or re-entrant shape. These disks are sealed to the glass tubing and extend beyond the envelope to permit attachment to the external cavity resonator. Fig. 7–29 illustrates how the resonator attaches to the tube. To vary the resonant frequency of the resonator, we vary its inductance by screwing plugs into it. The view of the resonator in Fig. 7–29 also shows the coupling loop which abstracts energy from the resonator.

FIG. 7.28. A klystron tube which requires an external cavity resonator. (*Courtesy Bell System Technical Journal*)

Another type of tuner, which is separate from the tube, is the coaxial cavity tuner shown in Fig. 7–30. This unit was specifically designed to be used with certain reflex klystrons developed by Sylvania Electric. (See Fig. 7–31.) The tube itself contains the electron beam-forming structure, the repeller plate, and the resonator grids. Contact to the two resonator grids is made through copper disk seals extending through the glass envelope of the tube. The diameters of these disks are not alike, the lower

Fig. 7.29. The reflex klystron tube of Fig. 7.28 with the resonator. (*Courtesy Bell System Technical Journal*)

ring being slightly larger. This permits the tube to be inserted into the coaxial cavity like a tube being plugged into a socket. Within the resonator, spring fingers slide over the upper smaller ring when the tube is inserted, as indicated in Fig. 7–30. Contact to the lower ring is made by a toroidal spring located in a groove of the resonator. Movable plungers at one end of the resonator cavity enable the frequency to be changed. The advantage of an arrangement of this type is the large frequency range which can be achieved.

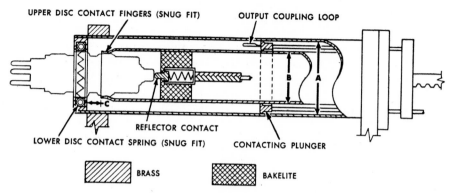

UPPER DISC CONTACT FINGERS (SNUG FIT)   OUTPUT COUPLING LOOP

REFLECTOR CONTACT

LOWER DISC CONTACT SPRING (SNUG FIT)   CONTACTING PLUNGER

BRASS   BAKELITE

FIG. 7.30. Diagram of a typical coaxial cavity suitable for use with the reflex klystron shown in Fig. 7.31. The length is determined by the operating frequency and the range of plunger motion is established by the frequency band to be covered. Essential dimensions: (A) Outer cylinder inside diameter, $1\frac{1}{2}''$; (B) Inner cylinder outside diameter, .937″; (C) Distance between contactors, 5/16″; Recess in contacting plunger, $\frac{1}{2}''$; Loop size for 800–3500 mc, 9/16″; Loop size for 3000–5000 mc, 9/32″; Loop width for both sizes listed above, .175″. (*Courtesy Sylvania Electric Products*)

A reflex klystron in which the cavity resonator is an integral part of the tube structure is shown in Fig. 7–10C. The resonant cavity possesses a re-entrant shape and is formed partly by the frames which support the two cavity grids and partly by the volume between the upper flexible diaphragm and one of the frames. The electron beam-forming assembly, consisting of the cathode, a cathode spike, and a beam-forming circular plate, are located within the re-entrant cavity which shields the beam-forming assembly from the r-f magnetic and electric fields within the cavity resonator. The repeller plate is located above the second resonator grid and is supported by the flexible diaphragm.

The peculiar design of the electron gun is such as to make the electrons which give up energy to the resonator on their return trip strike the frame supporting the bottom grid and so be removed from the circuit.

To obtain energy from the resonator, a small diameter coaxial line is constructed into the tube. The inner conductor of the line extends beyond

FIG. 7.31. A reflex klystron manufactured by Sylvania Electric.

the outer conductor and is shaped into a small loop which links with the magnetic field within the resonator, obtaining energy from the field by inductive coupling. The line extends down through the tube and through a special hole drilled in the octal base. Within the line, the inner conductor is supported by a polystyrene insulator from the vacuum seal to the external end of the line. At this end the inner conductor projects beyond the outer conductor, but this time as a straight wire. To transfer energy from the

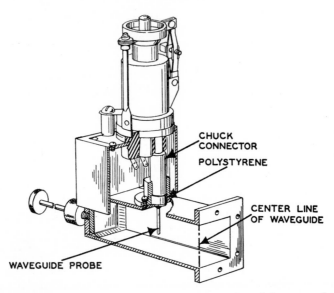

Fig. 7.32. The manner in which energy can be transferred from a reflex klystron (such as shown in Fig. 7.10C) to a waveguide. (*Courtesy Bell System Technical Journal*)

line to a waveguide, the tube socket is mounted over a waveguide in such a manner that when the tube is inserted into the socket, the inner coaxial conductor extends into the waveguide. (See Fig. 7–32.) The outer conductor then connects to the waveguide wall mechanically. The projecting inner conductor now functions as a vertical antenna, transmitting electric (and magnetic) fields which are propagated down the guide either to an antenna if the oscillator is used in a transmitter, or to a crystal detector if the unit is part of a receiver.

Tuning of this klystron is accomplished by varying the distance between the two resonator grids. Some appreciation of the mechanical difficulty that faced the designers of this tube can be gained when it is realized that a frequency change of 200 mc occurs for each thousandth of an inch displacement of the grids. Therefore, to change the frequency by 1 mc requires that the tuner be mechanically adjustable to an accuracy of five millionths of an inch. Fig. 7–10C shows the type of mechanical arrangement employed. The upper part of the tube which is mounted on the flexible diaphragm is mechanically fastened on the right-hand side to a strut which extends from the top of the tube to the base and which acts as a hinge for the pair of steel strips mounted on the left-hand side of the tube. These strips are fastened together at the arm leading to the top of the tube and also at the base of the tube. At the center of each strip is a nut. One nut is fixed while the other nut can be rotated, increasing or decreasing the spacing between the strips. When the nut is rotated so that the steel strips separate, the repeller housing at the top of the tube tilts toward the left, increasing the separation between the resonator grids. This decreases the capacity acting between the grids and increases the resonant frequency of the cavity. Rotation of the nut forcing the strips to come closer together has the opposite effect. All in all, a rotation of five full turns of the frequency-adjustment screw are generally sufficient to tune the tube over its rated frequency range.

Actual operation of this klystron in a microwave television relay is shown in Fig. 7–33. The tube is mounted in a temperature-controlled compartment which is placed directly over a waveguide so that energy from the klystron can be fed directly into the guide. The entire chassis is then mounted in a cylindrical case which, in turn, is attached to a parabolic reflector. A J-shaped waveguide extension which is mechanically connected to the guide receiving the output of the klystron directs this energy into the center of the reflector from which it is transmitted by line-of-sight to a similarly shaped reflector at the receiving end. Here the signal is converted back to the original video voltage and applied to the main transmitter for radiation to the surrounding community.

The parabolic reflector at the transmitting (and receiving) end has a diameter of 4 feet and a gain of 5000 over a simple dipole. The power output of the klystron is 100 milliwatts, but because of the gain of the reflector, we obtain the equivalent power of 500 watts.

Electronic Tuning. In each of the foregoing tuning methods, some component of the resonator (either its inductance or capacitance) was varied to achieve a new resonant frequency. It is also possible to alter the frequency of any signal generated by changing the voltages applied to the tube.

We have previously seen that a klystron would oscillate only when the voltages applied to it were such as to cause the electrons to give up energy to the oscillating circuit. In a two-resonator klystron this meant that the electrons had to arrive at the second set of grids (the catcher grids)

FIG. 7.33A. A klystron reflex oscillator used as the r-f generator in a microwave television relay. (*Courtesy RCA*)

when the r-f field here is at a negative maximum. Furthermore, the length of the feedback coaxial line between catcher and buncher resonators had to be the right length in order that the energy fed back possessed the proper phase to sustain oscillations. In the reflex klystron, the construction was simpler, but again the phase relationship had to be such that the returning electrons gave up energy to the resonator.

In each of these oscillators, maximum output depended upon the selection of proper operating voltages. Variation of these voltages resulted in variations in power out-

FIG. 7.33B. The entire transmitter complete with parabolic antenna. (*Courtesy RCA*)

put in a manner similar to that shown in Fig. 7–9. At the same time, the frequency of the generated oscillations changed, this being due to the desire of the circuit to maintain oscillations. By changing frequency, the phase (or time of arrival) of the electron bunches was shifted enough still to permit energy to be transferred from the beam to the resonator. Within certain limits, change in frequency is linear with change in voltage and the power output decreases only slightly. As the voltage is still further shifted, the phase of the electron bunches changes sufficiently to reduce the power output to zero, whereupon all oscillations decrease to zero. Frequency ranges of as much as 25 to 35 mc can be achieved by electronic tuning.

MODULATION OF KLYSTRONS

Klystrons may be employed as the local oscillator in a superheterodyne or their output may be modulated and used to transmit intelligence from one point to another. Klystrons can be modulated as to frequency, amplitude, or phase, although the most frequent application is frequency modulation for which the tube seems to be ideally suited.

To understand how the tube can be frequency-modulated, all we need to do is to remember that, if we vary the reflector or accelerating voltage on a reflex oscillator or the beam voltage in a two-resonator oscillator, the transit time of the electrons through the tube will change. If, for example, the electron bunches are caused to arrive at the grids slightly earlier in the r-f cycle, the result is an increase in frequency due to the desire of the circuit to maintain oscillations. By changing the voltages so that the electron bunches arrive slightly later than they should, rather than earlier, we find that the frequency decreases. Thus, over a limited range, changing the voltages in the tube will cause the frequency to vary, the frequency change being linear with voltage change over most of its range. (See Fig. 7–34.) Another important feature is the fact that the amplitude modulation produced in the signal while it is being frequency-modulated is relatively small and readily removed in the receiver by means of limiters. On the other hand, amplitude modulation is accompanied by appreciable frequency modulation, and since this cannot be removed at the receiver it introduces distortion.

In the reflex oscillator, the most common method of producing frequency modulation is by inserting the modulating voltage in series with the negative reflector voltage. The audio voltage from a microphone is amplified by one (or more) stages of audio amplification and then impressed across a resistor placed in series with the reflector voltage. The varying audio voltage appearing across the resistor varies the total negative voltage applied to the reflector and thereby varies the frequency output of the klystron. The range of voltage variations is restricted only to the region within which the frequency changes linearly with voltage. Within this region the amplitude modulation impressed on the signal is small.

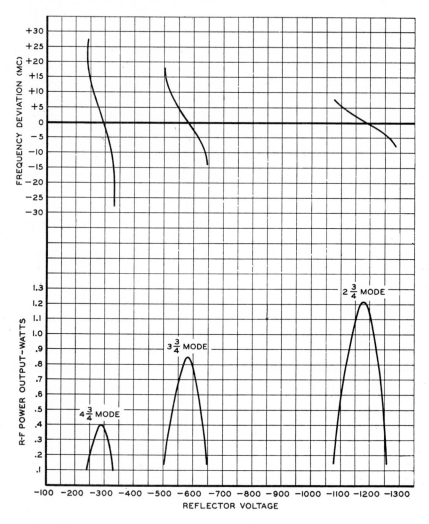

FIG. 7.34. By varying the reflector voltage of a reflex klystron, we can cause the generated frequency to vary, thereby achieving frequency modulation.

In the microwave television relay previously shown, the video signal developed by the field cameras is amplified to a level of 30 volts and then inserted in series with the negative repeller voltage of the reflex klystron to produce a frequency-modulated r-f output signal.

QUESTIONS

1. Describe the tuning unit used with a klystron oscillator.

2. What are the first set of grids in the klystron called? What do they do?

3. What are the second set of grids called? Are they placed close to or far from the first set of grids? Why?

4. Explain what occurs in the drift space of a two-resonator klystron.

5. How are the electrons arranged when they arrive at the second set of grids? Explain the reason for this.

6. Where is the d-c energy in the beam expended?

7. Give the requirements that the catcher grids must satisfy for proper operation of a two-resonator klystron.

8. What does the Applegate diagram illustrate?

9. How is the energy fed back from the second pair of grids to the first pair?

10. Describe the various phase shifts incurred in the klystron, considering its use as an oscillator.

11. Draw a diagram of this type of oscillator.

12. What type of power supply is needed here? Why?

13. Describe the action of the reflex klystron oscillator.

14. Draw its diagram.

15. How can the frequency of this oscillator be altered? Is the frequency variation very large?

16. Where is energy removed from the reflex oscillator? By what methods?

17. How can the two-resonator klystron be used as an amplifier? How does this differ from its use as an oscillator?

18. What feature of the klystron enables it to operate as a frequency multiplier with good efficiency? What changes must be made in a klystron amplifier to enable it to be used as a frequency multiplier?

19. Discuss the operation of a klystron containing three cavity resonators.

20. Describe two types of cavity resonators that may be used with klystrons.

21. How does one tune a cavity resonator capacitively? Inductively?

22. How can a klystron be frequency-modulated? Draw the circuit of a frequency-modulated klystron.

23. What is overbunching and what effects does it have?

Chapter 8

THE RESNATRON, TRAVELING-WAVE TUBES, AND OTHERS

THE RESNATRON

As described previously, electron transit time is one of the major obstacles in using conventional vacuum tubes in ultra-high-frequency circuits. During World War II the resnatron tube was developed which retained the conventional structure of a tetrode; yet, through a combination of cavity resonators and high voltages, this tube was able to surmount some of the effects of electron transit time and deliver continuous power output in excess of 50 kilowatts at frequencies from 350 to 650 mc. Furthermore, an efficiency as high as 60 to 70 per cent under the proper conditions was achieved.

The basic resnatron possesses a combination of the features of the ordinary tetrode and the beam-power tube (6L6, 6V6, etc.). In the conventional tetrode there are four elements: cathode, control grid, screen grid, and plate.

The presence of the screen grid, operating at a fairly high d-c voltage but at r-f ground potential, serves to reduce feedback of energy from the plate to the control grid. However, the screen grid, by itself, also created an undesirable effect, that of having secondary electrons knocked off the plate by oncoming electrons which, in turn, were drawn to the screen grid. This action is particularly noticeable when the plate voltage is less than the screen voltage.

The difficulties caused by the capture of these secondary electrons by the screen grid is overcome in the beam-power tube. (See Fig. 8–1.) In these tubes, the electrons are emitted by a flat cathode and concentrated into narrow sheets by the two grids and two beam-forming plates. The screen-grid wires are mounted directly behind and in the shadow of the control grid wires, forcing the electrons to form into a series of sheets.

224

At the same time, very few electrons are captured by the screen grid, reducing materially the amount of power dissipated in this element.   The presence of the two side beam-forming plates restricts the spread of the electrons.

The electron beam, plus the relatively large distance between the screen grid and the plate, gives the beam power tetrode electrical charac-

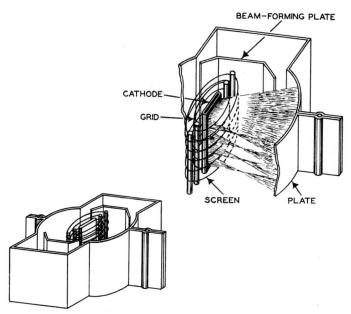

Fig. 8.1.   The internal construction of a beam-power tube.

teristics similar to a pentode.   In the latter tube, capture of plate secondary electrons by the screen grid is prevented by the suppressor grid inserted between the screen grid and the plate.   The suppressor grid is connected internally or externally to the cathode and any electrons tending to travel from plate to screen grid are repelled by this cathode-potential barrier. In the beam-power tube, the beam-forming plates and the spatial arrangement of the two grids cause the electrons to pile up and form a virtual cathode at low plate voltages in the region between screen grid and plate. Thus, a suppressor grid effect is achieved.   When the plate voltage is high, no virtual cathode is formed, but it is improbable that electrons knocked off the plate will be able to leave the strongly positive plate.

In the resnatron the screen grid wires are placed close to and exactly behind the control grid wires.   Also, the distance between screen grid and plate is made relatively large. However, unlike the beam-power tube, sharp beam focusing is achieved not by using side plates, but by carefully designing and shaping of the cathode, control grid, and screen grid elements.

In the resnatron, cavity resonators are combined directly with the cathode, control grid, screen grid, and plate electrodes, inside the vacuum tube envelope. Tuning is accomplished by changing the volume of the resonators by inserting rods or collapsing a bellows-like cavity.

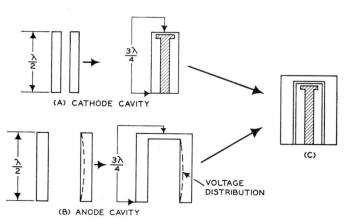

FIG. 8.2.   The manner in which the tuning cavities of a resnatron tube are formed.

A sketch of the resonant cavities used in the resnatron tube is shown in Fig. 8–2. The cathode cavity, formed between the cathode and control grid as shown in Fig. 8–2A, is three-quarters wavelength long and has the shape of a cylindrical "U". A tuning rod extends up through the center of the cavity and can be moved up or down by metal bellows. The cathode cavity is equivalent electrically to a three-quarter wavelength transmission line shorted at the lower end and open at the upper end.

A second cavity, also three-quarters wavelength long, is formed between the screen grid and plate of the tube. (See Fig. 8–2B.) It, too, has a "U" shape, but the open end is wider, permitting the unit to be placed over the cathode cavity as indicated in Fig. 8–2C. Tuning of the anode cavity in one type of resnatron is achieved by exerting pressure on the top of the cavity, altering the space within the cavity. Electrically, the change in volume is equivalent to capacitive tuning in low-frequency circuits.

It may appear that, if the larger anode cavity is three-quarters wavelength long, then the smaller cathode cavity cannot possess the same electrical characteristics. However, the cathode cavity, by being narrower, possesses greater shunting capacity which compensates electrically for its shorter length. Resonators, to be resonant to the same frequency, need not possess the same length. The shape and separation of their sides determine their resonant frequency.

The electrical length of three-quarters wavelength for the cavity resonators was chosen for two reasons. First, it permits capacitive tuning at the center of the cavities where the r-f voltage is the highest. Second, it so happens that this high r-f voltage point occurs at the center of the

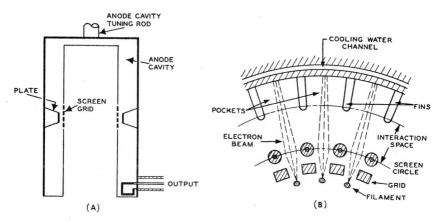

Fig. 8.3.   (A) The anode cavity showing the placement of the screen grid wires and the plate.   (B) A cross-section of the electrode structure showing the relative position of all the elements.

sides (see Fig. 8–2B) and, as we shall see in a moment, it is through this point in the resonators that the electrons travel in going from cathode to plate. This second feature is especially important since operation of the resnatron could only occur if the electrons traveling from cathode to plate are subjected to the r-f voltages existing in the circuit.

To utilize these resonators in the resnatron tube, their side structure is altered to include the tube elements. The anode cavity contains the screen grid and plate of the tube. The screen grid can be formed by drilling a series of holes around the center of the inner cylinder wall. (See Fig. 8–3A.)   (It is necessary for the reader to remember that the diagrams shown are flat and two-dimensional, whereas, in actual appearance, the resonator structures are cylindrical cans with partially hollow centers. The screen grid holes would then be drilled all the way around the inner cylinder wall.)   However, since the heat dissipation in this tube is high and the tube requires water cooling, the screen grid consists of a series of copper tubes. Water is circulated through these tubes, carrying away whatever heat is generated here.

The anode is formed by a series of cooling fins protruding from the inside surface of the outer cylinder wall of the anode cavity. There are 25 of these fins, dividing the anode into a series of 24 pockets, each pocket having two side walls (formed by cooling fins) and a back wall (the anode resonator), but having no top or bottom walls. The electrons arrive at these anode pockets in the form of 24 separately focused beams. (See Fig. 8–3B.) The cooling fins serve not only to dissipate the heat formed by the beams, but to prevent secondary electrons from reaching the screen grid.

Notice the alignment of filament, grids, and anode pockets. A filament wire faces an open slot. The screen grid tubes are in the shadows of the grid bars, and the anode fins are in line with the two grids. The entire arrangement of the tube elements causes the electrons to flow from the cathode to the anode in sheets characteristic of the beam-power tube.

The anode resonator is metallic throughout, presenting a continuous d-c path from plate to screen grid. If it is desired to break this path, without affecting the r-f currents, the cavity construction shown in Fig. 8–4A may be utilized. The outer wall of the screen structure is extended over the outer wall of the anode structure for one-quarter wavelength. The quarter wavelength spacing, with one end open, produces an effective r-f short at the point where the two walls first overlap, preventing the escape of any r-f energy contained in the resonator and, at the same time, completing the r-f circuit. The overlap, of course, breaks the d-c path between elements.

The cathode cavity contains the control grid which consists of slots in the copper resonator structure. Facing the grid slots are the filaments, consisting of 24 tungsten wires, each bent in the shape of a paper staple. These wires are mounted at equal intervals in a circle facing the grid slots in the cathode cylindrical cavity. All of the filaments are in parallel with each other, being soldered on two circular copper rings. Fig. 8–3B shows quite clearly that the filaments are so mounted that the electrons they emit pass between the control grid and screen grid wires on their way to the plate. This construction is purposely chosen to focus the electrons into beams so that relatively few of the electrons strike the positive screen grid wires. This prevents the screen grid dissipation from becoming excessive.

The cathode resonator is also divided into two sections because of the high negative biasing voltage on the grid. The control grid and cathode are each mounted on separate sections which overlap one-quarter wavelength to form the same type of arrangement that was used to separate the plate and screen grid elements. (See Fig. 8–4B.) The manner of applying d-c voltages to this tube is shown in Fig. 8–5.

Cross-sectional views of two types of resnatron tubes in Fig. 8–6 illustrate how the preceding resonator structures are combined to form

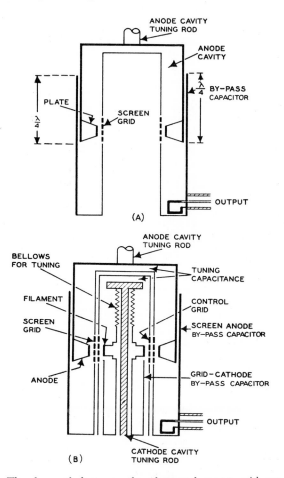

FIG. 8.4. (A) The d-c path between the plate and screen grid can be broken, as shown, without disrupting the r-f path between these elements. (B) A similar separation between the control grid and cathode to permit application of a d-c biasing voltage.

the tube. In Fig. 8–6A tuning of the cathode cavity is achieved by moving a rod up and down by means of metal bellows. When the upper end of the rod approaches the top of the cathode cavity, the capacitive loading on the resonator increases and the frequency decreases. When the rod is moved farther away, the capacitance decreases and the frequency rises. Tuning of the anode cavity is achieved by pressure on the top of the cavity which varies the capacitance between the top of the anode housing and the cap on the screen grid structure. With this system of tuning it is possible to achieve a frequency variation of 30 mc at a center frequency of 500 mc.

In Fig. 8–6B, capacity tuning of the cathode cavity is also employed, but in a slightly different way. A cup-like arrangement is attached to

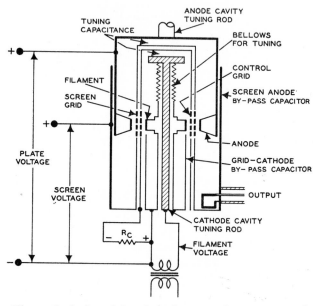

FIG. 8.5.   The method of applying d-c voltages to the resonator tube elements.

the top of the movable rod, and this moves in and out of two small circular cylinders. The tuning method is still capacitive, but the variation with frequency is more linear. The anode cavity of the second resonator also differs slightly from the arrangement in Fig. 8–6A. For one thing, the d-c path between screen grid and plate is not broken, and both operate at the same potential. Secondly, tuning is accomplished by a movable shorting bar between the screen and plate walls. Since both ends of this cavity resonator are shorted, it is one-half wavelength rather than three-quarters wavelength long. The shorting bar can be moved a distance of 30 cm.

As with any of the cavity resonators previously discussed, energy may be removed or introduced by coupling loops or rods. In the resnatron, a coupling loop externally connected to a 50-ohm coaxial line is matched to a waveguide which, in turn, conducts the power to an electromagnetic horn radiator.

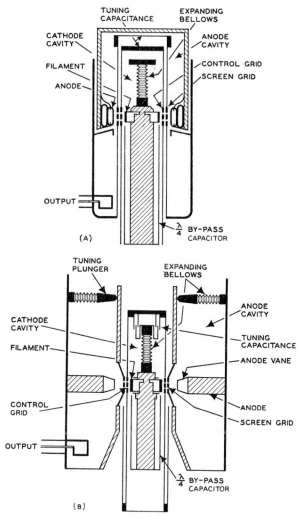

FIG. 8.6. Cross-sectional drawings of two types of resnatron tuning structures.

To utilize the resnatron as an oscillator, energy must be fed back from the output to the input circuits. This may be done either by connecting a short length of coaxial line between the two resonators, or by means of a capacitive probe which extends from the top of the cathode cavity through the grid spaces to the top of the anode cavity. The latter method, shown in Fig. 8–7, is the one most frequently used since it permits the generation of oscillations over a wide frequency band. If the tube is to be used as an amplifier, the feedback line is removed.

Since the resnatron essentially is a tetrode, one may wonder why its efficiency is so much greater than other tetrodes. The answer lies in the fact that electrons are drawn through the interelectrode space with tremendous velocity due to the structure of the screen grid and the relatively high voltages (10 to 15 thousand volts) which are used. It should be remembered that one method suggested previously for overcoming the

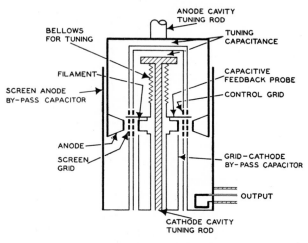

FIG. 8.7.   The resnatron may be converted into an oscillator by inserting a feedback probe between the anode and cathode cavities.

effect of electron transit time was the use of high accelerating voltages. In the ordinary low-power tube this was not feasible because the heat generated could not be removed by air alone. However, in the resnatron, high power is desired, and a water-cooling system is incorporated into the tube. The complete tube structure has an overall length of approximately 5 feet and a weight of 250 pounds, but it is capable of operating efficiently at the ultra-high frequencies.

A second advantage obtained by using high voltages is a reduction in the number of secondary electrons which travel from the plate to the screen grid. The secondary electrons produced at the plate are unable to develop enough momentum to leave the high potential anode field. At lower screen potentials, secondary emission becomes appreciable, loading down the anode cavity and reducing the efficiency of the circuit.

The physical appearance of a resnatron is shown in Fig. 8–8.

Recent research on the resnatron indicates that the power output and the operating frequency can both be raised. Resnatrons are being developed now to operate as high as 2000 mc with peak pulse power outputs in the megawatt range. Another foreseeable application of this tube is in

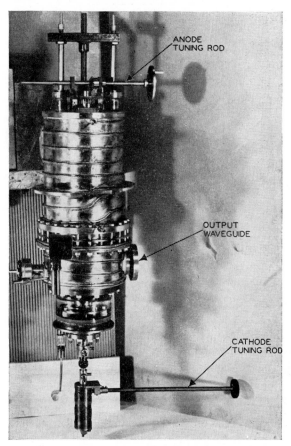

Fig. 8.8.   The physical appearance of the resnatron tube.   (*Courtesy Westinghouse*)

UHF television broadcasting where high power and high efficiency are especially desirable.

LOW- AND MEDIUM-POWER UHF TUBES

There is as much need for low- and medium-power tubes in the UHF region as there is for high-power tubes. Not all broadcast services require as much power output as a resnatron will furnish. Furthermore, low-power tubes must be used frequently to drive high-power tubes. A considerable amount of work has been done toward the development of suitable low-power UHF tubes and a number of these are discussed in the paragraphs to follow.

A widespread practice, adopted by commercial designers and radio amateurs alike, is to reach a desired UHF frequency by starting with a lower VHF frequency and then frequency-multiplying this to the desired

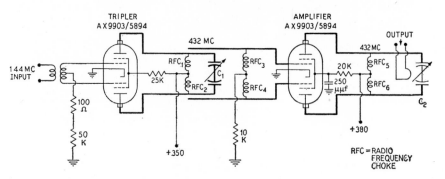

FIG. 8.9.   Diagram of a tripler-amplifier for 432 mc.   (*Courtesy QST Magazine*)

value.   For example, to operate in the 432-mc band, amateurs often start with a 144-mc oscillator, similar perhaps to the oscillator shown in Fig. 5–5, Chapter 5.   To this is then added a frequency tripler and an amplifier, such as illustrated in Figs. 8–9 and 8–10.   The tripler-amplifier consists of two push-pull tetrodes working into half-wave tuning lines, each tuned with small split-stator capacitors at the open ends.   The interstage coupling, with the grid line of the amplifier overlapping the plate line of the tripler, is essentially capacitive in nature.   The amplifier input line is formed of small strips of stiff copper soldered to the grid terminals of the amplifier tube socket and then run closely parallel to the tripler plate line.*   Thin sheets of mica or teflon inserted between the tuning lines prevent physical contact between them.

The tube used in this circuit is a AX9903/5894 high-frequency double tetrode.   (See Fig. 8–11.)   Element connections extend straight through the glass envelope, permitting the tube to be closely integrated with the rest of the circuit.   A power output of 40 to 50 watts is obtainable up to approximately 500 mc; at lower operating frequencies this can be increased to a maximum of 85 watts at 250 mc.

Better performance can be attained from the AX9903/5894 and similar tubes if forced air cooling is used and the tuning circuits are shielded or otherwise enclosed.   Commercial equipment almost always follows this practice; amateurs frequently do not because of the simplicity of the open type of construction.

* "Better Results on 420 Mc," by Edward P. Tilton. *QST Magazine*, August 1950.

FIG. 8.10. Physical appearance of the 432-mc tripler-amplifier. The tripler stage is at the left; the amplifier and output at the right. (*Courtesy QST Magazine*)

A high-efficiency beam tetrode using a co-axial electrode form of construction is shown in Fig. 8–12A. The tube, a 4X500A, will handle 500 watts of plate dissipation (using forced air cooling) and operate with frequencies as high as 400 mc.

A cross-sectional view of the 4X500A tube is shown in Fig. 8–12B. The control grid (and the screen grid, too) consists of a number of vertical bars equally spaced about a cylindrical cathode. Electrons leave the cathode from all points on its circumference and head toward a cylindrical anode after passing by the control grid and screen grid bars. All electrode connections are made through a base pin. The cathode pins are on a large pin circle to minimize cathode-lead inductance and to provide a short grounding path. The control grid is brought out through the center pin to facilitate coaxial input-line connection.

To employ such tubes adequately requires coaxial tank circuits and forced air cooling. One such tank circuit designed for a companion tube, a 4X150A, is shown in Figs. 8–13, 8–14, and 8–15. Electrically, the circuit is quite simple, being a straight tetrode amplifier, with

FIG. 8.11. The AX9903/5894 high-frequency beam tetrode. (*Courtesy Amperex Electronic Corporation*)

the input coupled to the grid coil L_1, and the output drawn in similar fashion from the plate coil, L_3.

FIG. 8.12A. The Eitel-McCullough 4X500A UHF tetrode. (*Courtesy Eitel-McCullough*)

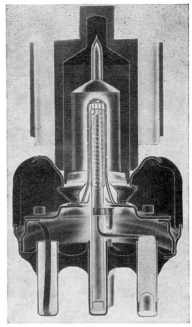

FIG. 8.12B. Cross-sectional view of the 4X500A tetrode. (*Courtesy Eitel-McCullough*)

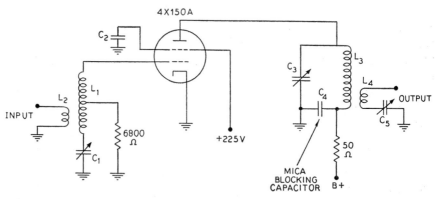

FIG. 8.13. Schematic diagram of the 4X150A amplifier. (*Courtesy QST Magazine*)

The chief feature of this amplifier is its physical construction, shown complete in Fig. 8–14 and in cross-section in Fig. 8–15. The plate circuit

for the tube is a quarter-wave section of coaxial transmission line. The
inner hollow rod makes contact to the plate ring of the tube by means

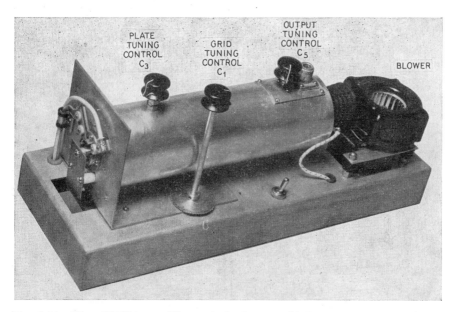

FIG. 8.14. The 4X150A amplifier completely assembled. The grid line may be
seen at the left, where it makes a right-angle bend under the bracket on which the
unit is mounted. (*Courtesy QST Magazine*)

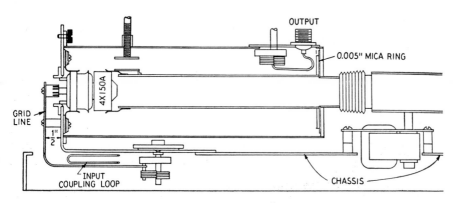

FIG. 8.15. A cut-away drawing of the 4X150A amplifier (side view). (*Courtesy
QST Magazine*)

of special flexible fingers formed by notching a flat phosphor bronze strip
and then soldering it around the end of the inner coaxial rod.

A blocking capacitor in the form of a mica ring is built into the shorted (or far) end of the coaxial line. This prevents the high plate B + present on the inner conductor from reaching the outer surface of the larger conductor. The latter can then be grounded to provide the necessary shielding action while, at the same time, protecting the operator from possible electrical shock.

Two small disks mounted near the plate end of the coaxial tank enable the operator to vary the operating frequency within rather narrow limits.

Fig. 8.16.   A 1.5-kw 500-mc triode (at the left) with watercooling plug for the anode (at the right). (*Courtesy Bell Telephone Laboratories*)

At the other end of the line is a coupling loop for extracting energy from the circuit. This loop has a small capacitor in series with it.

In the grid circuit of the amplifier we find a half-wave parallel plate line. One end of the line connects directly to the grid terminal of the tube; the other end is terminated in a small variable capacitor which tunes the input circuit. The grid line is bent into a 90-degree angle to enable it to fit down and around the coaxial assembly. Ceramic stand-off insulators hold the line firmly in place. The grid resistor is soldered to the electrical center of the line while the other end of the resistor is grounded to the coaxial tank. Position of the input coupling can be seen in Fig. 8–15.

A blower is attached to one end of the coaxial tank circuit and sends air down the inside conductor and through the radiating fins of the tube's plate assembly. The air also circulates around the tube base, effectively carrying off the heat generated during operation.

A 1.5-kw 500-mc triode is shown in Fig. 8–16. It was developed by The Bell Telephone Laboratories for use as a grounded-grid amplifier for A–M or F–M signals. The elements are mounted in parallel planes in much the same fashion as the planar lighthouse tube. Nominal spacing between the grid and cathode is 0.015 inch, and the spacing between grid

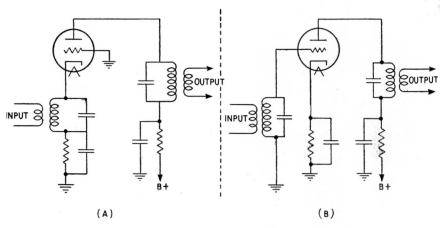

(A)   (B)

FIG. 8.17. A comparison between the grounded-grid (A) and the conventional amplifier (B).

and plate is on the order of 0.075 inch. The tube operates with 3000 volts on the plate and requires cooling water at the rate of 0.7 gallon per minute.

For those who may not be familiar with a grounded-grid amplifier, a comparison between the grounded-grid and conventional amplifier is made in Fig. 8–17. Note that the grid of the tube is at r-f ground potential* and that the incoming signal is fed to the cathode. The tube still functions as an amplifier because the flow of plate current is controlled by the grid-to-cathode potential. Instead of varying the grid potential and maintaining the cathode fixed, the grid is fixed and the cathode potential is varied. The net result is still the same. In addition, the grid, being grounded, acts as a shield between the input and output circuits, thereby preventing the feedback of energy between them. This arrangement is

* The grid in Fig. 8–17 is shown connected directly to ground. This places it at both d-c and r-f ground potential. If it is desired to apply a negative d-c biasing voltage to the grid, but still keep the r-f potential zero, then a small by-pass capacitor from grid to ground is employed. The capacitor breaks the d-c path to ground but has no effect on the r-f voltage. The d-c biasing voltage now goes directly to the grid element.

quite effective in preventing undesirable oscillations in the UHF region.

The 5588 tube, shown in Fig. 8–18, is a 100-watt grounded-grid triode which will operate up to 1200 mc. Efficiency as a straight amplifier is 30 per cent. The cathode, grid, and anode are closely spaced cylindrical elements (Fig. 8–19) designed for good mechanical stability and low inductance. The external electrode terminals of this tube are also sections of cylinders which, starting from the cathode, have progressively larger diameters.

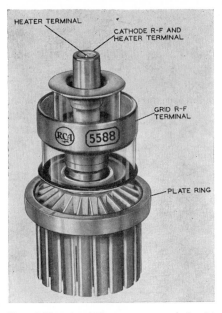

HEATER TERMINAL

CATHODE R-F AND HEATER TERMINAL

GRID R-F TERMINAL

PLATE RING

FIG. 8.18.   A   100-watt   grounded-grid triode which will operate up to 1200 mc. *(Courtesy RCA)*

This tube may be employed either as an oscillator or amplifier up to 1200 mc. Fig. 8–20A illustrates an arrangement for use as an oscillator employing a coaxial type of tuner. The plate and cathode circuits are shorted concentric transmission lines which are three-quarters wavelength long. Feedback is provided by a small loop linking the plate and cathode cavities. Cylindrical mica capacitors are inserted in the inner conductors of both plate and cathode lines to isolate the d-c plate and cathode-bias voltages.

Fig. 8–20B shows this tube used as an amplifier. This is a folded-back type of arrangement in which the grid-plate tuning cavity is folded back over the grid-cathode cavity. The neutralizing probe between plate and cathode cavities is to prevent oscillation from arising from energy feedback within the triode tube. R-f power is applied to the amplifier by a capacitive probe in the cathode cavity. Power output is obtained by a similar arrangement in the plate cavity.

The foregoing tubes illustrate the solutions to the problems of designing low- and medium-power UHF tubes. That the basic form of the tubes will change in the future seems unlikely. In any event, whatever tube structure does finally evolve, it must possess:

1. High power gain.
2. Stability.
3. Simple adjustments.
4. Good efficiency.
5. Practical circuits which can be used with these tubes.

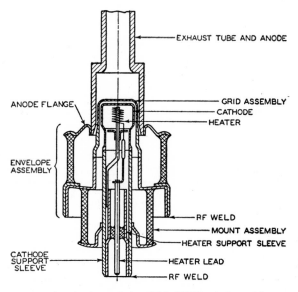

FIG. 8.19.   A cross-sectional view of the 5588 UHF triode. (*Courtesy Institute of Radio Engineers*)

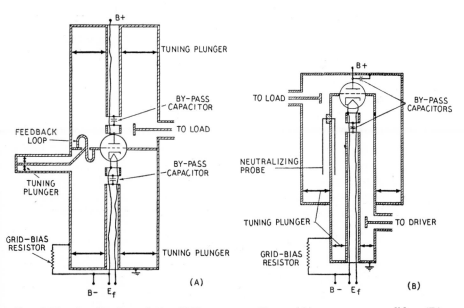

FIG. 8.20.   Application of the 5588 as an oscillator (A) or as an amplifier (B). (*Courtesy Institute of Radio Engineers*)

TRAVELING-WAVE TUBE

In microwave relay networks, there is a definite need for wideband amplifiers which are capable of operating above 3000 mc with good gain and low internal noise. Of all the tubes discussed thus far, only the klystron is capable of functioning as an amplifier at that frequency. But it has limited application because of the relatively high level of noise which it generates and the relatively narrow bandpass of its resonators. The comparatively poor coupling between the electron beam

FIG. 8.21A. The physical appearance of the traveling-wave tube. (*Courtesy Bell Telephone Laboratories*)

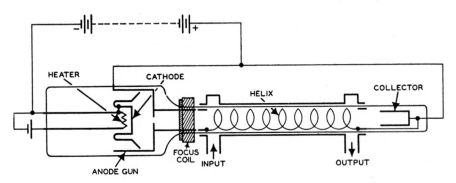

FIG. 8.21B. Schematic of the traveling-wave amplifier tube.

and the electromagnetic field of the cavity resonators is one of the chief difficulties of the klystron. If the beam and the energy were permitted to remain in contact longer than the time afforded them by the narrow resonator gaps, the efficiency of the energy transfer would be higher. Unfortunately, the transit time of the electrons when crossing the resonator gap must be kept small, and this, in turn, prevents any extended interaction between the beam and the field.

In order to extend the region over which the electrons and the fields may come in contact with each other, the traveling-wave tube was developed. The tube, shown in Fig. 8–21A, consists of a tightly wound helix of wire mounted in a glass tube and supported by four ceramic rods. The length of this helix is 11 inches. The ends of the helix are connected to short, straight conducting stubs parallel to the axis of the tube and close to the glass wall. The stubs pick up or transfer electromagnetic energy to two waveguide sections through which the tube projects. (See Figs. 8–21B, 8–22, and 8–23.) One waveguide section is placed at the input

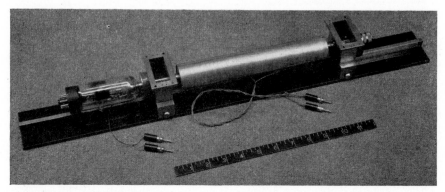

FIG. 8.22. The traveling-wave tube in place between the input and output waveguide sections. Note also the circular metallic shield. (*Courtesy Bell Telephone Laboratories*)

end of the helix and one section at the output end of the helix. Input and output waveguides are connected to the short waveguide sections through which the tube passes. The remainder of the tube is enclosed in a circular pipe to shield it from stray electromagnetic fields.

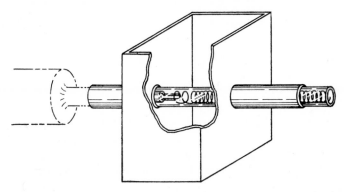

FIG. 8.23. Coupling between the helix and the waveguide. (*Courtesy I.R.E.*)

Thus far we have a relatively long helix coupled to an input and output waveguide. If energy were fed into the input waveguide, it would travel along the helix and appear at the output waveguide. The electromagnetic waves follow the helix wire with a velocity very close to that of light.   However, since the wire is wound in the form of a spiral, and the waves follow the twisting wires, the actual forward velocity of the wave is only about one-third that of light.

If the tube contained only the helix, energy traveling along the coil from end to end would experience a 33-db loss due to the resistance of the wires.   However, the tube, in addition to the helix, has an electron gun at one end and a collector plate at the other.   When the gun is emitting electrons, electromagnetic waves traveling along the helix receive a gain rather than a loss.

A beam of electrons formed by the gun is shot through the tube, passing through the center of the helix winding and impinging on the collector plate.   The helix winding is given a relatively high positive potential (approximately 1600 volts), drawing a beam current of about 10 milli-amperes.   By properly adjusting the focusing coil at the gun end, the major portion of the beam will reach the collector plate.   At the acceleration voltage of 1600 volts, the electrons travel axially through the tube with a velocity which is only slightly greater than the forward velocity of the electromagnetic wave along the helix.

The amplification of the tube depends upon the interaction of the electromagnetic field which is set up along the axis of the tube and the electrons traveling through the coil.   The electromagnetic field carried by the helix contains a magnetic and an electric component.   Both of these components extend axially along the tube.   Since the electrons are traveling parallel to the magnetic field, there will be no interaction between them.   There will, however, be an interaction between the electric component of the electromagnetic wave and the beam electrons.

The electromagnetic energy of the wave enters through the input waveguide and travels along the helix.   An electron leaving the electron gun and entering this field will do so at one of two times: either when the electric field of the wave is positive at the gun or when it is negative. If the field is positive, the electron will receive a greater acceleration than it would have received from the d-c voltage alone.   If the field is negative at this instant, the electron will not receive as much acceleration.

Now, the electron velocity is adjusted so that it is slightly greater than the forward wave velocity.   This is an important point to remember. If an electron emerges from the electron gun at a time when the electric field of the wave is positive, it will travel even faster and move fairly rapidly out of the positive electric field and into the preceding negative field.   Here it will gradually slow down with the result that it will remain in this negative or decelerating field for a longer period of time than it remained in the positive electric field.   It will, therefore, give up more energy to the wave than it absorbed from it.

Electrons which emerge from the electron gun when the electric field of the wave is negative will receive less acceleration than they would have in the absence of the field. The field will slow them down and force them to remain for a comparatively longer time in this negative electric field. The result, again, is a transfer of energy from the electrons to the wave.

Since the electrons are traveling faster than the wave, we can visualize the wave as standing still and the electrons slowly moving past it. Wherever the electric field of the wave is positive, the electrons will move forward faster than at those points where the electric field is negative. Consequently, at any one instant of time more electrons are being slowed down than speeded up and therefore more energy is being received by the wave than it is giving. The amplitude of the wave will increase as it travels through the tube. At the end of the helix the energy is radiated into the waveguide and conducted away from the tube.

The gain achievable in the traveling-wave tube depends on the relative velocity between the wave and the electron beam. Beam velocity is a function of the d-c accelerating voltage. In order that reasonable voltages may be used, the helix is wound so that the forward velocity of the electromagnetic wave is reduced to a value about one-thirteenth that of light. At this velocity, an acceleration voltage of 1600 volts forces the electrons to move slightly faster than the wave. Experimentally it was discovered that the tube gain rises as the beam velocity increases until this velocity slightly exceeds that of the wave. Beyond this, the gain decreases again.

Gain is a function of the length of the helix also. The longer the tube, the more intimate the contact between the electron beam and the wave, and the greater the possibility of energy transfer from the beam to the wave. However, if the tube is made too long, difficulties in beam focusing and beam spreading arise, both of which result in a reduction in gain. The tube shown in Fig. 8–16A was designed for a mid-frequency of 3600 mc. Its gain as an amplifier is about 23 db and it possesses a bandwidth of 800 mc, which is extraordinarily large. There are about 40 wavelengths at 3600 mc along the helix, the gain being slightly greater than 0.5 decibel per wavelength. Since gain depends upon the number of wavelengths along its axis, gain decreases as the frequency is lowered because fewer wavelengths are present along the helix. An upper frequency limit exists for any given tube because, as the frequency rises, the electromagnetic wave tends to concentrate closer to the helix wires, reducing the electric intensity near the axis. Since the electrons move along this axis, reduced field intensity means less bunching with less power transferred from the electrons to the wave. Operation at a higher frequency could be achieved by using another traveling-wave tube designed for this frequency.

THE DOUBLE-STREAM AMPLIFIER*

The double-stream amplifier shown in Fig. 8–24 is a variation of the traveling-wave tube. In this tube two streams of electrons traveling at different speeds but in the same direction will amplify high-frequency signals. The two streams of electrons are emitted by two separate cathodes, C_1 and C_2, and are accelerated through the tube by G, an accelerating grid. The cathodes are at different potentials with respect to grid G, and

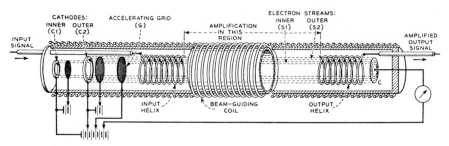

FIG. 8.24. The double-stream amplifier tube. (*Courtesy Bell Telephone Laboratories*)

this is the reason why the beams travel at different speeds. The beams travel side by side down the nearly foot-long tube. To prevent the beams from spreading out, the tube is placed within a special beam-guiding coil. The axial magnetic field set up by the coil brings an electrical force to bear on any diverging electrons.

Two smaller coils are placed within the tube, one at each end of the beam path. The left-hand coil, labeled input helix, couples the input circuit to the electron streams. The right-hand coil, labeled output helix, transfers the amplified signal to the output circuit. The incoming signal is brought in to the input helix and modulates the electron streams moving by. The amplitude of the signal modulation on the streams increases as the beam travels down the tube. This increase is attributed to the interaction of the streams on each other. At the output helix the amplified energy is removed and transferred to the output circuit. The beam electrons are collected by electrode C and brought back to the cathode.

The secret of the tube's operation is the interaction of the beams. With both cathodes cold, no signal passes from the input to the output helixes. When one stream is in operation, the signal is transmitted through the tube with little loss in amplitude. It is only when both streams are turned on that the signal amplification is obtained.

---

* "The Double-Stream Amplifier," by A. V. Hollenber. *Bell Laboratories Record,* August 1949.

It is interesting to note further that the electron streams must exceed a certain current density before amplification takes place. Beams possessing lower densities will yield no amplification. When the minimum value is exceeded, the gain increases rapidly at first and then approaches a limiting value as the current density is increased indefinitely. The gain is limited to about 27 db per wavelength in the streams per unit "velocity separation." The term "velocity separation" is defined as the difference in velocity between the two streams divided by the average velocity. The result is a small value, on the order of 0.1.

Thus, if a tube is 16 wavelengths long, its theoretical limiting gain would be

$$16 \times 27 \times 0.1 = 43 \text{ db}$$

It is evident that the longer the tube, the greater its gain. However, as the tube is made longer, difficulties arise, such as trying to keep the beams together, and maintaining electron velocity. As it is, the tube is many wavelengths long in terms of the wave that travels on the electron streams, and each electron takes part in the amplifying process over a number of cycles. Note that the wavelength in the electron stream is much smaller than the free space wavelength because the electrons are traveling far below the speed of light.

This tube, in common with the traveling-wave tube, is capable of amplifying a large bandwidth of signals with almost uniform gain. The gain does vary with frequency, but it does this so slowly that its value over relatively large frequency ranges can be considered as essentially constant.

QUESTIONS

1. Describe briefly the structure and operation of the resnatron.

2. Why can this tube operate successfully between 350 to 650 mc, while the conventional tetrode or beam-power tube cannot?

3. How does the resnatron overcome the undesirable effects of secondary emission?

4. In what respects does the operation of the resnatron as an amplifier differ from its operation as an oscillator?

5. How is the resnatron tuned?

6. Why is the traveling-wave tube capable of greater amplification than the klystron when the latter is employed as an amplifier?

7. Describe the various components of a traveling-wave amplifier.

8. Explain how a traveling-wave tube operates.

9. Upon what factors does the gain of a traveling-wave amplifier depend?

10. For any given traveling-wave tube, what limits the highest and lowest frequencies at which it may conveniently and efficiently be used?

11. How is energy fed to a traveling-wave tube? How is it abstracted?

12. Explain briefly the mode of operation of the double-stream tube.

13. Describe the electrode arrangements used in low-power UHF triodes and tetrodes.

Chapter 9

UHF ANTENNAS

In any communications system, it is desirable to convert as much of the available signal at the transmitter into radiated energy and, at the receiver, to pick up as much as possible. Although these objectives are true at all frequencies, they become especially important in the ultra-high-frequency range because of the difficulty of generating efficiently large amounts of power, the high losses that are incurred in wave travel between transmitter and receiver, and the lower sensitivity of the receivers. To achieve adequate signal strength at the receiving point, either the power transmitted must be raised by a large factor or the efficiency of the radiating and receiving antenna systems must be increased. Previously, it has been more economical to erect elaborate and high-gain antennas than to attempt to obtain greater power from transmitters. Fortunately, the wavelengths are quite small and hence even fairly complex arrays can be built having moderate dimensions.

If the energy transmitted by an antenna system is radiated equally in all directions, the antenna is said to be nondirectional. On the other hand, if the energy is concentrated principally in one or two directions, the system is said to be directional. The type of array used will depend upon the purpose of the transmission. If signals are to be broadcast to a city, then the antenna would most likely be erected in the center of the city and its radiation made nondirectional. This is true, for example, in television and F–M broadcasting.

On the other hand, for radar and commercial point-to-point communications such as relay systems or on remote broadcasts, the energy radiated is concentrated in a narrow path and beamed to the receiving point. The antenna arrays used in each instance would differ because of the differing requirements.

The following pages show how the simplest types of antennas are built and how they may be fashioned into highly directional antennas possessing gain factors of several hundred or more.

248

Simple Antennas. A very simple type of antenna is shown in Fig. 9–1A. It consists of a metal rod, one-half wavelength long, mounted vertically.

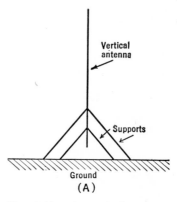

FIG. 9.1A. A vertical antenna (side view).

Now, the most important information that can be given concerning an antenna is the manner in which it will radiate the energy it receives. For this, a special graph, known as a radiation pattern, is plotted on circular coordinate paper. Energy is fed to an antenna, and the signal strength at various angles around the antenna is measured. The values obtained are marked on the graph and, when all these points are connected, we have a curve which shows the radiation pattern of the antenna. Consider, as an example, the curve in Fig. 9–1B. This reveals that, for a vertical half-wave antenna, the signal strength is the same at all points which are equally distant from the radiator. The distance from the antenna for each field strength measure-

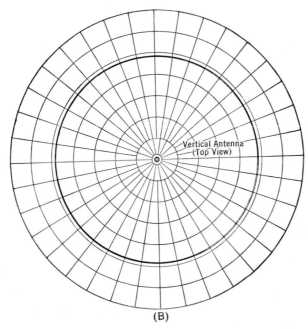

FIG. 9.1B. The signal strength pattern of a vertical antenna. Notice that it remains constant at all points about this antenna (in the horizontal plane).

ment at each angle was the same. Hence, it is seen that vertical antennas are nondirectional in a horizontal plane. The horizontal plane is any plane which is parallel to the ground. Strictly speaking, this type of horizontal plane could not be flat since the earth's surface itself is not flat. However, for practical purposes, it will be considered as such. The vertical plane is at right angles to the horizontal plane and hence deals with the energy radiated in the skyward direction. (See Fig. 9–2.)

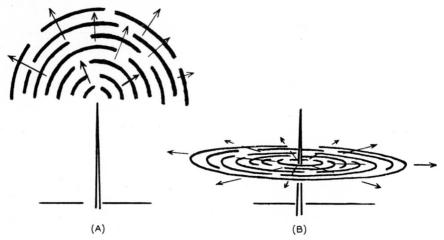

(A)   (B)

FIG. 9.2. (A) The vertical plane. (B) The horizontal plane.

Consider a half-wave dipole that is placed parallel with the ground, a horizontal antenna. Fig. 9–3 shows this antenna, together with its radiation pattern. Here, in the horizontal plane, there is greater signal strength in the direction at right angles to the antenna, or broadside, as it is called. As the angle made with the center-line AA' increases, the signal strength decreases, until at 90 degrees, when we are facing one end of this antenna, there is no signal strength or radiation. This, then, is a directional antenna since it concentrates energy in the broadside direction and radiates nothing off the ends.

The radiation patterns, thus far, have dealt only with the signal strength transmitted in the horizontal plane. However, antennas also radiate energy upward, toward the sky. For long-distance communication, extensive use is made of the sky wave. Hence radiation patterns are also desirable showing the variation in signal strength at various angles in a vertical plane. Referring to Fig. 9–4, imagine that you were standing on the ground looking up at a horizontal antenna. The circle would represent the signal strength at various angles above the wire, with the center of

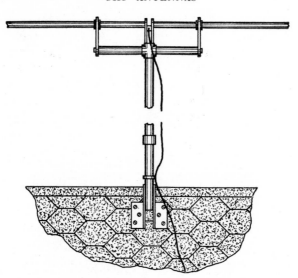

FIG. 9.3A. A half-wave dipole with lead-in line.

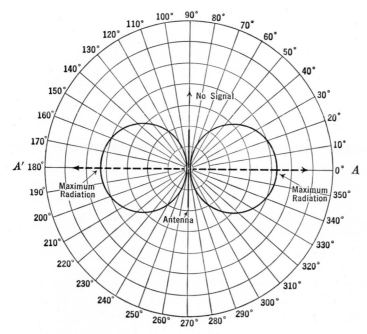

FIG. 9.3B. Horizontal radiation pattern of half-wave dipole antenna above.

the wire as the origin. Line *A* shows the strength of signal which might be expected at a 50° angle, line *B* at a 90° angle, and line *C* for a 135° angle. Maximum radiation in the upward direction is at right angles, or broadside, to the wire.

A little thought will show that a half-wave dipole, no matter in what position it is placed, will always radiate a maximum amount of energy at right angles to the wire axis. When the wire is held vertically, right angles to the wire is the horizontal plane and since this plane exists at

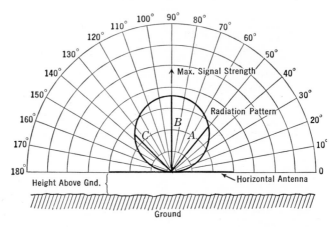

Fig. 9.4. Side view of a horizontal antenna, placed above the ground. The radiation pattern shows how the signal strength varies in the vertical (or upward) direction.

all points around the wire, the radiation pattern is nondirectional. However, when the wire is laid on its side or held horizontally, there are only two points in the horizontal plane that are at right angles to the wire. All other points in the horizontal plane make an angle of less than 90 degrees with the wire, and the energy radiated in that direction varies accordingly.

If we were to illustrate the complete radiation pattern of a half-wave antenna in all directions, the radiation pattern would possess a doughnut shape. (See Fig. 9–5.)

There is so little useful sky wave propagation at the ultra-high frequencies that patterns depicting signal radiation in the vertical plane are not required. All patterns shown from now on, unless otherwise stated, will refer to the type of signal laid down in the horizontal plane, parallel with the ground. In analyzing these radiation patterns, the reader should know that the type of ground below the antenna will considerably influence

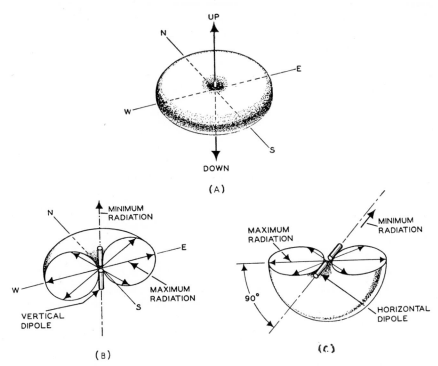

FIG. 9.5. (A) The complete three-dimensional radiation pattern of a vertical dipole. (B) Cross-sectional view of the radiation from a vertical dipole. (C) Cross-sectional view of the radiation from a horizontal dipole.

and modify the radiation graph obtained for the radiator. For idealized curves, a fictitious, perfectly conducting and reflecting earth is assumed. Actual conditions, however, may differ substantially from this perfect ground, resulting in patterns that do not have the same shape as the theoretical curves. However, in many instances it will be found that the actual patterns agree quite closely with the derived curves and this warrants the continued use of these patterns.

Another practice, sometimes used, shows the radiation patterns without the background of angles. A diagram of this type is given in Fig. 9–6 for a vertical antenna. Very little confusion is caused by this method, since it is simple enough to draw in the necessary angles, if needed.

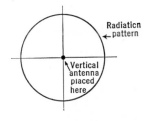

FIG. 9.6. Radiation pattern of a vertical antenna without the various angles shown. Compare this with Fig. 9.1B.

Although the foregoing deals with the properties of antennas when employed for transmission, the same characteristics hold true when the antennas are utilized for reception.

Antenna Arrays. The simple half-wave dipole antenna, shown in Fig. 9–3, may be used in a variety of combinations to give rise to directive radiation patterns, wherein the signal strength in one direction is increased but in some other direction reduced to small values, possibly zero. These systems are known as arrays and are of two general types, the driven and parasitic array. In the driven array, each individual wire comprising the array receives its energy from the transmitter. In a parasitic array, some of the elements are not connected to the transmitter; instead they develop currents by intercepting energy from the driven wires.

Directional arrays are more widely used with UHF than the simpler vertical or horizontal antennas because of the increased gain due to the concentration of energy in one or two directions. The gain is obtained from the energy which normally would have gone in other directions. It does for a signal what a megaphone does for the voice. When speaking with normal loudness into a megaphone, it will be noted that the forward projected sound has greater intensity because of the concentration of energy that ordinarily would not have gone forward.

Gain. The gain of a directional array is a ratio of the signal strength that it would develop to that which a standard or reference antenna would develop if both were placed at some identical distant point to the signal. The standard or reference antenna frequently chosen is the dipole. Thus, a gain of 10 means that it would be necessary to put 10 times as much power in the half-wave antenna as in the directional array in order to have the same strength signal at some distant point. Or, if the power in the standard antenna were kept constant and the power in the directional system lowered to 1/10, the signal strength at the distant receiving point would be the same.

Many times, the decibel is used as the unit of gain. In this case, since power is being employed, the formula is:

$$db = 10 \log_{10} \frac{P_1}{P_2}$$

A ratio of P_1 to P_2 of 100 would give the equivalent decibel rating of 20. This follows from the fact that the $\log_{10} 100 = 2$, and 2×10 equals 20 db.

Directivity. The directivity of a directional antenna means the sharpness with which the signal is confined or directed to a particular direction. To describe this directivity accurately, the term *beam angle* is often employed. Beam angle is the angle between the two points on the radiation curve at which the signal voltage is 0.707 (or 70.7%) of its maximum value. In Fig. 9–7, the angle between points A–B, or the angle θ, is the beam angle for this radiation pattern. At each of the points (A and B), the signal strength is 0.707 of its value at point C.

Points A and B are also known as the half-power points because the radiated power here is one-half of its value at point C. This is an equivalent expression because power is proportional to the square of the voltage and $(0.707)^2$ is approximately equal to 0.5.

It should be noted that, if a system of wires possesses a certain directional pattern for sending, it will show the same directivity when used for reception.

Parasitic Arrays. A parasitic array, by definition, contains one or more wires which receive their energy solely from the energy radiated by the driven element or elements. The parasitic wires are placed parallel to and some small distance from the driven antenna and, because of the currents set up by the induced emf, likewise give rise to their own radiations. At some points, the energy radiated directly by the

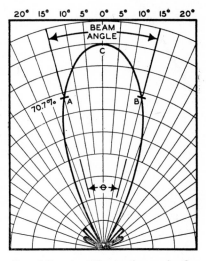

Fig. 9.7. An illustration of the standard definition of beam angle.

driven element will be in phase with the energy re-radiated by the parasitic element. At other points partial or total neutralization will occur. When the signal strength in all directions about the array is measured and plotted on a graph, a directional pattern will be obtained.

The phase difference that exists between the current in the parasitic element and that which flows in the driven antenna depends on two factors:

1. The relative length of the parasitic antenna.
2. Distance between the driven and parasitic elements.

The length of the parasitic wire will determine whether it is operating above, below, or at the resonant frequency of the wave being intercepted. As in any ordinary tuning circuit containing capacitance, inductance, and resistance, the current flowing in the wire will bear a definite relationship to the induced emf, the amount dependent on how much the inductive reactance neutralizes the capacitive reactance in the wire. At resonance, the impedance is completely resistive. The influence which the distance between the wires plays in determining the phase difference is easily seen.

It is directly related to the amount of change which occurs at the driven antenna during the time the energy it radiates is traveling the intervening space between the wires. The two factors of length and spacing will determine the directivity of the antenna array and, in addition, the field strength of the signal at some distant receiving point.

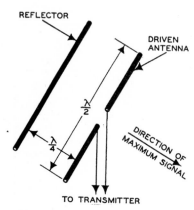

FIG. 9.8.   A dipole and reflector.

Reflector Wire. A simple parasitic array containing two wires is shown in Fig. 9–8. One wire, one-half wavelength long, receives energy from a transmitter. The second wire is placed behind and parallel to the driven element. This, the parasitic element, is known as a reflector and serves to concentrate the radiated energy of the driven element principally in one direction. (See Fig. 9–9.) Very little signal appears behind the reflector. Thus, by the addition of the reflector, the bidirectional radiation pattern* of a dipole can be changed to one which is essentially unidirectional.

Addition of the reflector changes the response pattern of the dipole because the energy picked up and reradiated by the reflector differs in phase from the energy radiated directly from the dipole. Whenever these two waves meet, the manner in which they combine will depend upon the phase difference between them. At some points the two waves add, at others they completely cancel, and at intermediate points, only partial cancellation occurs. The resultant radiation pattern then appears as shown in Fig. 9–9.

If the separation between the reflector and the driven element is one-quarter wavelength, both wires will have the same length. It is possible to increase the gain of the array by bringing the reflector wire closer to the dipole. When this is done, however, the reflector wire length must be increased. By making the reflector wire longer, we cause it to resonate at a lower frequency than the energy transmitted by the driven dipole. Hence, when the signal reaches the reflector, the current in this wire is made to lag. By properly cutting the reflector wire, the lag introduced will equal the lag which would have been incurred had the spacing between the two wires been kept at a quarter wavelength.

---

* The term *radiation pattern* is used when the antenna is considered from the standpoint of transmission. For reception, the same characteristic is called a *response pattern*.

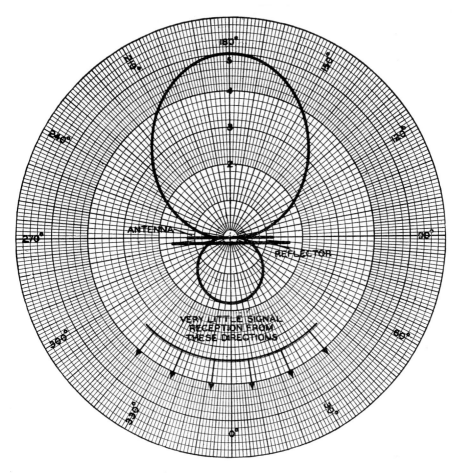

FIG. 9.9. Response of a dipole and reflector.

Directors. A unidirectional effect with a two-element array may also be obtained if, instead of using a wire of slightly longer length behind the driven element, a parasitic antenna is placed in front of the driven element. This wire is known as a director. (See Fig. 9–10.) If the distance between the director and the dipole is less than one-quarter wavelength, the length of the director must be made less than that of the driven dipole. In a director, we desire to have the current lead. This condition can be achieved by making the length of the reflector less than the dipole.

It may be noted in passing that the addition of reflectors and directors to any array tends to reduce the input impedance of the active element.

Thus, a dipole antenna, which has an input impedance of 72 ohms, by itself, will show approximately a 50-ohm impedance when used with a reflector. Just what the exact impedance will be is governed by the diameter of the rods used and the spacing, shape, and length of the reflector.

In the foregoing discussion, the simple dipole with reflector and/or director has been treated more or less from the standpoint of transmission.

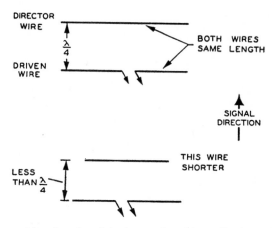

Fig. 9.10.   A parasitic wire placed in front of a driven dipole. The length of the director depends upon its position.

That is, energy was fed into the system and then radiated. This particular approach was taken because it is easier to understand antenna operation from the standpoint of transmission than reception. However, what is stated for one use is just as valid for the other. Thus, although simple dipoles are seldom employed for transmission, they are extensively employed for reception.* This is particularly true of television and F-M. In addition to the arrays shown in Figs. 9–3, 9–8, and 9–10, there are some variations and these are described briefly below. They are useful up to approximately 400 mc.

Beyond this, in UHF television (470-890 mc), more elaborate receiving arrays are frequently employed in order that the increased antenna gain may partially offset the weaker signals.

1. *Folded Dipole.* (Fig. 9–11A.) This consists essentially of two dipole antennas connected in parallel with each other. The separation between the two sections is approximately 3 to 5 inches. The folded dipole has the same bidirectional pattern as the simple dipole and approximately

---

* In reception, especially where the general public is concerned, simple arrays are popular because they are economical, easy to install, and provide good results. For transmission, high gain and the proper directivity are the controlling factors.

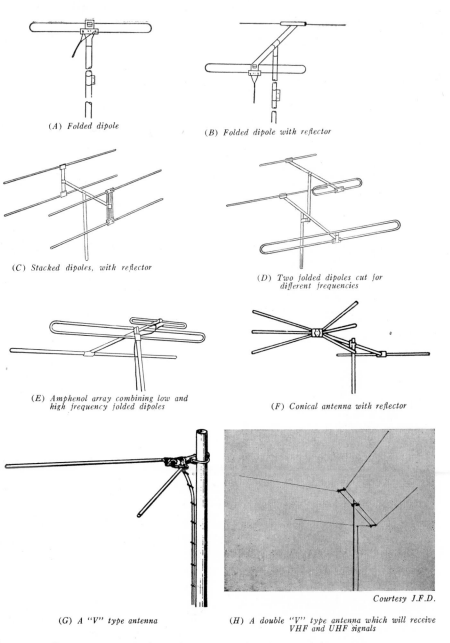

(A) Folded dipole

(B) Folded dipole with reflector

(C) Stacked dipoles, with reflector

(D) Two folded dipoles cut for different frequencies

(E) Amphenol array combining low and high frequency folded dipoles

(F) Conical antenna with reflector

Courtesy J.F.D.

(G) A "V" type antenna

(H) A double "V" type antenna which will receive VHF and UHF signals

FIG. 9.11. A number of popular television receiving antennas.

the same gain. The input impedance is 300 ohms against 72 for the simple dipole.

2. *Folded Dipole with Reflector.* (Fig. 9–11B.) The addition of a reflector has the same effect here as with the simple dipole, namely, increased gain and directivity.

3. *Stacked Dipoles with Reflector.* (Fig. 9–11C.) Two half-wave dipoles are placed at the front of the assembly, one mounted above the other. The center terminals of each dipole are connected together by means of a parallel-wire transmission line. Each conductor of the lead-in line to the receiver attaches to a conductor of this connecting transmission line at a point midway between the dipoles. A reflector rod is mounted behind each dipole. Stacking of antennas usually results in approximately a 2-db increase in gain for each additional section.

4. *Two Folded Dipoles for Different Frequencies.* (Fig. 9–11D.) Two folded dipoles, with reflectors, are mounted one above the other. The upper dipole is cut for a resonant frequency approximately in the center of the upper VHF television band (174–216 mc), and the longer folded dipole is resonated at the center frequency of the lower VHF television band (54–88 mc). A short length of 300-ohm transmission line connects the upper dipole to the lower one. From the lower antenna, a 300-ohm line feeds the signals to the receiver. Each antenna can be oriented independently for best reception from stations within its band.

5. *Inline Array.* (Fig. 9–11E.) Essentially the same arrangement as Fig. 9–11D, except that the longer folded dipole acts as the reflector for the shorter folded dipole.

6. *Conical Array.* (Fig. 9–11F.) Instead of using a single rod for each section of a dipole, this array uses three. For the two halves of the dipole, this produces a total of six elements (not counting the reflector). Each individual rod is one-quarter wavelength long.

The addition of several elements in parallel to the ordinary dipole has the effect of broadening the frequency response of the array, enabling it to provide a more uniform response over a range of frequencies.

7. *"V" Antenna.* (Fig. 9–11G.) This antenna and variations of it have recently become popular for television reception. It does not stem from the dipole, but rather is basically a long-wire type of array in which gain increases with frequency and with length of the antenna wires. The best suitable "V" angle (which the wires make with each other) lies between 40° and 60° and the compromise figure of 50° is frequently chosen.

8. *"V" Antenna with Directors.* (Fig. 9–11H.) A "V" antenna with a director. Closer inspection, however, reveals that the director rods (up front) are electrically connected to the two rear rods. The reason for this is twofold. First, the connecting line serves as a transmission line to

conduct whatever signal is picked up by the two front rods to the two rear rods. In addition, the two rear rods also pick up that portion of the signal which passed over the front rods and combine this with the

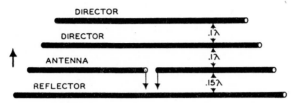

Fig. 9.12A. A simple directive array employing two directors and one reflector. The arrow indicates the direction in which energy would be radiated if this array was connected to a transmitter. For reception, the arrow indicates the direction from which energy would be received.

energy received from the front rods via the transmission line. Signal pick-up from the rear of the array is low because the energy which approaches the antenna from the rear and captured by the front and rear rods combine out of phase and is therefore cancelled.

The second purpose of the connecting transmission line (which is rigid) is to support both front and rear sets of rods and produce a mechanically sturdy array.

Several Parasitic Elements. To increase antenna directivity and gain, several directors and a reflector may be used, as shown in Fig. 9–12A. The separation between elements for a typical installation is 0.1 λ between directors and 0.15 λ between the reflector and the driven dipole. With these distances, parasitic elements behind the driven antenna are made longer, while those in front are made shorter, than the excited antenna. The radiation and frequency

Fig. 9.12B. A fan dipole with a screen reflector.

responses of this array are more selective than those of the two-element antennas, the unit responding uniformly to a much smaller range of signal frequencies confined to a narrower direction. In its most frequently encountered form, the array contains a single reflector with three or four directors. Additional elements could be added, but unless the unit is designed for UHF operation, it becomes too bulky. When the array is to be used for transmission or reception over a band of frequencies, it is frequently tuned for maximum signal strength at the center frequency of the range. The gain decreases the more we deviate from the center frequency, but the reduction can be made nominal for moderate band widths.

In VHF applications, usually only one reflector is employed and this is frequently a rod. Although this rod will reduce signal pick-up from the rear, it is far from being totally effective. A more efficient reflector is one constructed of a solid metallic sheet (or a wire mesh of similar size) placed behind the antenna. At VHF frequencies, antenna dimensions are such that use of a sheet reflector causes the array to become bulky and frequently difficult to erect. However, at UHF frequencies, the dimensions are sufficiently reduced so that sheet reflectors are entirely feasible. Mesh screens serve as well as solid metallic sheets. The fact that there are openings in the screen does not materially affect its performance as a reflector so long as the openings are on the order of 0.2 of a wavelength or less. Dimensions of the reflector are not critical, but the edges should extend for a short distance beyond the dipole elements.

Parallel bars are in common use as reflectors in place of a mesh screen. The same considerations of small spacing apply.

A modified dipole with a screen reflector is shown in Fig. 9–12B. This array is designed for the reception of UHF television signals over the band, 470 to 890 mc. The broadening of the dipole elements into triangular sheets, as shown, serves to provide good response over the entire UHF–TV band. The triangular construction also results in a 300-ohm input impedance.

Driven Arrays. While the emphasis thus far has been wholly on parasitic arrays, there are two types of driven arrays which have found application at ultra-high frequencies, especially in radar systems. These are the collinear array and the broadside array.

a. *Collinear Array.* The collinear array is a combination of half-wave antennas which are placed end to end and are excited so that the voltage variation along each antenna wire is the same. The simplest collinear array consists of two half-wave antennas connected to a transmission line as shown in Fig. 9–13A. Since the voltages across the open ends of a line are opposite in phase, the polarities at the two near ends of the half-wave wires will likewise be opposite in phase. On each antenna wire, the polarity will reverse itself between ends because each wire is one-half wavelength long. We can add additional elements to the array (Fig. 9–13B) by using a half-wave connecting link between each antenna element in order to preserve the same phase relationship between each of the radiating elements. The connecting lengths between each radiator is folded in half and both halves are entwined about each other. This is

not shown in Fig. 9–13B because it is desired to indicate that the length
of the connecting link is a half wavelength. In so doing, the oppositely
flowing currents in each half cancel and hence the connecting links have
very little effect on the over-all radiation pattern.

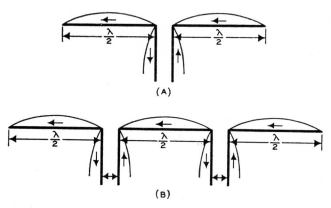

Fig. 9.13. (A) A two-element collinear array. (B) A more extensive collinear
array.

As many elements as desired may be added to the array, the directivity
and gain increasing with the number of elements. The radiation pattern
is a "figure-8," closely similar to that of the simple half-wave dipole, but
possessing greater gain and directivity. If radiation in one direction only
is desired—and this is true in most
radar installations—then a metal
screen is mounted behind the radiating antennas. The unit now is a
combination driven and parasitic
array.

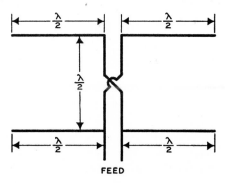

Fig. 9.14. A simple broadside array.

b. *Broadside Arrays.* Instead of
mounting the half-wave elements in
a line, it is also possible to mount
them one above the other, in which
case we obtain a broadside array.
The antenna elements are mounted
one-half wavelength apart in order
to simplify the problem of feeding the array by means of a single transmission line. In one-half wavelength, voltage (and current) values reverse,
and by reversing the connections between the antenna wires and the transmission line, all of the elements in a vertical line can be fed in phase.
This is shown in Fig. 9–14. A more extensive array, containing 16 elements,

is shown in Fig. 9–15. Again note the simplicity of the feeding system, requiring only one transmission line feeder from the transmitter or receiver.

Because of the vertical mounting or stacking of the radiating elements, and of the phasing of the currents and voltage, the vertical radiation from this array is small. Practically all of the energy is concentrated in the horizontal plane, and by employing enough elements in the array, the horizontal directivity can likewise be sharpened considerably. The result is a very narrow beam having a high concentration of energy. Further-

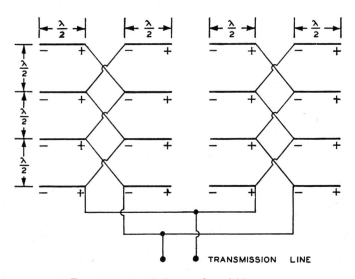

FIG. 9.15.   A 16-element broadside array.

more, by placing a metal screen behind the array, all energy is radiated in one direction. Large structures containing as many as 100 radiating elements are used in radar installations enabling the system to develop signals with high effective power when transmitting and to receive very weak signals when listening for echoes.

Metallic Parabolic Reflectors. Metallic parabolic reflectors are not new. For many years, before anyone thought of using them for the concentration of radio waves, they were employed for light beams. Their concentrating action is due to the shape of the reflecting surface and the fact that, for reflection, the incident and the reflected rays make equal angles with any line drawn perpendicular to the surface at the point of reflection. To understand this, refer to Fig. 9–16A. Here we have the ray AB hitting the parabolic surface at point A. Let the line N be perpendicular to the parabola at point A. Then, for reflection, angle a must equal angle ϕ. It will be found that the reflected ray AC will pass through the focal point F. Furthermore, it can be shown that all parallel rays reaching the parabolic surface will likewise meet at point F. Going the other way, rays starting from F will strike the parabolic surface and travel outward in parallel lines, as in Fig. 9–16B. Spherical surfaces do not possess this property. The parabolic reflector may be used either to concentrate a set of rays coming toward it or to produce a group of parallel rays. In ultra-high-frequency communication, both are desirable.

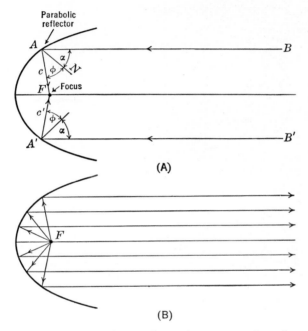

(A)

(B)

Fig. 9.16. (A) Action of a parabolic reflector in concentrating all parallel rays at its focus, F. (B) Rays originating at the focal point, F, leave the parabolic surface in parallel rays.

It should be noted that the concentrating action or focusing occurs only when the rays arrive at the reflector along parallel lines. For all other angles of incidence, the rays do not pass through the focal point, F. The reader might think this would impose a limitation on the unit, but experience has shown that radio waves coming from points as close as 3 or 4 miles away arrive essentially as parallel rays. At greater distances the effect is even more positive.

For reception or transmission, the antenna is placed at the focal point, F. In order to achieve the proper focusing action, the antenna must be kept as small as possible. For this reason, only simple antennas are used.

If portions of the antenna extend beyond the focus point, energy transmitted will diverge or spread out after reflection from the parabolic surface. Thus, a radiating element placed between the focal point F and the surface will produce rays that diverge or spread out after reflection from the parabolic surface. A radiating element placed at a distance greater than the focal distance will cause the rays to meet at some point P and then spread out. Both conditions are shown in Fig. 9–17, and both are generally undesirable because they reduce the sharpness of the beam.

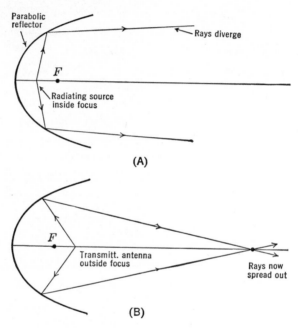

FIG. 9.17. Illustrations of what occurs when the antenna is not correctly placed at the focus, F, of a parabolic reflector.

The radiated energy of a parabolic reflector (known also as a rotational parabola or as a paraboloid) is concentrated into a beam, like the light from a flashlight, and projected in the direction that the reflector is facing.

A parabolic reflector can concentrate energy into a narrow beam because of its ability to take the spherical waves radiated by a dipole placed at its focus and to convert this energy into a plane wave. Now, energy radiated into space will travel in a direction perpendicular to its wave-front. If we have a plane wave, such as shown in Fig. 9–18A, then the energy will travel forward in a straight line, because this is the only direction which is perpendicular to the wave-front. The energy will have no tendency to spread out because all sections of the wave-front, being in the same plane, will move forward in the same direction. When the wave-front is spherical, all sections of the wave-front will move in a direction perpendicular to the wave-front, similar to the plane wave. However, since the wave-front surface is curved, perpendiculars drawn to various points of the wave will not all be parallel to each other. (See Fig. 9–18B.) As a result, this energy, as it travels, will spread out, producing a radiation pattern which is not as sharp or directive as that obtained with a parabolic reflector.

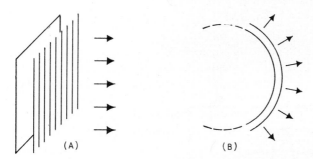

FIG. 9.18. A plane wave (A) tends to travel in a straight line, maintaining a close concentration of energy. A spherical wave (B) tends to spread out.

As a general rule, then, the directivity of any radiating system depends upon its ability to convert whatever energy it receives into a plane wave.

In order for a parabolic reflector to produce a plane wave, its shape must be truly parabolic in all directions, the antenna must be placed precisely at the focal point, and the dimensions of the antenna made small in comparison to the dimensions of the parabolic "dish." If any of these conditions are not adhered to, the radiated energy does not remain as shown in Fig. 9–18A but begins to curve. This causes the beam width to increase, and energy is radiated off to the sides through the establishment of minor lobes. Parabolic reflectors, when carefully constructed, are capable of providing considerable gains over that obtained from a simple dipole alone.

In order to achieve an appreciable amount of directivity and gain, the parabolic reflecting surface must be large in comparison to the antenna (and, in the same sense, to the wavelength of the signal). This is the chief reason why these units find application only at the ultra-high frequencies.

The gain of a parabolic reflector is given by

$$G = \frac{4\pi A}{\lambda^2}$$

Where A = aperture area of the reflecting "dish",
λ = wavelength of the signal to be transmitted (or received).

The aperture area of a parabolic reflector is very closely equal to the area across the mouth of the reflector. As this area becomes greater, in comparison to the wavelength of the signal, the gain increases accordingly. The angular width of the beam, between the half-power points, for the reflector is given by

$$\text{Width} = \frac{70\lambda}{d}$$

where d = width of aperture.

A radiation pattern of a parabolic reflector 5 feet in diameter, radiating a signal of 10,000 mc, is shown in Fig. 9–19. There is one large lobe, the primary or principal lobe, surrounded by several small secondary lobes. Increasing the size of the reflector or decreasing the wavelength will cause the width of the large lobe to decrease and its gain to increase. At the same time the minor lobes will decrease in size and move in closer to the main lobe.

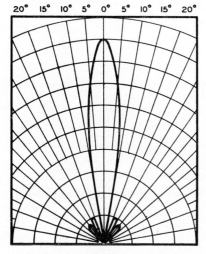

Fig. 9.19. The radiation pattern of a parabolic reflector 5 feet in diameter, operating at 10,000 mc.

A simple dipole placed at the focal point is generally used to feed the reflector. However, merely using the antenna by itself results in a broadening of the beam because not all of the radiated energy travels to the reflector. Some of it travels directly forward from the dipole itself. To reduce this extraneous radiation to a minimum, a small reflector may be placed behind the antenna to cut off any direct radiation and force all the rays to strike the reflector. (See Fig. 9–20A.) The reflector should not be too large or it will intercept many of the reflected rays and lower the radiating efficiency of the system. Other types of reflectors, such as straight rods and curved plates, are also used. (See Fig. 9–20B.) Furthermore, the entire dipole with its reflector may be enclosed in a plastic shell for protection from the weather.

It might be instructive to examine the radiating dipole and the coaxial cable which feeds energy to it from the transmitter (or which receives the signal from the dipole and feeds it to a receiver). Merely connecting two rods to the end of a coaxial cable to form a dipole antenna would not

be suitable because of an impedance mismatch between the dipole and the
cable and, further, because of the unbalanced current and voltage conditions
that exist in coaxial cables. To effect a match between coaxial cable

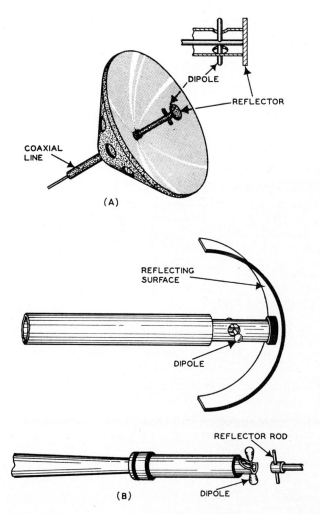

FIG. 9.20.   (A) A dipole and reflector mounted at the focus of a parabolic reflector.
(B) Two additional types of reflectors used with dipoles and parabolic reflectors.

and the dipole and, at the same time, provide the two elements of the
dipole with equal currents, the arrangement shown in Fig. 9–21 is employed.
A bazooka is attached to the outer surface of the coaxial line effectively
transforming the unbalance of the coaxial cable to the balanced condition

required by the dipole antenna. Ordinarily, at this point, a two-wire line would be connected to the coaxial cable. However, since the additional length of line required is small, the coaxial cable is merely extended beyond the bazooka. The dipole rods are then connected to the coaxial line, one rod attaching to the outer conductor of the line and one rod connecting to the inner conductor through a hole cut out of the outer conductor. A disk reflector is positioned a quarter wavelength distance from the dipole to direct all of the radiated energy to the parabolic reflecting surface. To

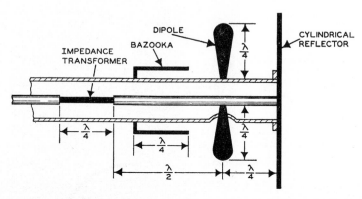

FIG. 9.21. The detail construction of a dipole and reflector frequently used with parabolic reflectors.

support the reflector mechanically, the coaxial line is extended beyond the dipoles, and the reflector is connected to the inner and outer conductors of the line, effectively shorting them together. This short circuit, reflected through the quarter wavelength distance between dipole and reflector, appears as a high impedance at the dipoles. This has negligible effect on the system since the 60-ohm impedance* of the dipoles is in parallel with this reflected high impedance, presenting a resultant impedance which is only slightly less than 60 ohms.

One further match is required in this system, that of the dipoles (60 ohms) to the coaxial line (50 ohms). This is accomplished with an impedance transformer. The 60 ohms of the dipole is reflected without change to the impedance transformer by the half-wave section connected directly to the dipole. The transformer is a quarter-wave section of line whose characteristic impedance is such as to enable it to match the coaxial line's 50 ohms on one end to the dipole's 60 ohms on the other.

There is no reason why a waveguide cannot be used to bring energy to the parabolic reflector by placing the mouth of the guide at the focal

* The decrease from 72 to 60 ohms for the dipole is caused by the reflector.

point of the parabola and positioning it so that the energy strikes the parabolic reflector. A typical application is shown in Fig. 9–22. The most easily constructed waveguide feed is simply an open-ended waveguide. The energy from the transmitter comes streaming down the guide, passes out through the open end, and, if this is facing the parabolic reflector, strikes the reflecting surface. Sometimes the end of the waveguide is tapered in so that the energy may be distributed horizontally or vertically to produce a desired pattern after it is reflected by the paraboloid. By modifying the shape of the feeding waveguide, we can concentrate energy in one direction and, in conjunction with the parabolic reflector, achieve a desired radiational pattern.

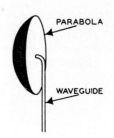

Fig. 9.22. A parabolic reflector with a waveguide feed.

One difficulty that is encountered when using waveguides to feed energy to parabolic reflectors is the fact that the guide, passing in front of the reflector, tends to obstruct or block part of the energy reflected by the

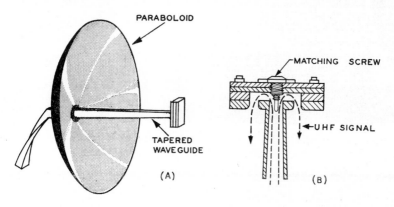

Fig. 9.23. (A) Energizing a paraboloid with a rear-feed arrangement. (B) A top view of the waveguide termination which directs the waveguide energy to the reflector surface.

paraboloid. To avoid this difficulty, several rear waveguides have been developed. In this form of feed, the waveguide passes through the center or vertex of the paraboloid and extends to the focus, at which point the energy is redirected back to the reflecting surface of the paraboloid and then radiated in the forward direction. The most widely used and most successful of these "rear-feed" arrangements is the "Cutter" feed shown in Fig. 9–23. The energy from the transmitter travels through a waveguide

until the paraboloid is reached.   Here the guide tapers down to a matching
section containing two slots or openings through which the energy is
directed toward the reflector.

Other Types of Parabolic Reflectors.   It is possible to concentrate
energy in one plane only, by using a section of a parabolic reflector.   Thus
with the parabolic cylinder shown in Fig. 9–24A directivity is obtained in

FIG. 9.24A. A parabolic cylindrical reflector
with a group of dipole antennas. (*Courtesy
Bell System Technical Journal*)

FIG. 9.24B. A modified cylindrical parabolic reflector using
only a small section of the parabolic surface. (*Courtesy TACO*)

the plane perpendicular to the length of the cylinder.   For Fig. 9–24A this
would mean extremely sharp vertical directivity.   Parabolic cylinders do
not have single focal points, as paraboloids do, but rather a focal line.
Small dipole antennas are mounted along this line, the useful energy
radiating back toward the reflector and then forward by reflection from this
surface.   The horizontal directivity of this reflector is determined by the
number of half-wave dipoles used and the phasing of the currents and
voltages fed by a transmission line to the dipoles.   The greatest directivity,
however, is obtained in the vertical plane and this is determined by the
parabolic surface.

A modified cylindrical parabolic reflector using only a small segment of the parabolic surface is the array shown in Fig. 9–24B. This unit is designed for UHF–TV application and uses a folded dipole as the active element. A 300-ohm twin-lead transmission line connects the dipole to the television receiver.*

Another section of a paraboloid which is of interest is the truncated paraboloid shown in Fig. 9–25. This is energized by either a single dipole

Fig. 9.25. A truncated parabolic reflector. (*Courtesy Raytheon*)

or a waveguide placed at the focus point. Directivity in the horizontal plane is essentially the same as that obtained from a paraboloid; directivity in the vertical plane is not quite as good. Therefore, the main directivity is in the horizontal plane.

The Corner Reflector. Instead of using curved surfaces as reflectors, it is possible to use two flat, solid conducting sheets which are so placed as to intersect each other at some angle, forming a corner. This type of reflector, shown in Fig. 9–26, is known as a "corner reflector" antenna. The driven element, usually a dipole antenna, is placed at the center of

* The reader is again cautioned to regard all of the antenna systems described in this chapter as being suitable for both transmission and reception.

this corner angle and at some distance, S, from the vertex of the angle. Fig. 9–26B shows the antenna as it could be used for the transmission of vertically polarized waves. By turning the system on its side, horizontally polarized waves could be sent (and received) as well. These two

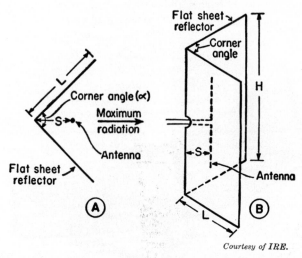

Courtesy of IRE.

FIG. 9.26. Corner reflector in cross section (A) and in perspective (B).

flat surfaces may form any angle up to the limiting value of 180 degrees, at which position the reflector becomes a flat surface.

The radiation pattern obtained for this reflector depends not only on the corner angle but also on the distance between the antenna and the vertex of the reflector corner. For relatively large distances (large compared to the wavelength used) a pattern containing more than one main lobe is obtained as, for example, Fig. 9–27B. As this is generally undesirable, there are limits for which maximum gain will be had with only one lobe in the directional pattern (Fig. 9–27A).

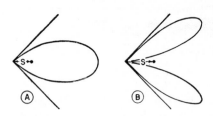

FIG. 9.27. Typical directional pattern for the corner reflector antenna (A). When S is large, a double-lobed pattern is obtained, as in (B).

Instead of using a solid sheet, a set of parasitic bars may be placed behind the dipole, as shown in Fig. 9–28. Essentially the same results will be obtained using this grid-type reflector as would be obtained with a solid metallic sheet. The corner angle in the reflector is 90 degrees, and a similar bend is placed in the dipole.

At ultra-high frequencies all physical dimensions, both for the driven antenna and for the parasitic wires or sheets, are quite small, resulting in a compact unit that is easily transported from place to place. It is claimed that parabolic reflectors and electromagnetic horn radiators provide little or no improvement over corner reflectors of comparable size, and that the latter are less critical to adjust than the parabolic system. Other suggested applications are given in Fig. 9–29. In Fig. 9–29A, two corner reflectors are combined in a multiple-unit structure, with both antennas fed in phase. At B, a bidirectional

FIG. 9.28. A commercial corner reflector. (*Courtesy RCA*)

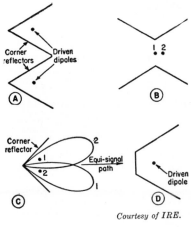

Courtesy of IRE.

FIG. 9.29. Two-unit corner reflector (A) and a bidirectional type (B). Single corner reflector with two driven dipoles for producing double beams (C). At (D) we have a modified corner reflector with three sides.

pattern is obtained. If the driven dipole is moved from position 1 to position 2, the right-hand direction would receive more of the signal than the left. For position 1, both directions, right and left, would be equally favored. At C in Fig. 9–29, with two antennas placed at equal distances from the central bisecting line, the radiation patterns shown will be obtained. One suggested use for this would be with radio beacons for landing aircraft. And, finally, Fig. 9–29D shows a modification of the two-sided reflector.

Metal Horns. It was only natural for the men who first investigated the properties of waveguides (both cylindrical and rectangular) to wonder how efficient these devices might be as radiators. And it was just as natural to start with the usual types of waveguides, using them as they were, with the open end for the emission of the ultra-high-frequency waves. The waves in these guides traveled along until they reached the open end where part of the energy continued out into space while part was reflected back along the guide.

It was reasoned, however, that perhaps better results could be obtained if the transition from the waveguide to the open space was made less abrupt. To effect a slow transition, horns of varying diameter were resorted to, as shown in Fig. 9–30, for cylindrical waveguides. These horns actually are sections of waveguides, except that the diameter of the cylindrical forms increases gradually, that is, flares. In the diagrams that

Courtesy of IRE.

Fig. 9.30.   Various electromagnetic horns that were used in tests.

follow, the various properties of these units, used as receivers, will be shown. However, the same relationships prevail for the transmission of waves, so that we are imposing no limitation. A good transmitting radiator is likewise a good receiver of electromagnetic energy (over the same range of frequencies). Although circular horns will be used as illustrations, we will, at the end of this section, generalize from the given diagrams to those that would be obtained if a so-called pyramidal horn is employed. The waves to be transmitted down the guides must, of course, be above the critical frequency.

In the investigation that followed the early work, three conditions were of general interest:

1. The type of radiation pattern obtainable with various lengths of the horn.
2. The variation of directivity and gain with change in flare angle.
3. The effect of frequency.

With patterns for these three factors worked out separately, it would then be possible to predict how to obtain the best results for any type of combination that it might be desired to use. The first set of diagrams in Fig. 9–31 shows how the directional properties of a circular horn vary with change in the angular openings. For this set of readings, the length of each horn was kept approximately constant, while the frequency used was 15.3 cm. Note that the greatest gain and directivity are obtained at flare angles of 40° to 50°, with decreases above and below this value. For very large openings, the radiation pattern starts to form other small lobes. These are called secondary lobes. The same result is found to occur with the rectangular horn and the sectoral horn soon to be described. The gain, as given in these diagrams, should have 2.15 deducted if we wish

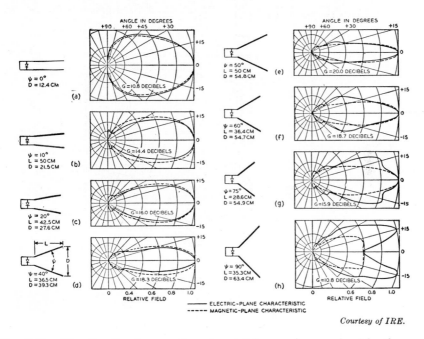

Courtesy of IRE.

Fig. 9.31. The directional properties of metal horns of approximately the same length but with different flare angles.

to compare them with half-wave antennas. The data were taken relative to a nondirectional radiator. The half-wave antenna is 2.15 times more directional than the nondirectional element. Gain is given in decibels.

For the effect of length of the horn, with the angle set at a value of 40°, refer to Fig. 9–35. In the first four diagrams in this figure, the greater gain available with increase in length is shown quite distinctly. Still greater lengths, however, seem to show very little increase in gain and are accompanied by a lessening of the sharpness of the beam. The reason for this relates to the optimum angle, as tested in the previous set of patterns (Fig. 9–31). It should be pointed out that, for each length there is a "best angle," so to speak. For the lengths used in Fig. 9–31, the angle was found to approximate 40°. In general, as the length increases,

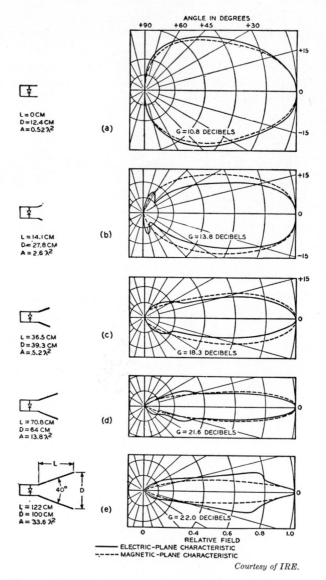

FIG. 9.32. These radiation patterns are for metal horns of the same flare angle but of different lengths. Wavelength used—15.3 cm.

the optimum angle needed becomes smaller so that, in the set of graphs given in Fig. 9–32, the radiation pattern improved with the length until the best length for that angle was reached. Beyond this, for improved results, the optimum angle should be decreased, which explains the fifth pattern in Fig. 9–32.

In the final test, the variable was frequency; the flare angle and length of the horn were kept constant. The results obtained appear to indicate

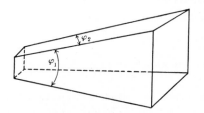

that the shorter the wavelength, the greater the gain. Actually, better results are obtained with the higher frequencies because, then, the relative dimensions of the horn increase. The length of a horn may be relatively small at one wavelength and yet quite large when compared to some higher frequency. When it is stated that the gain rose with increase in length, it was meant that the physical size of the horn was large in

FIG. 9.33. A pyramidal horn showing the two ways the flare angle may vary.

comparison to the wavelength used. A horn only 10 in. long might be a large unit if the frequency used is high enough.

Instead of conical horns, these experiments could have been performed using a rectangular waveguide or a pyramidal horn, the latter shown in Fig. 9–33. Note that here, when we speak of the flare of the horn, we mean either one of two angles, ϕ_1 or ϕ_2, or both. And it follows, from what has been presented before, that the resultant radiation pattern will depend on both these variables, in addition to the length of the unit itself. For equal angles, symmetrical radiation patterns are derived. On the other hand, increasing ϕ_2, for example, while ϕ_1 remained constant, gives a broader pattern in the horizontal plane. Likewise, if ϕ_1 is increased, a less well-defined beam is obtained in the vertical plane. The observations regarding length apply here, as well as to circular horns.

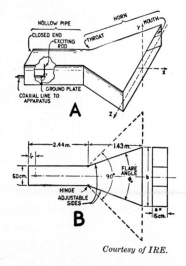

Courtesy of IRE.

FIG. 9.34. Perspective view (A) and cross-sectional view with dimensions in the x, z plane (B), of a sectoral electromagnetic horn.

The Sectoral Electromagnetic Horn.

Instead of having each of the four walls of an electromagnetic horn flare outward, it is possible to have only two walls flared, with the top and bottom walls remaining parallel to each other. This type of horn, shown in Fig. 9–34, is called by its originators a "sectoral horn." While the top and bottom portions remain fixed, the two side walls may be arranged to form any angle between 0 and 90 degrees. The angle is measured as shown in Fig. 9–34B. When the sides are straight, the angle is 0 degrees.

To permit ready adjustment of the flare angle, the movable sides are hinged at the throat. The antenna may be placed close to the throat, as shown in the illustration, and an adjustable backboard can be provided in order to obtain maximum intensity of radiation. However, there is no reason why the antenna could not be placed in a waveguide at some distance from the horn and the energy made to travel the length of the guide before it reached the attached horn. As before, the backboard tuning arrangement would still be behind the antenna.

Working with the sectoral electromagnetic horn, Barrow and Lewis[*] obtained the radiation patterns shown in Fig. 9–35. The data were taken with the flare angles indicated below each plot. It is seen that, as the

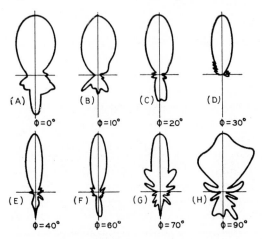

Fig. 9.35.   The radiation patterns of the sectoral horn for various flare angles.
(*Courtesy I.R.E.*)

flare angles increase up to the range of 40 to 60 degrees, the radiated beam becomes sharper and more defined. Above these angles, the directivity decreases and secondary lobes appear. In each instance the mouth of the horn may be considered as being placed at the origin of the curves, where the two straight lines intersect at right angles. With this in mind, it may seem strange to the reader that any radiation would occur in the backward direction, since this is behind the apparatus. Barrow and Lewis investigated this effect and, after experimentation, came to the conclusion that it was due to diffraction, or bending of the waves around the mouth of the horn. With suitable precautions this may be eliminated altogether.

With the flare angle kept at 40 degrees, the operation of the horn was checked at various frequencies. It was found that the horn may be

* Barrow, W. L., and Lewis, F. D., *Proceedings of the Institute of Radio Engineers,* Volume **27**, p. 41, January 1939.

employed over a wide band of frequencies without having its directive powers altered. The pattern is appreciably altered only when the critical frequency of the waveguide is approached.

The sectoral horn has been compared with the parabolic reflector, and the results seem to indicate that the horn is capable of better performance and is to be preferred. For example, the radiation pattern of a horn is devoid generally of any appreciable secondary lobes, while such lobes are evident in the parabolic radiation pattern. Furthermore, the parabolic reflector is more sensitive to wavelength variations than the horn and, even when operated at one frequency, requires careful adjustment for optimum operation. The antenna must be placed precisely at the focus of a parabolic reflector for best results.

Antenna arrays fare no better in comparison at the extremely short wavelengths. Arrays are seldom used at the very high frequencies, partly because of the difficulty of adjusting the system. The radiation patterns of the arrays usually contain appreciable secondary lobes which can be removed only by adding more parasitic elements. At the longer wavelengths, however, the horn or parabolic reflector becomes too large to handle and the antenna array must be employed. The same situation exists here as with transmission lines and waveguides. The method to be used depends upon the ease with which it can be assembled and adjusted.

It is interesting to note that the radiated beam of the horn may be made sharper by lengthening the sides of the horn. For compactness, it has also been suggested that small transmitting units be placed in the short rectangular waveguide connected to the horn, and in this way a decrease in the loss usually incurred by transmission lines that transfer power from the unit to the guide be effected.

Biconical Electromagnetic Horns. The patterns obtained with the radiators considered thus far have a concentration of the beam in a relatively narrow angle in one direction. There are times, however, when it is necessary to send out radiation in all directions with a uniform signal level throughout the entire 360 degrees—for example, when the signal is to be received by a large population scattered over a considerable area. One solution might be to use a vertical antenna, which has been shown to be nondirectional in the horizontal plane. There is another method, however, where the same nondirectional property may be obtained with the added advantage of additional gain. This type of system has been described by Barrow, Chu, and Jansen.* They combined two electromagnetic horns in various ways, some of which are shown in Fig. 9–36. Because only two elements are used in this system, it has been given the name of

* Barrow, W. L., Chu, L. J., and Jansen, J. J., *Proceedings of the Institute of Radio Engineers,* Volume 27, p. 769, December 1939.

"biconical electromagnetic horn." Note from the illustrations that the flaring of the horn may be gradual, as in B and C of Fig. 9–36, or sharp, as in illustration D. For E and F, one horn is partially placed within the other. In Fig. 9–36E, the radiation is downward; in F the beam is upward. The energy is applied to the horns by means of a coaxial cable, with the center conductor of the cable extending up between the horns. It is from this antenna that the radiated energy is obtained. The other end of the cable would be attached to a UHF generator.

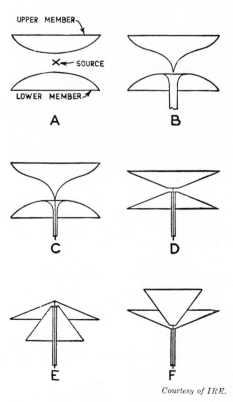

FIG. 9.36. Various combinations of biconical electromagnetic horns.

Courtesy of IRE.

There are many points of similarity between the radiational patterns of biconical horns and the horns previously examined. For example, just as with the sectoral horn, the sharpness of the beam in the biconical arrangement will depend on the length of the flared sides and the flare angle. As the length is increased, the optimum flare angle will decrease and, at the same time, the resultant beam will be sharpened. Also, if the length is kept constant, there is one angle which will give best results. An interesting diagram showing the relationship between flare angle and power gain is given in Fig. 9–37. Each curve is for a different length of horn. When the length of the sides is large with respect to the wavelength used (in Fig. 9–43, this is a ratio of 50 for the top curve), a gain of approximately 50 times that of a half-wave dipole may be obtained. As the sides become smaller (with the same transmitted frequency), the flare angle must increase and the gain decrease.

The reader may be struck by the resemblance between the conical horn and a similar arrangement used with the corner reflector. Essentially these are the same except that the corner reflector, because of its structure, does not provide a nondirectional beam. The biconical horn does. To accentuate the beam more in one direction than at any other angle, it is possible to move the apex of one horn (say, the top one) slightly to one side. When the apex of the top horn is moved to the left, increased signal strength is observed to the right.

Metallic Lens Microwave Antenna. As the signal frequency rises and the wavelength decreases, the behavior of radio waves becomes more and more like that of light rays. The restriction of UHF propagation to line-of-sight distances and the manner in which large structures and obstacles block the passage of UHF signals indicate the semi-optical properties of these signals. It is not surprising, therefore, to find that optical lenses, which focus light beams, have their counterpart in metallic lenses which serve to focus microwaves into extremely narrow beams possessing a high concentration of energy. Beams of this type are well suited for radio and television relays where the energy must be transmitted from one fixed point to another fixed point with negligible interference or in radar where high concentrations of energy in narrow beams are desired.

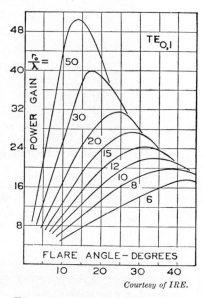

Courtesy of IRE.

Fig. 9.37. Curves showing the variation of power gain (not in db) with flare angle for various lengths of horn. Each number given with each curve represents the ratio of the length of the sides of the horn to the wavelength. The wavelength, of course, remains constant.

A metallic lens antenna (Fig. 9–38) contains three components—a waveguide which brings the energy from the generator, an electromagnetic horn which tends to match the impedance of the guide to that of free space, and the metallic lens which focuses the radiated energy into a highly directional beam. The lens structure consists of a large number of parallel, vertically mounted metal plates. The plates have a variety of shapes and are spaced from each other by slightly more than one-half of the operating wavelength. The front or outside surface of the lens is flat in appearance. This is the surface through which the electromagnetic energy passes as it leaves the radiating system at the transmitter and the first surface it reaches when this lens is used at a receiving point. The back or inner side of the lens consists of a series of circular steps as shown in Fig. 9–39. These plates are constructed of sheet metal and are fastened securely in place by means of interlocking joints.

The focusing action of the lens is due to its ability to take the spherical

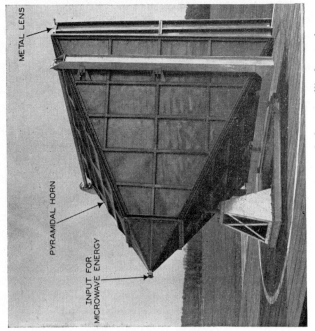

FIG. 9.38.   Two views of the metallic lens microwave antenna.   (Courtesy Bell Telephone Laboratories)

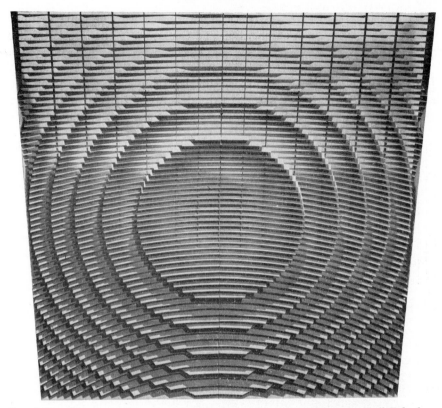

Fig. 9.39.   The stepped construction of the metallic lens.   (*Courtesy Bell Telephone Laboratories*)

wave-front of the energy transmitted by the electromagnetic horn and to transform this into a plane wave-front. It accomplishes this by causing the phases of the lagging portions of the wave to speed up and to catch up with the center section of the wave, thereby producing a flat wave-front. It is this type of wave which possesses extreme directivity, as noted previously.

At the receiving end, there is a similar grouping of apparatus. The arriving flat wave-front that enters through the lens is converted into a spherical wave and then, by means of the electromagnetic horn, is funneled back through a waveguide to a receiver.

A side or profile view of the metal lens is shown in Fig. 9–40, together with its effect on the spherical wave-front reaching it from the waveguide located in the throat of the electromagnetic horn. The center portion of the lens is thin because this section of the spherical wave is only slightly affected. As we progress from the center, the thickness of the lens increases, thereby accentuating its effect on the spherical wave. The outer sections of the wave require more acceleration and consequently the lens is thicker here.

The lens is mounted across the mouth of an electromagnetic horn so that all energy traveling forward in the horn impinges directly on the lens. (See Fig. 9–41.) If a space existed between the end of the horn and the lens, some of the energy would be able to escape, not only reducing

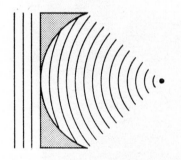

FIG. 9.40. An illustration of the focusing action of a metallic lens on electromagnetic energy.

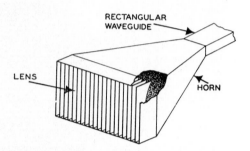

FIG. 9.41. The metallic lens is mounted across the entire mouth of an electromagnetic horn so that all energy traveling forward in the horn impinges directly on the lens.

the energy which is transmitted forward but possibly interfering with the other horns situated near by. In two-way relay systems there is one horn for receiving energy and a second horn for transmitting back along the same path. Both are placed close together, and it is desirable that there exists little or no interaction between the two units.

The radiation pattern of a metallic lens depends upon the shape of the vertical plates. While many different shapes and patterns are possible, of greatest interest in microwave relay application is the radiation pattern in which the horizontal and vertical widths are equal. This is a symmetrical radiation pattern. The "step construction" shown in Fig. 9–39 not only provides this type of radiation but has a band width of 400 mc. Throughout this range (from 3920 mc to 4320 mc for the unit shown) the radiation pattern remains essentially as shown in Fig. 9–42.

The graph in Fig. 9–42 is another way of indicating the radiation characteristics of an antenna. It is especially suited for those antennas (like the metallic lens antenna) where the directivity is so pronounced that all or substantially all of the energy is contained within a few degrees about the antenna axis. It would not be as suitable for systems radiating energy over large angles.

The size of the lens depends upon the operating wavelength. If a narrow beam is desired, the lens dimensions should be 40 wavelengths wide and 40 wavelengths high. Now, in an electromagnetic horn, we have seen that, as the opening or aperture of the horn or the length of the horn,

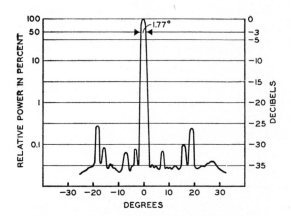

FIG. 9.42. The radiation pattern of the metal-lens antenna shown in Fig. 9.38.

or both, are increased, the diameter of the radiated beam decreases. To obtain comparable high gain and an extremely narrow beam from a horn alone, the opening across the mouth of the horn would have to

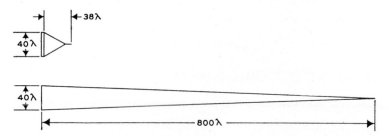

FIG. 9.43. A comparison of horn lengths (top) with a metallic lens and (bottom) without the lens in order to obtain comparable high gain and narrow beam width.

possess a minimum width of 40 wavelengths at the operating wavelength of the signal. In addition, the horn length would have to be at least 20 times the aperture width. Hence, even at extremely small operating wavelengths the length of the horn would be considerable. Fig. 9–43 shows a comparison of the horn lengths when the horn is used (A) with a metallic lens and (B) when it is used by itself. When combined with a lens, the length of the horn need be only 38 wavelengths long, compared to 800 wavelengths when employed by itself.

The metallic lens in Fig. 9–38, at 4000 mc, provides a power gain of 12,000 over a simple dipole. At approximately 1.8 degrees off the axis of the beam, the power gain drops to 0.01 of its maximum gain, which gives some idea of the extreme directivity of the radiated beam.

Metallic lenses not only are superior to electromagnetic horns, but they also possess many advantages over a parabolic reflector. A metallic lens will withstand a considerable amount of warping or twisting and not have

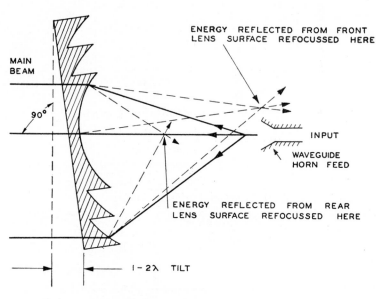

Fig. 9.44. Tilting the metallic lens to prevent reflected energy from entering the waveguide and developing undesirable standing waves.

its properties appreciably affected. A parabolic reflector, on the other hand, must maintain the shape of its surface at all times. Any physical change will alter both the width of the radiated beam and the gain of the system. Another serious disadvantage of the parabolic reflector is the diffraction of energy around the edges of the reflector, causing cross talk and interference to near-by microwave systems. Finally, the energy fed to the paraboloid must come from the focal point, and any misalignment here results in loss in efficiency and increase in beam width. The larger the surface of the parabolic reflector becomes, the more difficult it is to shape it accurately.

In metallic lenses, some energy is reflected from the front and rear surfaces of the lens and this energy, feeding back to the waveguide which feeds the horn, will establish standing waves and disrupt the match between guide and horn and lens. The result will be some loss of power. To minimize the effect of such reflections, it is customary to tilt the lens slightly, as shown in Fig. 9–44. A tilt of one or two wavelengths causes the reflected energy to miss the mouth of the waveguide feeding the horn and consequently does not produce any standing waves in this passageway.

FIG. 9.45A. A metal delay lens using small conducting disks arranged in a special spherical lattice to form a convex lens. (*Courtesy Bell Telephone Laboratories*)

FIG. 9.45B. Another metal delay lens formed by metal-spraying tin directly onto polystyrene foam sheets. (*Courtesy Bell Telephone Laboratories*)

Delay Lenses. The metallic lenses of Figs. 9–38 and 9–39 serve to transform a spherical wave-front into a plane wave-front. Another approach employs small metallic elements or particles which are held together by a nonconductor in shapes that conform more closely to optical lenses. Two such artificial lenses are shown in Fig. 9–45.

The action of this lens is similar to that of a glass lens on light and therefore opposite to the action of the lenses of Figs. 9–38 and 9–39. In the latter, it will be recalled, the phase of portions of a wave-front passing through were speeded up, enabling them to catch up with the center section of the wave and thereby produce an outgoing plane wave-front. (See Fig. 9–40.) In the lens of Fig. 9–45, the reverse action occurs; that is, the phase velocity of a wave passing through is reduced. Thus, the lens shape is made thick at the center and thin at the ends because the center of the entering spherical wave-front is farther advanced in phase than it is at any other point. (See Fig. 9–46.)

The reduced velocity or delay is caused by the presence of the metallic particles which act as small dipoles. The manner of arranging these metallic elements was arrived at by studying the molecular lattice structure of conventional lenses such as those used with light waves and then positioning the metallic particles in a similar configuration. Two precautions to observe are: (1) the spacing of the elements must be somewhat less than one wavelength of the shortest wavelength to be transmitted and (2) the size of the elements must be small relative to this wavelength.

Fig. 9.46. Focusing action of a metal delay lens. Compare this with Fig. 9.40 where the focusing action of a metallic lens is shown.

The Bell Telephone Laboratories, the originators of these lenses, suggest that one way of looking at the delay caused by the metallic elements is to consider them as equivalent to capacitive elements which "load" down free space just as parallel capacitors placed across a transmission line slow down any waves traveling through the line.

The delaying action is also reflected in the name of these units, namely, metallic delay lenses. This is in distinction to the previous lenses, which are simply known as metal lenses.

There are a number of different ways in which suitable delay lenses can be made, with the two shown in Fig. 9–45 being typical of their present form. In Fig. 9–45A, small conducting disks are arranged in a special spherical lattice to form a suitable convex lens. Polystyrene foam sheets support the disks. In Fig. 9–45B, the lens is formed by metal-spraying tin directly onto polystyrene foam sheets.

Metallic delay lenses possess broad-band characteristics which enable them to be employed with wide-range microwave systems. Metal lenses will operate satisfactorily only over limited bands.

QUESTIONS

1. How are radiation patterns obtained?

2. What is their purpose?

3. Will the same antenna give rise to the same pattern under all conditions? Explain.

4. What is the simplest nondirectional radiator? Is this true for both the horizontal and vertical planes? Illustrate.

5. What is the difference between driven arrays and parasitic arrays?

6. Why are arrays to be preferred over the simple single-wire antenna?

7. Give the characteristics of a parasitic array formed with one driven element, one reflector, and two directors. Draw a diagram of the layout, showing correct distances between elements.

8. What is the effect of adding more parasitic wires to an array?

9. How does a parabolic reflector function?

10. What precautions must be observed when using parabolic reflector systems?

11. What are the advantages of a corner reflector over the parabolic reflector?

12. Are the directional properties of waveguides increased by the use of horns? Explain.

13. Describe the general effects of flare angle on the directional properties of electromagnetic horns.

14. Do the same for the length. How are the two effects correlated?

15. Draw a sketch of a biconical horn and discuss its directional effects.

16. In the biconical horn, what are the effects of the flare angle and length of the sides? Explain in terms of horizontal and vertical plane radiations.

17. Where might the radiating antenna be placed for use with any of the electromagnetic horns? What adjustments should be made for best transmission?

18. What might be some advantages that multi-unit horn arrays could offer over a single horn?

19. Define beam angle. How could the beam angle of an array be determined without resorting to its directional response curve?

20. What is the difference between a collinear array and a broadside array? Illustrate your answer.

21. Describe several suitable methods for feeding energy to parabolic reflectors.

22. How is the radiation pattern altered by the use of a parabolic cylinder in place of a parabolic reflector (a paraboloid)?

23. Name the various components of a metallic lens. Describe briefly the function of each component.

24. How is the focusing action of the metallic lens achieved?

25. What is the difference between a metal delay lens and the metallic lens?

Chapter 10

UHF MEASUREMENTS

Factors Governing UHF Measurements. One reason for the rapid advance of the radio art is due to the precision low-frequency measuring devices which have been developed. Without proper meters to guide the engineer constantly and to show him success or failure, there would not or could not be the compact and precise radios of today. Fortunately, at the low frequencies, inductance, capacitance, and resistance values are not appreciably affected by frequency change and a meter calibration at one frequency is applicable to other frequencies. Probe leads can possess lengths of one to two feet, lead inductance, resistance, and capacitance can be ignored, and conveniently sized components can be employed both in the measuring instrument and in the operating circuit without impairing meter accuracy. We find, however, that, as the frequency rises above 5 to 10 mc, those factors which previously could be disregarded now become influential and must be carefully accounted for. A study of these factors will reveal why the conventional types of meters at the high frequencies either had to be modified or completely discarded if satisfactory results were to be obtained.

In the ideal situation, when a meter is inserted into a circuit to measure current or voltage, the quantity indicated on the scale will be the true value, and the presence of the meter will have no effect on the circuit. To achieve this, all current-indicating meters should have zero resistance and all voltage-indicating devices should possess infinite resistance. The more actual meters depart from these specifications, the less accurate the readings become.

At low frequencies, good results can be obtained because these goals are closely attained. This is especially true of electronic meters, such as the vacuum-tube voltmeter. With sufficient increase in frequency, however, we find that certain changes occur which have significant effects on circuit operation. Consider, for example, the resistance of a length of wire. At

292

the low frequencies, currents flow through this conductor in a uniform manner, each small section of wire carrying the same amount of current as any other similar section of wire. Increasing the frequency of the currents causes them to crowd toward the outer surface of the wire. This is the well-known skin effect and results in an increase in the effective or a-c resistance of the conductor.

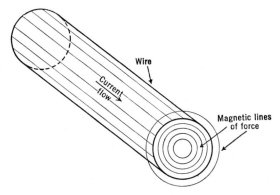

FIG. 10.1.   A small section of a wire carrying a current.

Skin Effect. The reason for the increase in resistance can best be understood if we consider what occurs within a length of wire when a current flows through it.   It is common knowledge that current flow has associated with it a magnetic field in the form of magnetic flux which encircles the wire carrying the current.   The definition of inductance depends upon these flux linkages and is given by the formula

$$\text{Inductance (henries)} = \frac{\text{Flux linkages encircling conductor}}{\text{Current Producing these linkages (in amp)}} \times 10^{-8}$$

Consider now the end view of a small round section of wire that has a current flowing through it.   (See Fig. 10–1.)   Each small section of current flowing through this wire has magnetic lines of flux encircling it, but the sections of current at the outer edges of the wire have fewer lines of flux around them than the currents at the center of the wire.   This is because the flux produced inside the wire by the central currents does not encircle the outer currents and so cannot influence their flow.   The flux produced by the currents at the surface of the wire, however, does encircle the currents at the center and hence exerts an influence upon them.   From the foregoing definition of inductance, it is seen that, since there are more flux linkages encircling the center of the wire than the outer surface of this wire, the inductance will be greater at the center than at the surface.

As the frequency of the currents increase, the inductance at the center of the wire will present more opposition (reactance) than the outer sections of the wire where less inductance exists. The current, seeking the path of "least resistance," will tend to concentrate more at the surface (or skin) of the conductor. Hence, the current, which formerly spread uniformly throughout the entire area, is now concentrated near the surface. This has, in effect, reduced the useful cross-sectional area of the conductor, and the resistance, because of this decrease in effective area, will rise.

The total resistance of a wire, at high frequencies, is thus seen to consist of the normal d-c resistance plus an additional amount which is dependent upon frequency. At frequencies above 300 mc, this latter factor becomes predominant and, at sufficiently high frequencies, is often many times the d-c resistance.

Inductance and Capacitance. Consider, too, the effect that the inductance in the wire might have on meter readings aside from the resistance increase due to skin effect. For a straight round wire of nonferrous metal such as copper, the inductance formula is:

$$L = 0.00508S \left(2.3 \log_{10} \frac{4S}{d} - 0.75\right) \text{ microhenry}$$

where S = length of wire in inches,
$\quad d$ = diameter of the wire in inches.
Using this formula for a length of No. 20 wire which is 3 inches long, we obtain an inductance of:

$$L = 0.00508 \times 3 \left(2.3 \log_{10} \frac{12}{0.032} - 0.75\right)$$

$$= 0.01524[(2.3)(2.574) - 0.75]$$

$$= 0.075 \text{ microhenry}$$

At 1000 cycles, the impedance presented by this inductance is:

$$X_L = 2\pi f L$$

$$= 2 \times 3.14 \times 1000 \times 0.075 \times 10^{-6}$$

$$= 0.00050 \text{ ohm}$$

At 100 mc, the impedance becomes 47 ohms and, at 1000 mc, 470 ohms. Thus at this latter high frequency, a small 3-inch length of wire has a complex impedance consisting of an appreciable amount of resistance and inductance. This impedance, introduced into the circuit as the leads from the measuring instrument, would certainly distort the meter readings.

A resistor that can be considered as possessing resistance only at low frequencies develops, at the high frequencies, inductance and shunting capacitance. (See Fig. 10–2.) In a carefully constructed resistor, the inductance arises solely from the inductance in the resistor-connecting leads. The shunting capacitance across the resistor is primarily the capacitance between these two leads. At sufficiently high frequencies, the shunting capacitance reduces the effective impedance of this circuit to relatively low values. Further, because of the presence of the inductance and capacitance, the impedance is complex and not simply resistive, as it is at lower frequencies.

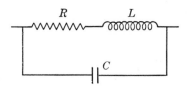

Inductance values change slightly with frequency, again because of the effect of flux linkages and the currents. With frequency increase, the distribution of the currents in the wire will change and, because inductance depends upon this distribution,

FIG. 10.2. Equivalent circuit of an ordinary resistor at the ultra-high frequencies.

it, too, will change. The result is generally a slight decrease. Inductive reactance, however, which is dependent upon both inductance and frequency, rises because of the frequency. This was noted in the foregoing example.

Finally, there is the matter of capacitance. The capacitance of any circuit may change because of stray couplings that might arise between adjacent wires, a wire and ground, points of difference of potentials, and in innumerable other ways that never were considered important before.

Leakage conductance can also be included in connection with capacitance and can become quite large at very high frequencies. Insulators, under certain conditions, may allow small currents to flow through them. They then act as high resistances, or poor conductors. The conductance is low and is termed *leakage conductance*. In a poorly constructed line, leakage may rise to large values. Care must always be taken with so-called insulators which are to be installed in high-frequency systems. They should first be tested for leakage at the short wavelengths.

The foregoing discussion does not present the complete story, but it will enable the reader to understand why present low-frequency measuring instruments must be modified to meet the new conditions of UHF. There may, in addition, be combinations of factors. For example, in the diode voltmeter the combination of interelectrode capacitance and lead inductance forms a resonant circuit which introduces sizable errors in readings made at the ultra-high frequencies. Furthermore, at the short wavelengths, current and voltage values of a small piece of wire in the circuit will change appreciably in a very small distance. This fact must be known before accurate measurements of these quantities can be made. Such limitations will be noted as the various instruments are described.

Some of the more widely used methods of measuring wavelength, frequency, voltage, and power will be considered in this chapter. There are good methods available for the determination of impedance, but the mathematical formulas are very complex, and hence they are omitted. Current-measuring instruments are not included for two reasons: (1) Thus far, very little use has been found for them. From known values of power, voltage, and impedance it is easier to calculate the currents than if these measurements were taken directly. (2) There is the difficulty of securing readings with any reasonable degree of accuracy using only modest equipment. Because of the inherently low resistance of a current meter, it is subject to stray pick-up from near-by electric and magnetic fields. This necessitates elaborate shielding and very careful placement in the circuit if a true indication is to be obtained.

It is important not to confuse the current-measuring instruments with those that are used in conjunction with diode and triode vacuum tubes or other rectifiers. The latter meters only measure an average d-c current which is produced by rectifying the high-frequency voltages.

HIGH-FREQUENCY WAVELENGTH

In studying the evolution of a particular scientific development, a common pattern can usually be found. As new problems arise, engineers try to use existing equipment. When it fails, the same equipment is tried again, this time with modifications designed to suit the particular problem. If still unsuccessful, new methods must be evolved. Examples may be found in the field of radio. Take the case of the frequency or wave meter. At the start, it consisted of a fairly large capacitor and a series of plug-in coils, each containing many turns. It can be constructed simply and is capable of an accuracy of 2 per cent or less. For use at the higher frequencies the unit was modified in accordance with the formula

$$F = \frac{1}{2\pi\sqrt{LC}}$$

until the desired frequencies were reached. The former multiturn solenoid became—in the final analysis—simply a one-turn loop attached closely to a small capacitor containing a few semi-circular plates, all mounted on insulators.

A very-high-frequency wavemeter, covering the range from 55 to 400 mc, is shown in Fig. 10–3. It contains a small light bulb which glows when the wavemeter is adjusted to resonance at the frequency of the signal being measured. The frequency is then read from the calibrated dial.

Fig. 10.3. The General Radio wavemeter—55–400 mc.

To cover a higher range, the tuning circuit of Fig. 10–4 might be utilized. This is a small butterfly tuner capable of covering the range from 250 to 1200 mc. Resonance indications are obtained by connecting a small crystal detector and a sensitive galvanometer across the tuner. The voltage

Fig. 10.4. An absorption wavemeter covering the range from 250 to 1200 mc. (*Courtesy General Radio Co.*)

developed in the tuner is rectified by the crystal and the resultant current indicated on the meter. Maximum meter reading occurs when the voltage is maximum. An accuracy of 2 per cent is possible with both meters.

Wavemeters of the foregoing type must be placed close to the signal source in order for sufficient energy to reach them.

The absorption wavemeters just described cannot be used much above 1000 mc, even if the butterfly construction is employed. The circuit Q soon decreases at these high frequencies to such a degree that reasonable accuracy cannot be achieved. At this point sections of transmission lines were substituted for the conventional coil and capacitor, and it was found that simple forms of open-wire and coaxial transmission line produced good results. They had a high Q, even at very high frequencies; the line lengths were moderate and would resonate at different frequencies by simply changing the length of the line, usually by moving a shorting bar.

Transmission Line Wavemeters. In order to understand how the transmission line may be employed to measure wavelength, let us review some of the facts of Chapter 2. It was shown there that, if a short length of line is excited by a generator, then, for all terminations of the line other than its characteristic impedance, standing waves will be set up. Fig. 10–5A reviews the distribution of these standing waves along a quarter-wave line, and Fig. 10–5B shows the same conditions on a half-wave line. The transmission line lengths do not necessarily have to be either of the above lengths; they may have any value. The important point is the formation of the standing waves. Generally a short-circuited line is used, for then it is easy to move the shorting bar back and forth.

The type of transmission line which is used most frequently is a circular coaxial cable containing a narrow slot in the outer conductor extending the length of the cable. (See Fig. 10–6.) A small probe is inserted through the slot and positioned so that it projects for a very short distance into the space between the inner and outer conductors of the line. In this way the probe comes in contact with the electric field existing inside the line. The other end of the probe connects to a crystal rectifier and a microammeter.

The probe circuit is shown physically in Fig. 10–7A and schematically in Fig. 10–7B. The actuating r-f voltage is developed between the end of the probe and the outer conductor of the coaxial line. The path for the resulting r-f current is along the probe rod to the crystal, through the crystal and r-f by-pass capacitor back to the wall of the coaxial line. Because of the presence of the crystal, current can flow in essentially one direction. This, then, is the rectified d-c current, and it flows through the meter and through the quarter-wave supporting stub back to the crystal. Since the other side of the crystal connects to the microammeter,

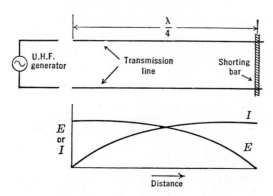

Fig. 10.5A. Current and voltage distribution on a shorted ¼ wavelength line.

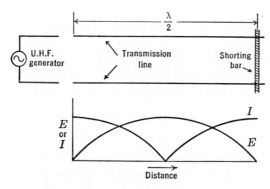

Fig. 10.5B. Current and voltage distribution on a shorted ½ wavelength line.

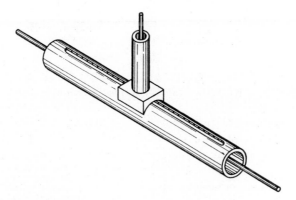

Fig. 10.6. To make precise standing wave measurements, a slotted coaxial line and a probe are required.

the d-c path is complete. The supporting stub thus serves two purposes:
to complete the d-c path for the meter and to support the probe without
affecting the high-frequency voltage on the probe. The probe assembly
is mechanically attached to a screw drive by which the probe can be
physically moved along the length of the line. (Refer to Fig. 2–36,

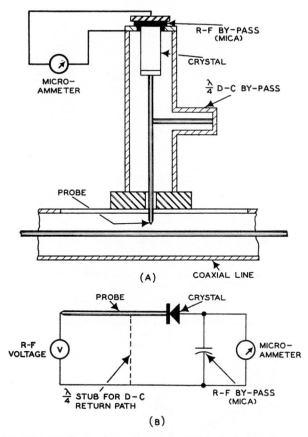

FIG. 10.7. (A) The physical appearance and electrical circuit of a probe detector.
(B) An equivalent electrical diagram.

Chapter 2.) Because of the existence of standing waves along the line,
the voltage induced into the probe by the electric field will vary with
the probe position and the meter reading will follow suit. By employing
suitable markings, the distance that the probe travels along the line may
be read from a scale calibrated either in inches or centimeters. Energy
is fed into the line, and the probe is moved along. The distance between
successive maxima is then noted and, when this figure is multiplied by 2,

the wavelength will be obtained. With a well-constructed line, possessing a reasonably high Q, the wavelength may be determined with an accuracy of better than one per cent.

A second type of coaxial wavemeter is shown in Fig. 10–8. One end of the line has a fixed short-circuit between the inner and outer conductors. Near this end, a magnetic probe consisting of a small loop antenna is inserted. This particular position was chosen for the probe because at the shorted end the current density and the magnetic field are high. The other end of the antenna loop connects to a crystal detector and a micro-ammeter. Another loop, near by, couples signal energy into the line.

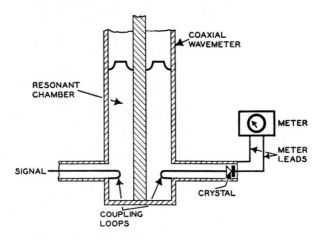

FIG. 10.8. A second type of coaxial wavemeter.

For the indicator used in this wavemeter, the coupling loop itself provides a d-c return path and hence no quarter-wave supporting stub is necessary.

The opposite end of the coaxial line contains a movable short in the form of a plunger. The plunger is connected to a screw drive, and a marker attached to the plunger indicates the distance through which the plunger moves. Since both ends of the coaxial line are shorted, resonance (when the standing wave amplitudes are maximum) occurs only when the distance between the shorted ends is a whole number multiple of a quarter wavelength at the frequency of the injected signal. As the plunger is moved forward, the meter will alternately rise to a maximum and decrease to a minimum. If the distance the plunger must travel between successive maxima is noted from the graduated scale and this figure is multiplied by 2, the wavelength of the signal will be obtained.

Fig. 10–9 shows essentially what has occurred. At A the line is shown as it would be if it were 1½ wavelengths long. The indicating device is placed at point O where it indicates a maximum. Then, as the shorting bar is moved along, the wave can be considered as being pushed before it. Since the current at O was a maximum at the start, moving the shorting bar along will cause the current standing wave, moving past this point, to decrease, eventually reaching a minimum at or near zero. Further movement of the shorting bar to the left will again cause the meter indication to increase until the second maximum is now at point O, opposite the

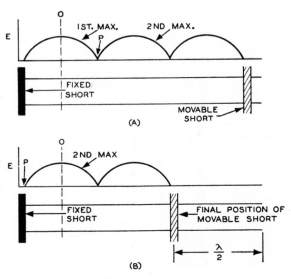

FIG. 10.9. An illustration of what occurs in the wavemeter of Fig. 10.8.

meter. (See Fig. 10–9B.) The distance moved by the shorting bar in this procedure should be exactly one-half wavelength long. The distance is read from a calibrated scale and multiplied by 2.

Cavity Wavemeters. When the frequency to be measured rises above 3000 mc, it is usually better to employ a cavity wavemeter than a coaxial line. Above 3000 mc, the length of a full wave becomes less than 10 cm, or approximately 4 inches. A half-wave then is 2 inches long, and in order to measure fractions of this distance with high accuracy, not only must the screw-drive mechanism be carefully constructed, but the resonance point must be sharply defined. The Q of a good coaxial cable in the region of 3000 mc is of the order of 6000, while for a cavity operating at the same frequency a Q of 20,000 is possible. Obviously the exact resonance point may be determined more accurately with the cavity wavemeter than the coaxial line meter.

For the range of frequencies up to approximately 10,000 mc, the cavity wavemeter is constructed generally in the manner shown in Fig. 10–10. A movable plate having a diameter almost as large as the diameter of the cylinder is attached to a screw drive which is similar in construction to the screw arrangement employed in micrometer calipers. This screw

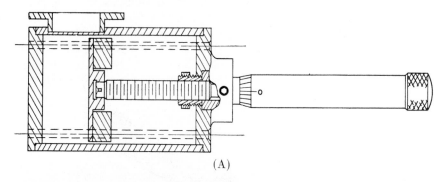

(A)

(B)

FIG. 10.10.   (A) Internal construction and (B) physical appearance of a cavity-type wavemeter for use at 10,000 mc.

is attached to a dial divided into a number of divisions. The dial may be calibrated directly in frequency, in which case its scale will generally not be linear, or it may be divided into arbitrary units. A separate tuning chart showing resonant frequency versus dial reading would be furnished with each unit.

The cavity wavemeter is mounted on a section of waveguide (through which the signal is sent) in such a way that it presents a high impedance in series with the guide when it is tuned to resonance. As a result, the output from the guide will drop sharply as the wavemeter is tuned to resonance. When this point is reached, the reading on the scale of the wavemeter is noted, and the corresponding frequency is determined. Coupling to the wavemeter is achieved by an opening (iris) in the cavity wall.

In some cavity wavemeter designs, a small loop is inserted into the cavity. The other end of this loop connects to a crystal rectifier and a microammeter, and therefore resonance is indicated directly on the meter. Again the dial reading is read and, from it, the frequency is determined.

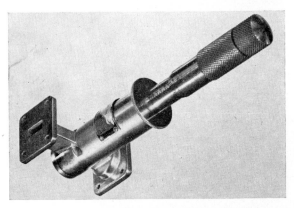

Fig. 10.11. A cavity wavemeter that tunes from 23,000 mc to 27,000 mc. (*Courtesy De Mornay-Budd*)

For frequencies above 20,000 mc, the tuning rate (frequency variation with dial rotation) of the cavity wavemeter of Fig. 10–10 is too large to permit accurate frequency measurement. By using a piston with a diameter considerably less than the cavity diameter, we can reduce the tuning rate and obtain a greater change in frequency per rotation of the dial. Such a cavity wavemeter is shown in Fig. 10–11.

In the design of any cavity wavemeter, the principal problem is that of avoiding the existence of modes of operations (and hence spurious resonances) other than the one desired. For each position of the plunger, only one resonant frequency should occur. Methods have been developed which suppress the undesirable modes, but these restrict the tuning range of the wavemeter. This is true of most cavity wavemeters.

Cavity wavemeters are calibrated by comparison with another cavity known as a reference cavity or, if more precise calibration is desired, against a crystal-controlled frequency standard.

VOLTAGE

The most precise voltage measurements are made with meters that present an input impedance which is large in comparison to the circuit impedance at the point where the voltage is to be measured. For d-c voltages, the engineer finds meters with internal resistances of 20,000 ohms per volt satisfactory in the majority of cases. The readings become inaccurate, however, when the voltage to be measured is small and the circuit resistance is high. To measure alternating voltages with frequencies up to 20 to 25 kc, a small copper-oxide rectifier may be used in conjunction with these meters. For higher frequencies, the capacitance inherent in the meter leads and the copper oxide rectifier generally produces serious inaccuracies.

Thermocouple Voltmeters. For the measurement of voltages in the range from d-c voltages up to several hundred megacycles, a thermocouple type of meter may be used. This instrument operates in a manner quite different from the conventional d-c voltmeter. It is based on the fact that, when two dissimilar metals are joined together and the junction heated, a d-c voltage will be produced which is proportional to the amount of heat generated. For practical use, a current is sent through this junction point and heat is thus generated. The heat developed is proportional to the square of the current, and the voltage generated by this heat is directly proportional to the temperature rise. Thus, by proper calibration, it is possible to measure currents and voltages. Fig. 10–12 shows the construction of the thermocouple meter. The junction, point 5, is called the thermocouple.

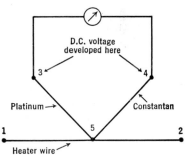

FIG. 10.12. A thermocouple meter arrangement.

The two dissimilar metals forming the junction are generally platinum and constantan, chosen because they produce a greater potential difference for a given amount of heat than most other combinations. The heater strip conducts the current to and from the junction and is quite short in length so that the current will tend to be uniformly distributed and each point will be evenly heated.

The d-c voltage produced at points 3 and 4 is measured by a conventional d-c meter. Note that this voltage will always be d-c, despite the fact that the currents flowing through the heater wire are a-c or r-f. Furthermore, it is not necessary to connect the meter directly to points 3 and 4; a transmission line may be inserted and the meter itself kept at some distance. (See Fig. 10–13.) Some manufacturers enclose the couple and heater strip within a glass envelope and evacuate the air. One such unit is shown in Fig. 10–14. It is called a vacuum thermocouple.

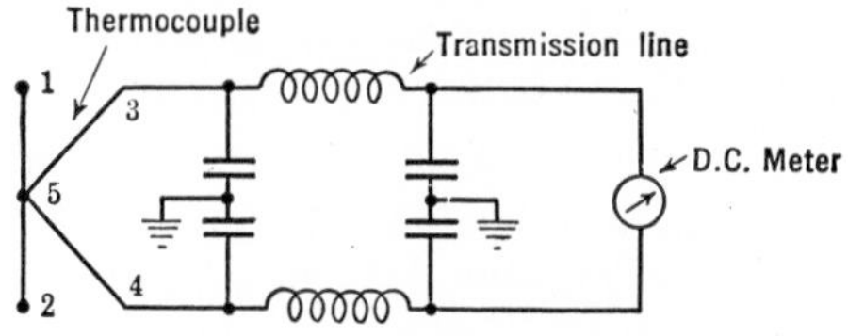

Calibration of the meter scale is made at low frequencies where known currents are easily obtained. Since the d-c current produced by the thermocouple is proportional to the square of the current flowing through the heater wire, the scale markings crowd together at one end. This will tend to limit the accurate range of any one scale, but, by the addition of

Fig. 10.13. A thermocouple meter arrangement where the d-c meter is placed at some distance from the thermocouple. A transmission line conducts the d-c voltage from points 3 and 4 to meter movement.

shunts, accurate readings over wide ranges may be achieved by changing the shunt whenever the indication occurs at the crowded end of the scale. The use of this meter at the high frequencies necessitates that there be practically no skin effect in the heater strip because this would invalidate the low-frequency calibration.

Two common methods are employed to achieve this. One method involves the use of a hollow conductor; the other employs a thin strip of metal. Both are illustrated in Fig. 10–15, together with a temperature-compensating strip to eliminate error due to changes in the surrounding temperature (ambient temperature). The compensating strips have the same thermal characteristics as the heater strip itself. The cold ends

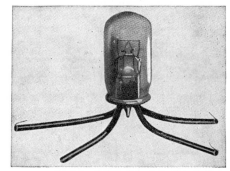

Courtesy of Weston Electric Instrument Co.

Fig. 10.14. A vacuum thermocouple.

of the couple are connected to the compensating strips, and the hot junction is placed on the heater wire. Since the compensating strips and the heater strip are made thermally equivalent, there is a temperature balance. However, when current heats the heater strip, there is a resultant difference in temperature between the hot and cold ends. This temperature difference produces a thermoelectric voltage due solely to the current flowing. Since any type of current flowing in the heater strip will produce this thermoelectric voltage, d-c, a-c, and r-f currents may be measured.

For use as a voltmeter, a high resistance is connected in series with
the heater wire. The electrical arrangement is indicated in Fig. 10–16.
The resistor chosen for this purpose should be as noninductive as possible.

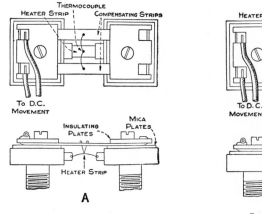

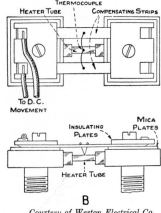

A   B

Courtesy of Weston Electrical Co.

FIG. 10.15. Two types of thermocouples which are accurate up to fairly high
frequencies.

Most manufacturers will supply a correction curve (error versus frequency)
for the instrument. Fortunately, many of the voltage measurements
made at the higher frequencies will
serve as well if they are merely
relative values, the exact quantities
being unnecessary. In this instance, the low-frequency calibration will serve effectively. The
upper frequency limit of a thermocouple voltmeter depends upon the
extent of the skin-effect error and
whether the heater length is more
than one-tenth of a wavelength at
the signal frequency. When the
heater length exceeds this value, the

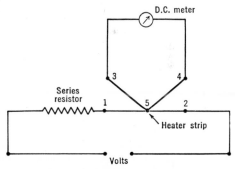

FIG. 10.16. A thermocouple voltmeter.

current variation from one end of the heater element to the other will be
appreciable and the meter indication will not be directly related to the
current. Thermocouple instruments can be made for use up to several
hundred megacycles. However, other measuring methods are available
which provide more accurate results and so the thermocouple is generally
relegated to use below 100 mc.

Vacuum-tube Voltmeters. A meter which has found wide acceptance throughout the radio industry is the electronic type of meter commonly

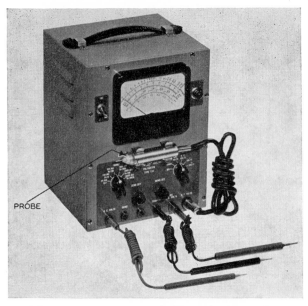

Fig. 10.17. A VTVM which will accurately measure voltages with frequencies to several hundred megacycles. (*Courtesy Sylvania Electric*)

referred to as a vacuum-tube voltmeter. (See Fig. 10–17.) Originally designed for d-c and low-frequency a-c measurements where it has an accuracy of 2 per cent or better, it can, by the use of a special probe, measure high-frequency voltages as high as 500 mc.

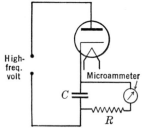

Fig. 10.18. A diode vacuum-tube voltmeter.

For high-frequency measurement, the probe receives the high-frequency voltage and converts it into d-c by rectification. A cable then conducts this d-c to the meter where it is measured like any other d-c voltage. Before we consider the probe structure in more detail, it may be instructive to analyze briefly the meter operation at d-c and low a-c frequencies.

Consider a simple diode arrangement such as a half-wave rectifier (Fig. 10–18). With the voltage positive at the plate, current will flow and charge capacitor C to the peak value of the voltage being measured. A high resistance and a sensitive milliammeter or microammeter are placed across the capacitor.

(This is essentially a voltmeter arrangement.) If the series resistance R is high enough, the peak value of the voltage under test will be obtained. This relates only to peak value of the positive peaks, since there is no conduction through the tube during negative plate voltage periods. For smaller values of series resistance, the capacitor will discharge partially and never reach peak value. In this instance, the voltage will depend upon the value of R. When the tube conducts, the impedance across the input terminals is not too high, perhaps not more than several thousand ohms. Hence, the meter will cause inaccuracies because of its shunting effect across the circuit under test. During the negative half-cycle, when no current flows, the resistance is very high. The more current that flows in this circuit, the lower the tube resistance and the greater its shunting effect on the circuit under test.

For more sensitive arrangements there are a number of triode tube circuits available, two of which are shown in Fig. 10–19. The first circuit, Fig. 10–19A, is the slide-back type vacuum-tube voltmeter and it is used to measure peak a-c or d-c voltages. To operate this meter, the input leads are first short-circuited and the resistance of R_1 is adjusted for zero plate current reading on meter M_1. Meter M_2 registers the grid bias voltage needed to cause this zero plate current. The leads are now placed across the voltage to be measured, and the grid bias voltage is adjusted, by means of R_1, to give again zero plate current. Meter M_2 should now read some new value, and it is the difference between this latter reading and the first reading of M_2 that indicates the peak value of the a-c voltage under test. Naturally, for d-c, this will be equivalent to the average value.

The advantage of this arrangement is that it requires no calibration. With careful design and construction, accurate readings can be obtained. For sinusoidal waves, rms values can be computed by multiplying the peak values by 0.707. Waves of other shapes, however, cannot be handled so easily.

The other vacuum-tube voltmeter illustrated in Fig. 10–19B is the one that is most widely employed today. The circuit is a balanced-bridge arrangement with the current flowing through each tube in the manner indicated by the various arrows. Thus, for $V1A$, the current I_1 flows from the plate through part of R_3 to B+ and from ground through R_1 back to the cathode of the tube. This current, in flowing through R_1, develops a certain voltage drop here which places point A at some positive value above ground.

A similar flow of current occurs through $V1B$ and its circuit, in consequence of which point B likewise develops a positive voltage with respect to ground.

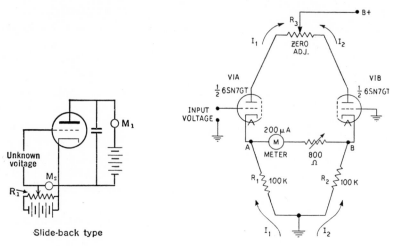

FIG. 10.19A. A slide-back type of vacuum-tube voltmeter.

FIG. 10.19B. The basic circuit used in most current vacuum-tube voltmeters.

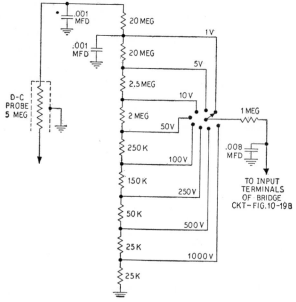

FIG. 10.19C. A voltage divider network for the VTVM of Fig. 10.19B.

Now, if the grid of $V1A$ is grounded (to place it at the same potential as the grid of $V1B$), then we might expect the potentials at points A and B to be equal and no current will flow through meter M. If the currents in both paths are not identical, then some difference in voltage will exist between points A and B. In this case, current will flow through meter M and its needle will deflect. To "zero the meter" and thus bring about a balance between both branches of this circuit, variable resistor R_3 is provided. Through its adjustment, the currents through $V1A$ and $V1B$ can be varied until points A and B possess identical positive potentials.

To employ this circuit for the measurement of voltages, a voltage is applied betwen the grid of $V1A$ and ground. If this voltage is positive, the current through $V1A$ will increase, and point A will become more positive than it was. Point B, on the other hand, will remain unchanged since the grid of $V1B$ is grounded.

With a very definite difference of potential existing now between point A and point B, current will flow through meter M from B to A. Just how much current will flow will depend upon the value of voltage applied to the grid of $V1A$. Consequently, the meter dial can be calibrated directly in volts.

When a negative voltage is applied to the grid of $V1A$, the current through this tube decreases, causing point A to become less positive and now current will flow through meter M from point A to point B. This will force the meter pointer to move from zero toward the left. Since on most instruments the zero position is already as far to the left as the pointer normally goes, applying a negative voltage to the VTVM would drive the pointer off scale. To prevent this, we may either reverse the test leads or incorporate a switch which will accomplish the same thing by reversing the meter connections.

In order to permit the VTVM to measure a range of voltages, a voltage divider circuit is placed across the input to the meter, as shown in Fig. 10–19C. The total value of the resistances in this string is 50 megohms and for the voltage ranges shown (that is, 1 volt to 1000 volts), 50 megohms is the input impedance of the VTVM. With an input impedance this high, it can readily be appreciated why the VTVM scarcely disturbs the circuit into which it is connected to measure voltages. This is one of the major advantages of the VTVM.

The foregoing vacuum-tube voltmeters are designed for the measurement of d-c voltages. To measure a-c voltages, a rectifier (usually a diode or a copper-oxide rectifier) is used. The voltage is converted to d-c by the rectifier and then applied to the vacuum-tube voltmeter circuits as any other d-c voltage. This arrangement will work satisfactorily for alternating voltages up to about 15,000 cps, with the use of a pair of ordinary test leads. Beyond this frequency, the inductance and shunt capacitance of the leads begin to have an increasingly greater disturbing effect on the circuit. The reason for this stems from the fact that, with frequency increase, the capacitance and inductance of a circuit decrease. Another way of looking at this is to say that, with frequency increase, a circuit becomes more sensitive to inductive and capacitive changes. Moving a wire only one-quarter of an inch in a 200-mc circuit will cause a greater frequency disturbance than moving a wire several inches in a low-frequency circuit.

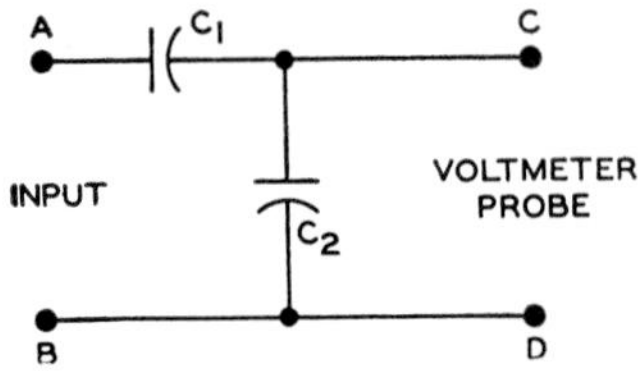

Because of this sensitivity, measurements in high-frequency circuits must be made with an instrument which introduces far less extraneous capacitance and inductance than a pair of test leads. Toward that end, special r-f or high-frequency probe attachments for vacuum-tube voltmeters have been designed wherein the rectifying element is brought as close as possible to the voltage to be measured. This reduces shunting capacitance to a minimum and, at the same time, keeps the amount of lead inductance extremely low.

FIG. 10.20A. Capacitive voltage divider.

Two types of rectifiers have been used in the probe: miniature diodes and crystal rectifiers. The diode is advantageous because it can be used to measure voltages up to several hundred volts. Its disadvantage is the error it introduces due to transit-time effects. The crystal unit does not possess the latter limitation, but to date the voltages which it can safely measure are seldom greater than 20 volts. It is partially possible to by-pass the voltage limitation of the crystal with capacitive voltage-dividing networks, but these introduce undesirable additional shunting capacitance.

FIG. 10.20B. View of capacitive voltage divider which provides a 10-to-1 reduction between the voltage applied to the multiplier and the voltage appearing across the voltmeter terminals. (*Courtesy General Radio Co.*)

A capacitive voltage divider which has been used with crystal rectifier probes is shown in Fig. 10–20A. The total voltage is applied to terminals A–B. The portion that appears across the output terminals leading to the voltmeter probe (C–D) is dependent upon the values of C_1 and C_2. The ratio of input to output voltages is given by

$$\frac{E_{\text{in}}}{E_{\text{out}}} = \frac{C_1 + C_2}{C_1}$$

Thus, if C_1 is 1 $\mu\mu$f and C_2 is 9 $\mu\mu$f, $(C_1 + C_2)\,/\,C_1$ will be equal to 10/1. When 10 volts is applied to the input terminals, only 1 volt will be applied to the voltmeter probe and indicated on the meter scale. Knowing that this is a 10:1 voltage divider, we would multiply all readings by 10 when using this network. An actual view of the divider is shown in Fig. 10–20B. One end is threaded so that the divider can be screwed on to the end of the voltmeter probe.

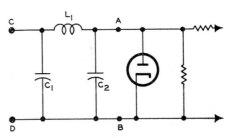

In both tube and crystal rectifier probes, an upper frequency limit is set by the resonance effects of lead inductance with circuit capacitance. The equivalent input circuit of a probe using either type of rectifier element is shown in Fig. 10–21. The input capacitance

Fig. 10.21. The equivalent input circuit of a probe.

C_1 is the capacitance of the probe rod to ground. The inductance L_1 is the inductance present in the probe rod plus whatever inductance exists in the connecting leads in the tube. The second capacitance C_2 is the sum of the tube (or crystal) input and socket capacitances plus the capacitance to ground of the shunt and series resistances connected to the rectifier.

Now, the voltage that appears across points A–B is the voltage to which the rectifier will respond. If the frequency of the voltage to be measured is not near the resonant frequency of L_1 and C_2, and C_1 is small, perhaps not more than 1 or 2 $\mu\mu$f, then the network of C_1, L_1, and C_2 will have no effect upon this voltage. However, if the frequency is high enough to excite L_1 and C_2 to resonance, the voltage across C_2 will rise. This is characteristic of all resonant circuits. Under this condition, the voltage presented to the rectifier will be higher than the actual voltage across points C–D. Above the resonant frequency, the voltage reaching the rectifier drops sharply because of the appreciable shunting effect of C_2. The resonant frequency of L_1 and C_2 thus sets an upper limit to the frequency range of the instrument. It is important to reduce both of these components to as small a value as possible.

A second cause for inaccuracy that arises when a diode is the rectifying element is none other than the previously discussed phenomenon of electron transit time. To see why this causes low readings, consider the following explanation of tube action. A diode vacuum-tube voltmeter (Fig. 10–18)

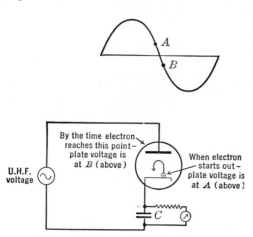

FIG. 10.22. When the voltage under test has a very high frequency, transit-time errors will cause *C* to be undercharged.

will be used for illustration, although the reasoning will apply equally to any other tube. When a high-frequency voltage is applied to the diode, the capacitor is charged by the current that flows through the tube during the positive half-cycles. If the electrons from the cathode reached the plate in zero time, the capacitor would charge to the peak value of the applied voltage. However, since an electron requires a finite time to travel the filament-to-plate distance, the positive voltage on this anode will change while some electrons are still in flight. Thus the electrons that left the cathode when the plate was at point *A*, Fig. 10–22, may not reach the anode before the voltage goes negative (point *B*). Hence they will be repelled. The capacitor, deprived of their added charge, will contain less voltage. This effect is present at all frequencies. At the longer wavelengths, the time required by an electron to travel the interelectrode distance is negligible in comparison with the time of one cycle, and the capacitor charges to essentially full value. In calibrating the meter, correction must be determined and applied to all readings in order to obtain the true value.

By carefully constructing the probe, the effects of transit time and resonance can be kept small for measurements up to 500 mc. Above this, the error increases quite rapidly and precise readings are not possible. Relative readings, however, when we wish to determine only whether certain voltages are larger or smaller than some other voltage, can be fairly accurately determined.

Cut-away and exploded views of a diode probe and a crystal probe are shown in Fig. 10–23. The diode probe uses a special tube chosen for its low input capacitance (0.3 $\mu\mu$f) and lead inductance. When the entire probe is assembled, the resonant frequency of the diode and its circuitry is approximately 1500 mc. The crystal probe has a natural frequency in the neighborhood of 1700 mc. This will vary slightly with the crystal used.

Bolometer Voltmeter. Each of the foregoing instruments suffered from some defect which restricted its use to frequencies of approximately 500 mc

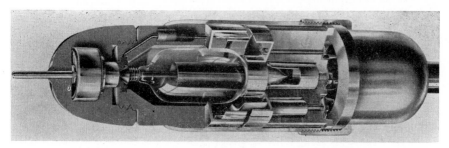

Fig. 10.23A. Cut-away view of high-frequency probe. (*Courtesy Hewlett-Packard*)

or less. A meter which is capable of making accurate measurements well up into the microwave region is a bolometer used in conjunction with a coaxial line. The bolometer, which is essentially a power measuring device, consists of a resistance whose value depends upon the power dissipated in it. In its most common form, the bolometer is either a small rod or a bead. It is incorporated as one arm of a Wheatstone bridge, and the change in resistance due to the dissipation of r-f power is measured. From the measured power dissipation P and the resistance R, the r-f voltage V can be computed from the relationship:

Fig. 10.23B. Exploded view of crystal probe. (*Courtesy General Radio Co.*)

$$V = \sqrt{PR}$$

When the frequency is relatively low, say, below 50 mc, the bolometer may be used by itself. However, increase in frequency above 50 mc soon introduces error because of the inductance of the bolometer wire. This becomes appreciable at 500 mc. However, by combining the bolometer element with a transmission-line matching section, it is possible to neutralize this inductance, and voltages having frequencies of several thousand megacycles may be measured. A diagram of the bolometer and the matching section are shown in Fig. 10–24. The method of using the bolometer is as follows:

The Wheatstone bridge is balanced with no r-f power applied, but with a d-c power dissipated in the bolometer in an amount greater than the r-f power to be measured. With this d-c power, the bolometer wire will possess a certain resistance. The r-f power is now applied to the slotted line and the line adjusted so that no standing waves are present. Under

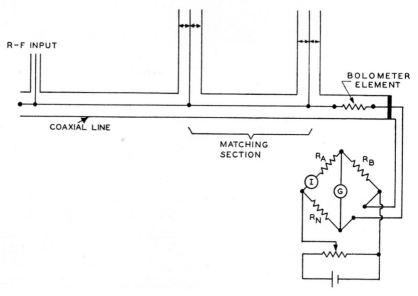

Fig. 10.24.   The schematic diagram of a bolometer voltmeter. (*Courtesy Radio News*)

this condition, the r-f voltage applied to the input of the line reaches the bolometer wire with its value unchanged.   However, the addition of the r-f power to the already existing d-c power raises the resistance of the bolometer and throws the bridge out of balance.   The d-c power is now reduced until the bridge is back in balance again and, when this point is reached, the reduction in d-c power is exactly equal to the added r-f power.

The next step is to convert this r-f power into r-f voltage. Since the power in the slotted line is equal to

$$\frac{V^2}{Z_0}$$

where Z_0 is the characteristic impedance of the line, we can, by knowing Z_0, solve for V. (The reader will recognize this formula as equivalent to

Fig. 10.25. A bolometer and coaxial line combination. (*Courtesy General Radio*)

the power relationship in a d-c circuit, $P = E^2 / R$. In a transmission line, Z_0 takes the place of R in a d-c circuit.)

D-c connection to the bolometer element is made in the following manner. One wire from the Wheatstone bridge attaches directly to one end of the bolometer, this point of connection being insulated from the outer shield of the coaxial line. A mica r-f by-pass capacitor at this point completes the r-f path from the bolometer to the outer conductor of the line. The d-c connection to the other end of the bolometer element is made by attaching the wire from the bridge to the outer conductor of the coaxial line. Because of the presence of the two side plungers, a continuous d-c path exists from the outer conductor, through the plungers, to the other side of the bolometer.

A bolometer-coaxial line combination used to check the output voltage of a signal generator is shown in Fig. 10–25. The same arrangement (Fig.

10–24) can be used to check the calibration of UHF voltmeters. The meter is connected to the end of the slotted section, with the r-f signal coming in as indicated. The line is then adjusted by means of the two side plungers, until there are no standing waves along the line. The voltage, as computed from the bridge, is then compared with the reading indicated on the voltmeter and the latter corrected, if necessary.

A limitation of the bolometer voltmeter is the necessity for retuning the matching section each time the frequency of the signal changes. On the other hand, it does not suffer from the transit-time effect of diodes or the power limitation of crystal rectifiers. The bolometer does not introduce any error with change in voltage level and hence may be employed to measure a wide range of voltages.

Calibration of UHF Voltmeters. Direct calibration of UHF voltmeters may be made with the bolometer and coaxial line. Where high accuracy is not necessary, good results may be obtained by calibrating the meter at some low frequency and then checking this calibration at the high frequencies by one of the following methods.

In one method, a length of transmission line and a source of variable medium-frequency power are required. The power is fed to the line and, if the line is not terminated in its characteristic impedance, standing waves of voltage and current will be formed. At regular intervals the voltage will pass through maxima and minima. Take a voltmeter whose calibration is to be checked, and measure the ratio of the maximum voltage to the minimum voltage at several points along the line so that an average set of values is obtained. Now change the power fed into the line and again obtain the average ratio of E_{max} to E_{min}. If the frequency is kept constant, the ratio should also remain constant and the point at which this ratio starts to change indicates the end of the linearity of the meter scale. This method indicates just how much of the meter scale to use and quickly shows up any changes in the low-frequency calibration. When the meter has not been calibrated, the method is still useful if only relative values are desired. Fortunately, this is true of many UHF measurements.

A variation of this method consists in finding the maximum voltage point on a suitably operated transmission line and then moving the indicator down the line for a distance of 45 degrees or $\frac{1}{8}$ wavelength. At this point the voltage should be 0.707 of the maximum voltage. This ratio is taken at several points along the line in order to obtain an average. Again a test is made to see whether this ratio is the same when the amount of power fed into the transmission line is varied. When the ratio ceases to agree with the above 0.707 value, the meter is no longer linear. Sinusoidal waves are used to obtain the 0.707 ratio, and the line is terminated so that appreciable mismatching will occur.

POWER

For the measurement of power, there are two methods in general use, both based on the principle of dissipating power in the measuring device. In one method, which is designed specifically for the measurement of power in excess of 1 watt, the power is absorbed by a water load and the resultant heat rise measured by a calorimeter. In the second method, the power is dissipated in the resistance of a thermocouple, a filament of a tube, or a bolometer. In the thermocouple, the d-c voltage developed by the thermocouple is measured by a millivoltmeter whose scale is calibrated directly in power. When the filament of a tube is used, the brightness of the filament wire is matched against the light emitted by a lamp whose filament is being activated by known amounts of d-c power. In the bolometer, the change in resistance is determined by a Wheatstone (or other suitable) bridge and, from this, the power dissipated is ascertained.

The second method is used principally for the measurement of powers less than 1 watt since the heat that would be developed by greater amounts of power would cause the resistance element to burn out. To dissipate greater amounts of power safely in each of the instruments used for the second method, the wire diameter would have to be made larger. This, however, would introduce variations in skin resistance with frequency. Hence, small diameter wires are required which, in turn, limit wattage dissipation.

MEASUREMENT OF LOW POWERS

Thermocouples. The thermocouple element used in thermocouple meters has already been discussed earlier in this chapter. It was noted there that the heat developed at the thermocouple junction caused a d-c voltage to develop at the opposite ends of the thermocouple wires which was proportional to the amount of heat. By connecting a suitable millivoltmeter and calibrating its scale in terms of watts (or fractions thereof) instead of in volts, a relatively simple system of power measurement can be developed. The thermocouple element, using a suitable mount such as a glass bead or an evacuated glass bulb, is inserted in a waveguide or across a coaxial line where its resistance is matched to the generator whose power is to be measured. The power absorbed by the thermocouple produces a d-c voltage which is then measured by a suitable voltmeter.

The principal disadvantage of thermocouples to date has been the difficulty of maintaining their resistance constant with power dissipation. A change in resistance invalidates the meter calibration and causes the readings to be in error. The effect is similar to the resistance change with frequency. Several fairly accurate UHF thermocouples for power measurements have been developed by the Bell Telephone Laboratories and work is continuing on others. If these units could be developed to provide accurate measurements for powers up to 1 watt, they would be extremely useful because of their simplicity.

Calibration at the low frequencies is generally employed. Since the resistance of the very thin heater element is relatively unaffected by

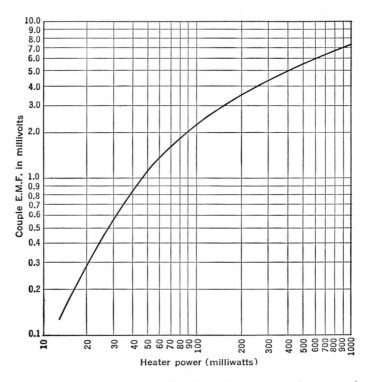

FIG. 10.26. Low frequency calibration of a vacuum thermocouple.

frequency, the emf registered on the d-c meter connected to the couple will be proportional to the square of the current. Power is likewise proportional to this quantity, and a calibration chart between the emf of the meter and the power may be constructed. A typical graph is given in Fig. 10–26.

Power-measurement Tubes. Power measurement may also be achieved by means of tubes. Several tubes developed for this purpose are shown in Fig. 10–27. Each contains two similar filaments, one of which is used as the load, where the unknown power is dissipated. The other filament is for calibration, either on d-c or 60-cycle a-c, and is adjusted until its brightness is equal to that of the load filament. The unknown power then equals the d-c or 60-cycle a-c power. Sample calibration curves applicable to these tubes are given in Fig. 10–28.* It may be seen from these graphs and the rating chart given in Table 10–1 that the measurable power range extends from 0.05 watt to 25 watts. The normal power range of the lamps

FIG. 10.27. Six power measurement tubes. (*Courtesy Sylvania Electric Products Co.*)

will give a brightness variation from red to yellow which allows direct visual comparison. The lamps may be used up to the maximum power rating, provided a dark glass filter is used for visual comparison or a

TABLE 10–1. CHARACTERISTICS OF THE SIX P–M LAMPS

	PM 3	PM 4	PM 5	PM 6	PM 7	PM 8	
Maximum freq. for $R_{a.c.} = R_{d.c.}$	100	100	150	200	400	900	Mc
Normal power (min.)	1.35	0.8	0.7	0.33	0.12	0.05	Watt
Normal power (max.)	10.00	5.5	3.8	1.75	0.95	0.41	Watt
Power dissipation (max.)	25.0	12.0	7.5	3.5	2.0	1.0	Watt
Applied d-c volts (max.)	48	48	55	28	24	16	Volts

Courtesy of Sylvania Electric Products Co.

photocell detecting device is employed. Measurements can be made to 5 per cent accuracy without special calibration of either filament. For more accurate results, the lamps can be calibrated by either impressing a known voltage or current to the calibration side, applying a voltage to the load side and measuring this load voltage when the two sides are equally bright. The power in the load is then known in terms of voltage or current in the calibration side and the accuracy will be independent of any difference between the two filaments.

Because of the high heat conductivity and small diameter of the filament material, the temperature and color will be constant for a given amount of

* Calibration curves for only three P-M tubes are shown. There would be similar curves for the other three tubes.

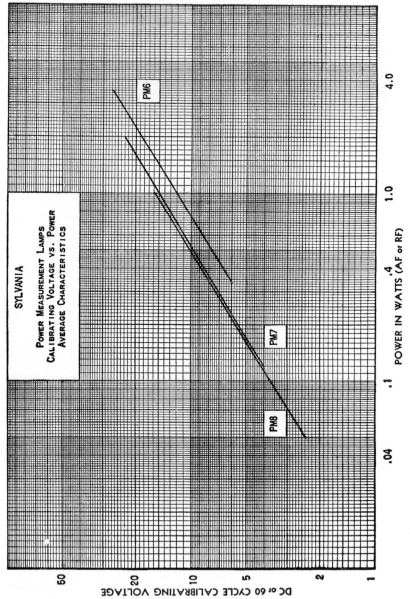

FIG. 10.28.   Calibration curve for six P-M tubes.   (Courtesy Sylvania Electric Products Co.)

energy dissipated, regardless of whether the heat is liberated uniformly throughout the cross section, as with d-c, or nonuniformly due to skin effect at the ultra-high frequencies. Generally, power can be measured at any frequency at which it is possible to couple the energy to the lamp filament.

The high-frequency resistance of any one of the power lamps of Fig. 10–28 does not differ appreciably from its d-c resistance up to the frequencies given in Table 10–1. This is due to the fact that the wire is so

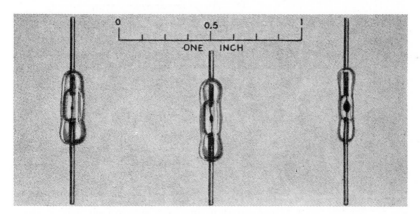

FIG. 10.29. Power-measuring thermistors with different-sized beads. (*Courtesy Bell System Technical Journal*)

small that the depth of penetration is greater than, or at least equal to, the wire radius. When the lamps are used at higher frequencies, skin effect becomes a factor and the resistive component increases.

Bolometers. By far the most widely used method of measuring low power in the UHF range is by means of bolometers. As previously noted, bolometers are resistances whose value depends upon the power dissipated within them. There are a variety of substances which possess this property and all could be used as bolometer elements. However, there are two bolometers which have found wide application, the thermistor and the barretter. The thermistor is a mixture of metallic oxides which are formed into beads, rods, and disks. For use in power measurement (they have a variety of other applications), the bead form is most frequently employed. (See Fig. 10–29.) It is made by applying a mixture of the metallic oxides to two platinum wires which have been set parallel to each other but separated by a spacing equal to five to ten times the wire diameter. The oxides on the wires form a bead because of surface tension. It is in this bead that the resistance of the unit resides. The bead is allowed to dry and then heated slightly until the mass is solid. The entire assembly, which is extremely small, is then enclosed in a glass capsule that is sealed at each end by heat.   The Thermistor has a negative temperature coefficient of resistance.

The barretter type of bolometer consists of a thin platinum wire which is generally suspended between supports of heavier copper wire which also serve as the leads for carrying the high-frequency currents.   Contrary to

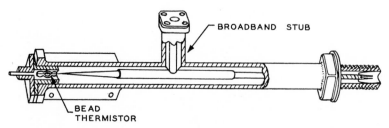

FIG. 10.30.   A broadband coaxial thermistor mount.   (*Courtesy I.R.E.*)

the thermistor bolometer, this unit has a positive temperature coefficient of resistance.   The entire assembly is mounted in an insulated cartridge of glass or polystyrene.

The two bolometers have fairly high impedances which must be matched to the impedance of the transmission line or waveguide in which they are mounted.   A typical illustration of how a thermistor-bead bolometer is

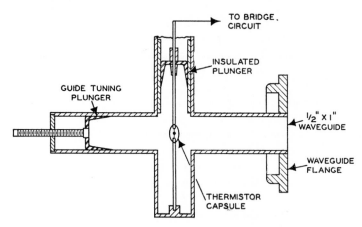

FIG. 10.31.   Waveguide thermistor mount.   (*Courtesy I.R.E.*)

matched to a 50-ohm transmission line is shown in Fig. 10–30.   The bead is mounted between the center conductor and the end of the line.   The inner conductor to which the bead is attached is not the regular conductor of the line but a tapered section designed to match the high impedance of the bolometer to the 50-ohm impedance of the coaxial line. A quarter-wave broad-band support holds the center conductor in place and acts as an insulator over a band of frequencies. It also functions as one of the d-c return leads to the bolometer when this is connected to the measuring bridge. Connection from the bridge to the outer side of the bolometer wire is made through a coaxial connector screwed into the end of the line. The line is terminated in a small polystyrene disk which acts as a short circuit for the UHF energy but as an open circuit for d-c. This type of connection is necessary in order to prevent shorting the two bolometer wires going to the bridge.

Mounting bolometers in waveguides is illustrated in Fig. 10–31. The bolometer (in this case a thermistor) is placed across the guide which has two tuning plungers designed to help match the thermistor impedance to the line as closely as possible.

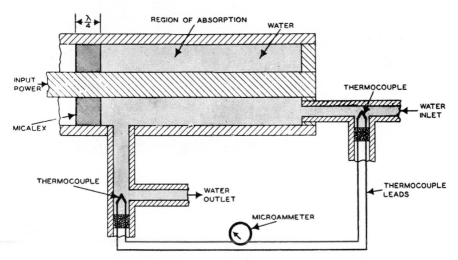

Fig. 10.32. A continuously flowing water load calorimeter. (*Courtesy Radio News*)

HIGH-POWER MEASUREMENT

To measure power in excess of several watts, a continuously flowing water load calorimeter is used. (See Fig. 10–32.) The power traveling down the coaxial cable or waveguide is absorbed completely by a water column at the end of the line. The water load is enclosed by the end of the line and a thick dielectric bead. The bead, micalex, is a quarter-wavelength thick and is chosen so that its impedance is the geometric mean between the impedance of the cable or guide and that of the water.

Water flows continuously through the end of the line and is heated by the high-frequency energy.   The rise in temperature is measured by placing thermometers or thermocouples at the water input and outlet terminals, and, from this rise, the power absorbed by the water can be computed.

This type of power-measuring device is good for powers in excess of several watts.   For smaller powers, the determination of the change in water temperature is difficult and the heat loss is large enough to make their use of doubtful value.

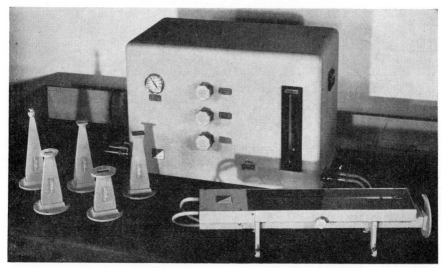

Fig. 10.33.   Calorimeter system for measurement of absolute r-f power at frequencies between 2600 and 26,500 mc.   (*Courtesy De Mornay-Budd*)

A commercial calorimeter which will measure power in the 2600 to 26,500 mc range is shown in Fig. 10–33.   The unit consists of the following:

1. A pump housing assembly containing a water reservoir holding 3 gallons of distilled water and a motor which pumps the water through the calorimeter and back to the reservoir.

2. A calorimeter unit containing a glass water load with input (cold) and output (hot) thermometers plus a scale calibrated in watts.

When the unit is turned on, the motor draws water from the reservoir at a constant rate of 3 gallons per minute.   Of this amount, only 0.04 gallon per minute flows through the water load of the calorimeter.   The remainder of the 3 gallons (3 − 0.04 or 2.96 gallons) is by-passed back to the reservoir to facilitate mixing of the reservoir water.   To insure that precisely 0.04 gallon of water flows through the calorimeter, an accurate flowmeter is used. This quantity must be accurately known because the scale calibration depends upon it.

When energy is received by the water load from a waveguide, the water circulating through the calorimeter will heat up. The "hot" thermometer at the water load output will then indicate a higher temperature reading than the "cold" thermometer at the calorimeter input. A movable scale with a zero reference marker (Fig. 10–34) is now positioned so that the zero line is in line with the mercury level of the input thermometer. The power in watts being received by the load may then be read directly from the scale at the mercury level of the output thermometer.

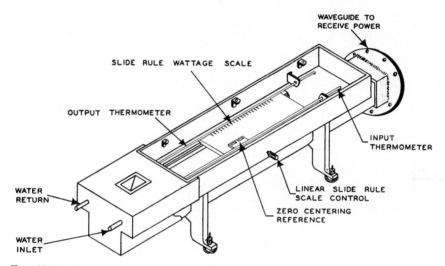

FIG. 10.34. Detail drawing of the calorimeter with various parts marked as to function. With proper calibration, unit is direct reading. (*Courtesy Radio News*)

Note again that the constant flow of water through the water load is the chief reason why power may be read directly from the calibrated scale. These readings are accurate to within two watts regardless of the average power reading from zero to 500 watts. To measure greater amounts of power, the water flow rate through the load is increased and the wattage scale readings are increased in the same proportion. Thus, if the rate of flow is raised to 0.08 gallon per minute, all markings on the calibrated wattage scale are multiplied by 2.

A detail drawing of the calorimeter is shown in Fig. 10–34. Input and output water connections from the calorimeter to the pump are made by means of flexible rubber hose. The zero reference on the calibrated scale is controlled by a rack and pinion. Coupling between the guide section of the calorimeter and waveguides from which the power is taken is achieved by a set of fine waveguide transformers or tapered adapters shown in Fig. 10–33.

The heated water, after it leaves the outlet terminal of the calorimeter, passes through a cooler which removes this added heat so that when the water returns to the reservoir for its next trip through the system, its temperature is back to the value it possessed before passing through the calorimeter.

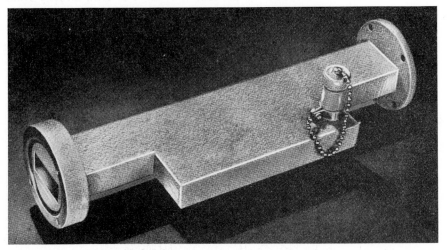

FIG. 10.35.   A directional coupler.   (*Courtesy De Mornay-Budd*)

DIRECTIONAL COUPLERS

In many instances, it is necessary to monitor the r-f energy that is being transmitted or received by an UHF system to determine whether the system is operating as desired. Perhaps the best way of doing this without disturbing the system is by means of directional couplers. These devices are attached to the sides of waveguides from which they extract a small amount of power. This power, however, comes only from the power traveling in one direction and therefore it is possible to determine the energy which is being put into a guide by a generator without picking up any of the reflected energy which is usually present to some extent in every system. Thus, the directional coupler permits an independent measurement of the forward traveling energy and the reflected energy.

A directional coupler is shown in Fig. 10–35, and the manner in which it operates is indicated in Fig. 10–36. The directional coupler is mounted on the side of a small section of waveguide, and this waveguide is inserted as part of the regular waveguide network of the UHF system. Between the waveguide and the directional coupler there are two sets of openings (in the form of small holes) through which energy in the waveguide may pass into the coupler. These two openings are spaced from each other by one-quarter wavelength at the frequency of the energy being sent down the guide. Inside the coupler there is a matched detector at one end and a matched termination at the other. The termination is to prevent any energy from reflecting from this end of the coupler, and the detector indicates the amount of energy present in the coupler.

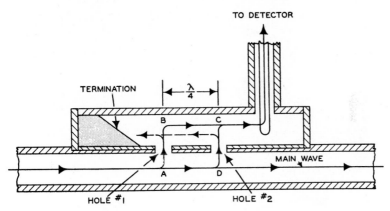

Fig. 10.36. Schematic drawing of a directional coupler. (*Courtesy I.R.E.*)

The manner in which the coupler operates is as follows: A small amount of energy traveling along the guide in the direction shown (which we will call the direction in which the main wave is traveling) will pass through hole #1 and into the coupler. The remainder of the energy of the main wave will travel along the guide to the second opening, and again some of the energy will pass into the coupler and combine with the energy from the first opening. Since the distance over path *A–B–C* is the same as that over path *A–D–C*, the two waves meeting at point *C* will be in phase and aid each other. From point *C* the energy in the coupler passes on to the detector where an indication of its power level is obtained. Power measurement is achieved by one of the methods described previously.

To demonstrate that only this forward traveling energy in the waveguide will affect the detector and none of any reflected energy that may be traveling along the guide in the opposite direction, consider what effect reflected energy would have on the unit. This energy, reaching hole #2 first, would pass into the coupler. The remainder of the reflected energy, traveling back along the guide, reaches hole #1 and some of it also passes into the coupler. The energy now travels from B to C and combines with the reflected energy that entered through hole #2. However, both these bits of reflected energy are 180 degrees out of phase with each other and they cancel. The 180-degree shift arises because the reflected energy which enters the opening near point A must travel from point D to point A (which is a quarter wavelength) plus another quarter wavelength from B to C before it combines with the reflected energy that entered hole #2.

FIG. 10.37. Bidirectional coupler that samples outgoing and reflected power. (*Courtesy De Mornay-Budd*)

A half wavelength distance is equivalent to a shift of 180 degrees, and hence the two waves combine out of phase and cancel. Thus, the power indicated by the coupler is dependent only on the forward traveling wave and not at all on the reflected wave.

The coupler abstracts only a small fraction of the power in the waveguide. The ratio of the power in the main wave to that which the coupler obtains is known as the coupling of the directional coupler. It is usually given in decibels according to the formula

$$\text{Coupling (db)} = 10 \log_{10} \frac{P_{\text{main}}}{P_{\text{coupler}}}$$

In the coupler shown in Fig. 10–35, the coupling is 25 db $\pm$ 1 db over the frequency range from 6250 mc to 6575 mc. There is also available a bidirectional coupler (Fig. 10–37) in which separate samples of energy traveling in each direction may be abstracted and measured. A major use of this device is to obtain the reflection coefficient of a waveguide system by measuring the amount of forward and reflected power.

QUESTIONS

1. Explain how skin effect causes the resistance of any wire to change with frequency.

2. What effect does change in frequency have on inductance? Why?

3. Name some factors that would cause low-frequency instruments to become inaccurate at the ultra-highs.

4. What is meant by leakage conductance and why is it important?

5. Describe how an ordinary wavemeter works. Why does this instrument become unsuitable for UHF work?

6. Explain how transmission lines are utilized for wavelength measurements at the ultra-high frequencies.

7. Draw a diagram for a set-up using a transmission line wavemeter.

8. Name several different voltmeters that are suitable for UHF work.

9. Why is the ordinary a-c voltmeter limited to relatively low frequencies?

10. Describe the action of a thermocouple and show how this may be applied to UHF voltage measurements.

11. In order to use the low-frequency calibrations, what precautions in thermocouple construction should be observed so that the same calibrations hold at the high frequencies?

12. What is meant by ambient temperature? Explain what effect a change in this temperature would have on a thermocouple meter movement?

13. Draw the circuits of a diode and of a triode vacuum-tube voltmeter. Why are pentodes, as such, seldom used in vacuum-tube voltmeter arrangements?

14. What two effects tend to make a vacuum-tube voltmeter inaccurate at the ultra-high frequencies? Explain each one in detail.

15. What is the common principle upon which many UHF power meters are built? Does this differ from low-frequency meters? Explain.

16. Explain one method that might be employed to calibrate a voltmeter, at least for relative readings.

17. Name several UHF power-measuring devices. What precautions must be observed in the construction of the power-dissipating element?

18. Explain the operation of special P–M tubes.

19. What property of a transmission line permits its use for the measurement of power?

20. How does a bolometer voltmeter function?

21. What property of a bolometer makes it useful for power measurement? How are bolometers connected into the circuit?

22. Why is the use of water to measure power restricted to power in excess of several watts?

23. Describe the operation of a commercial calorimeter.

24. What is a directional coupler? How does it operate?

25. A slotted transmission line is being used to measure the frequency of a certain signal. If it is found that the distance between two successive maximum points on the standing wave developed by this signal is 4 cm, what is the frequency of the signal?

26. Draw the electrical circuit of a probe detector commonly used in slotted-line wavemeters.

Chapter 11

UHF RECEIVERS

In the preceding chapters we have considered in some detail the structure and operation of many of the components of ultra-high-frequency systems. In the present chapter we will utilize these components to form the UHF receiver and to compare this type of set with the conventional receiver.

The superheterodyne type of receiving circuit is employed most extensively in the microwave region, although such receivers as the super-regenerative and the tuned-radio frequency (TRF) also have found application. Superheterodynes have been favored, however, for the same reasons that they are favored at the lower frequencies: greater selectivity, higher sensitivity, and ease of operation. In many instances, the set designer has little choice other than to employ the superheterodyne in the microwave region. It is difficult and usually economically impractical to attempt to amplify a signal by a group of r-f amplifiers since these can provide only an extremely small amount of gain. At frequencies which are comparatively low, such as those below 200 mc, it is possible to obtain a gain of 8 from a well-designed r-f amplifier. On the other hand, in a well-designed i-f amplifier operating at the comparatively high i-f value of 60 mc, gains of 25 or more can be obtained. As the signal frequency goes above 300 mc, the gain of present r-f amplifiers decrease, their principal function now being to provide selectivity improvement of the circuits preceding the mixer in order to reduce interference from unwanted or spurious signals.

The basic outline of stages in a superheterodyne receiver is fairly well known by now. (See Fig. 11–1.) The signal is received by an r-f amplifier, if one is used, amplified, and applied to a mixer. At the same time, another signal is obtained from a local oscillator and also applied to the mixer. By properly combining both signals, a third signal is obtained which possesses a frequency equal to the difference between the frequency of the incoming signal and that of the local oscillator. The intermediate frequency signal, however, retains the modulation or other information present in the original incoming signal. While the incoming frequency may be 1000 mc, or more, the intermediate frequency seldom exceeds 100 mc.

The signal, at this point, is still extremely weak and further amplification is required. This is furnished by a group of amplifiers known as i-f (or intermediate-frequency) amplifiers. There is no fixed number of such amplifiers for all sets, the number differing with each design. This section of the receiver furnishes both the sensitivity and selectivity for the

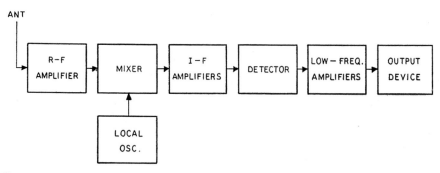

FIG. 11.1. The basic arrangement of stages in a superheterodyne receiver. In low-frequency receivers, the local oscillator and mixer are combined in one tube; in high-frequency receivers they are kept separate.

entire set. The sensitivity is established by the amplification of the stages and the selectivity by the number of tuned circuits.

The second detector follows the i-f amplifiers. Here the intelligence is removed from the carrier and made available to audio or video amplifiers where further amplification builds up the signal to the point where the output reproducing device, generally either a loudspeaker or cathode-ray tube, can be driven properly. The detector may be either A–M or F–M, depending upon the nature of the transmission.

This, in essence, is the form of practically all ultra-high-frequency receivers, whether they be employed for A–M, F–M, television, or radar. In each case a certain minute voltage, the signal, has to be received and amplified until it possesses an amplitude of several volts. When this has been attained, the intelligence is removed from the signal (by the second detector), further amplified, and then used for whatever purpose is desired. In television, this would be an image on a screen; in radar, an outline of the surrounding territory; in A–M or F–M, speech or music.

The front-end section of an ultra-high-frequency receiver must be capable of receiving the UHF signal, amplifying it if provision for this exists, and then converting the signal to the lower intermediate frequency. Since the generating of large amounts of ultra-high-frequency power is quite difficult, only relatively small or moderate signals are transmitted. Add to this the loss in energy suffered in traveling from transmitter to receiver, and it is quite obvious that any voltage received is quite small.

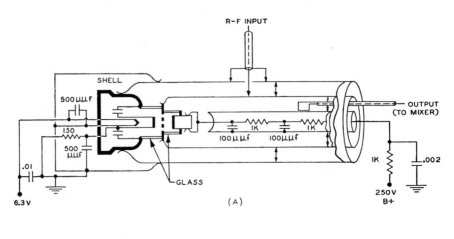

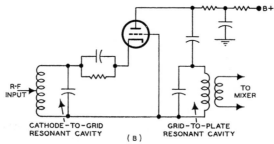

Fig. 11.2.   (A) Circuit of an r-f amplifier designed to operate at 1000 mc. (B) Low-frequency equivalent circuit.

If the signal frequency is below 1000 mc, it is possible to construct r-f amplifiers for use ahead of the mixer which will provide a small but nevertheless useful gain. Above 1000 mc, vacuum-tube amplifiers are generally unsatisfactory, and the signal is fed directly to a mixer where it combines with the local oscillator voltage to produce the i-f signal.

R-f amplifiers operating at frequencies up to approximately 1000 mc have employed the lighthouse tube to a great extent. A simplified diagram of a lighthouse tube r-f amplifier is shown in Fig. 11–2A. The circuit contains a separate input and plate tuning circuit. The mechanical layout consists of a coaxial tuner, in which the resonant frequency is altered by a sliding plunger. (See Fig. 11–2B.)   The tuning circuits are arranged to incorporate the lighthouse tube as an integral part of the structure. A probe extending into the input or grid-to-filament cavity couples the incoming energy from the coaxial line (or waveguide) leading to the antenna. Output transfer of energy is achieved by inserting a coupling loop in the cavity between the grid and the plate. B + plate voltage for the lighthouse tube is brought in by a wire placed inside the innermost coaxial conductor.

The output signal is transferred from the r-f amplifier to a mixer by means of a short length of 50-ohm coaxial cable. At a frequency of 1000 mc, the voltage gain of this amplifier is 4 or, in terms of db, 12 db. The noise figure, however, is 14 db, the significance of which will be indicated soon.

There are two types of mixers that are used in UHF receivers—vacuum tubes and silicon crystals. Vacuum tube mixers are useful up to about 500 mc and provide fairly good conversion gain and have a low noise figure. Above 500 mc, the noise characteristics of crystal rectifiers are superior to those of vacuum tubes and the crystal units are used—this in spite of the fact that a vacuum tube mixer is capable of some gain, whereas a crystal mixer introduces a 6 to 9 db loss.

Since noise plays such an important part in determining the type of front-end components suitable for a UHF receiver, a discussion of it and its significance is in order.

Noise Figure. The ability of a receiver to amplify a signal is not limited by the amplification which can be obtained from vacuum tubes but by the noise which arises from the tubes and the associated receiver networks. This noise is known as random noise because it possesses no fixed frequency, but extends from zero to frequencies far above any being used today. The noise, therefore, affects every type of receiving circuit.

The noise that is developed in a receiver is due to two sources, thermal agitation in conductors and electron flow through tubes. Thermal agitation arises from the random motion of electrons within a conductor. There is no external voltage applied, but the electrons, using their own energy, move to and fro along a conductor. This movement of electrons constitutes a current flow. Since, at any given instant, a few more electrons are moving in one direction than in the other, a voltage is set up in the conductor which is proportional to the net current flow and the value of the conductor resistance. The polarity of the voltage due to thermal agitation changes constantly, electrons moving first in one direction, then in another. Because of this, there is no definite pattern to the random voltage or, for that matter, any one frequency at which the energy changes. It has been found that the energy of the disturbance is distributed uniformly throughout the entire frequency spectrum used for communications.

The amount of voltage that is developed by thermal agitation in conductors can be computed from the following relationship:

$$E^2 \text{ (rms)} = 4KTR \times (f_2 - f_1)$$

where E = the rms value of the noise voltage generated across the
            resistance,

$K = 1.37 \times 10^{-23}$,

T = the temperature of the conductor (this is expressed in
      absolute degrees, Kelvin, which is equal to 273 plus
      the temperature in degrees Centigrade),

R = the value of the resistance of the conductor, in ohms,

$f_2 - f_1$ = the bandwidth of the receiver, in cps.

An inspection of the formula indicates that, with all other factors constant, the wider the bandwidth which the set is designed for, the greater the amount of thermal agitation voltage developed. Note that the actual frequency at which the set is operating is not a factor in the equation; only the bandwidth is important. Thus, a receiver having a bandpass of 1 mc and operating at 200 mc will develop as much thermal agitation voltage as another set having the same bandwidth but operating at 10 mc.

The second source of receiver noise is developed in the tubes. There are several components to this noise.

1. *Shot Effect.* The current that flows in a tube is not a continuous fluid but a moving aggregation of separate particles, the electrons. Noise voltages are produced, even when so-called steady currents are flowing, because at any single instant the number of electrons impinging on the plate differs from the number reaching the plate at any other instant. Over a measurable period, the current is steady, but instantaneously it fluctuates rapidly. It is these instantaneous fluctuations that cause the noise.

2. *Noise Due to Current Division.* The noise voltages produced by the foregoing shot effect increase as more positive elements (grids) are added to a tube. This is due to the random division of the current between the plate and the other electrodes.

3. *Induced Grid Noise.* At sufficiently high frequencies, when the frequency of the signal has a period comparable to the electron transit time, the number of electrons approaching and the number receding from the grid are seldom equal. This produces an induced grid current which fluctuates irregularly, developing a noise voltage at the grid.

Investigation has revealed that the noise energy developed by these three effects is distributed evenly throughout the frequency spectrum. In this respect it resembles the noise voltage due to thermal agitation. Both together can be combined under the general heading of random noise.

It is customary (and convenient) to express the noise voltage produced by a tube in terms of a noise voltage applied to the grid—the tube itself is assumed to be noise-free. The rms value of this voltage is then such that, when amplified by a noise-free tube, it produces at the output just as much voltage as would be produced by a noisy tube with its input shorted.

In a receiver, the noise that is developed by the first stage is actually the most important because at this point the level of the incoming signal is more closely on a par with the noise level than at any other point in the receiver. In this respect an r-f amplifier, if used, is more important than the mixer, because whatever noise voltage appears at the grid of the r-f amplifier is amplified by the tube and appears that much larger at the grid of the mixer. Thus even if the noise voltages of both tubes are comparable, that appearing at the grid of the r-f amplifier is effectively more important because it receives the amplification of the r-f amplifier while the noise developed at the grid of the mixer does not. Hence, what we seek in the first tube is low internal noise and high gain.

Every receiver must be used with some type of antenna in order that signals be received. Now, every antenna possesses resistance, and a noise voltage due to thermal agitation will therefore be developed by the antenna wires and fed to the receiver. We thus have two sources of noise to consider, although at frequencies beyond 100 mc, the noise developed in the receiver is considerably greater than the noise generated by the antenna.

As an indication of the ability of a receiver to take a weak signal and amplify it so that an intelligible output is obtained, a quantity known as a noise figure frequently is used. This noise figure compares the total noise present in the output of the receiver (with antenna connected to set) to that portion of the total noise generated by the antenna alone. This particular ratio is chosen because every receiver must be used with an antenna. Since the antenna generates some noise voltage because of thermal agitation in its wires, noise would be present at the receiver output even if the receiver generated no noise itself. However, if the receiver introduced no noise, then the ratio of the total noise output of the system to the noise output due to the antenna alone would be 1. In all receivers, the noise figure is greater than 1 because the receiver introduces noise.

The noise figure of a system generally rises with frequency because the noise output of tubes has been found to increase with frequency. This is due to the greater influence of electron transit time, resulting not only in a lower input impedance, but also to the greater induced currents flowing in the grid circuit.

At the low frequencies, when the input impedance of the first tube is high, the signal from the antenna is generally applied to the grid of the tube through a step-up transformer in order to achieve an impedance match.

Under these conditions, the tube noise voltage is small in comparison to the applied signal, and a good signal-to-noise ratio is maintained. The sensitivity of the receiving system, then, is limited only by the amount of noise voltage developed by the antenna and this is generally small. With increase in frequency, the tube input impedance decreases, and a step-up transformer is no longer needed to match the antenna impedance to the input impedance of the receiver. Tube noise now is on a level with the received signal and exerts a limitation on how small a signal can be received to develop a useful output. The sensitivity of the receiving system has decreased.

The choice between using or not using an r-f amplifier in a UHF receiver will thus be governed by whether or not the noise figure of the receiver will be decreased by the addition of this amplifier.* This, in turn, depends upon the noise figure of the mixer. If this value is high, then the signal-to-noise ratio may be improved by the addition of an r-f amplifier possessing a fair amount of gain. However, if the noise figure of the mixer is low, then the small degree of selectivity which an r-f amplifier might furnish would not warrant the expense occasioned by the inclusion of this stage in the receiver. At frequencies around 1000 mc, the lighthouse tube may be used as an r-f amplifier, increasing the r-f gain and helping to improve the noise figure. In the region between 2000 and 3000 mc, there are no vacuum tubes commercially available which possess moderate noise figures and r-f amplifiers are seldom used.

To illustrate why an r-f amplifier will not improve the sensitivity of a receiver if it itself does not provide high gain and low noise, consider the following. Assume that the equivalent noise voltage existing at the grid of a mixer is 10 microvolts and the signal amplitude required to provide an intelligible output is 30 microvolts. This is a signal-to-noise ratio of 3 to 1. Now, let us add an r-f amplifier ahead of the mixer which possesses a gain of 8 and has an equivalent noise voltage at its grid of 20 microvolts. The question is: How much signal voltage would be required now to maintain the same 3 to 1 ratio at the mixer grid?

As a first step, let us compute the total equivalent noise voltage at the grid of the mixer. The noise voltage of the r-f amplifier is 20 microvolts and, when this receives a gain of 8, it becomes 160 microvolts at the mixer input. This must be combined with the 10 microvolts of the mixer. However, direct addition is not permissible since the noise voltages consist of many different frequency components. The rms value of the sum of

* Where competition is important, the additional cost engendered by the addition of an r-f amplifier also enters the picture. Thus, although r-f amplifier tubes are available in the 500 to 1000 mc region, UHF television receivers and converters do not use them because of their relatively high cost. However, when and if a low cost r-f amplifier tube is developed, it will undoubtedly find extensive application.

these two voltages is obtained by taking the square root of the sum of the squares, or

$$= \sqrt{(160)^2 + (10)^2}$$

$$= \sqrt{25,700}$$

$$= 160.3 \text{ microvolts}$$

This is the total noise voltage effective at the mixer grid. It is interesting to note that it is governed almost wholly by the amplified noise voltage from the r-f amplifier.

To maintain the same 3 to 1 signal-to-noise ratio, we would need approximately 480 microvolts of signal at the mixer grid. With a gain of 8 available from the r-f amplifier, the signal at the grid of this tube would have to be 480/8, or 60 microvolts. Thus, by adding an r-f amplifier, we have made the set less sensitive. Before its addition only 30 microvolts of signal were required; with the amplifier, the value rose to 60 microvolts.

However, an r-f amplifier would be useful if the mixer equivalent noise voltage were high and the amplifier itself offered good gain with a low noise voltage. Thus, suppose that the mixer noise voltage was 40 microvolts before the addition of an r-f amplifier. Under these conditions, a signal voltage of 120 microvolts would be required to provide the necessary 3 to 1 signal-to-noise ratio. Using the same r-f amplifier as above, the total equivalent noise voltage at the mixer grid now becomes:

$$= \sqrt{(160)^2 + (40)^2}$$

$$= \sqrt{27,200}$$

$$= 164 \text{ microvolts}$$

The required signal for this much noise voltage is 3×164, or 492 microvolts. Dividing 492 by 8, the gain of the r-f amplifier, we see that approximately 62 microvolts of signal is needed at the input to the r-f amplifier. Since the required signal was 120 microvolts without the r-f amplifier, addition of this stage has doubled the receiver sensitivity.

UHF Mixers.* An illustration of a vacuum tube mixer at 1000 mc is shown in Fig. 11–3, together with a simplified circuit diagram. The incoming signal and the local oscillator voltage are probe-coupled to the grid-cathode coaxial resonant circuit where they introduce their respective voltages simultaneously. The output coupling network is, in this instance, tuned to 60 mc and consists of an inductance and a variable capacitance.

---

* The terms *mixer* and *converter* are used interchangeably by the industry and the same practice will be followed here.

The i-f output voltage is fed to an i-f amplifier section through a 75-ohm coaxial transmission line.

Above 500 mc, the noise characteristics of crystal rectifiers are considerably better than those of vacuum tubes and hence are used almost universally. The internal structure of a silicon crystal is shown in Fig. 11–4. It consists of two metal terminals separated by an internally threaded ceramic insulator. The silicon wafer is the rectifying element and it is soldered firmly to one of the terminals. The other terminal has a contact spring (known widely as a "cat's-whisker") which is made of tung-

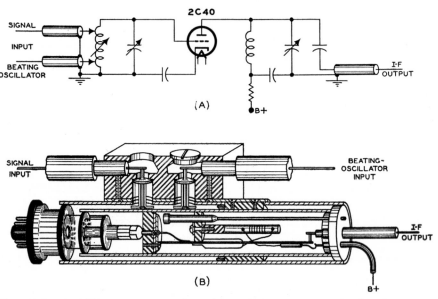

Fig. 11.3. A 1000-mc vacuum-tube mixer. (A) represents the low-frequency equivalent circuit and (B) the actual physical construction of the converter unit.

sten wire and shaped into the form of an S. One end of this wire is attached firmly to the metal terminal while the other end presses up against the surface of the small silicon block and establishes rectification.

Another type of silicon detector which has been used possesses the structure shown in Fig. 11–5. In this unit the rectifier terminates a small coaxial line. The central conductor forms one terminal, while the outer surrounding conductor forms the other terminal. The central conductor is molded into an insulating block of bakelite which forms a base for the central conductor and prevents it from shorting to the outer conductor.

To employ these silicon rectifiers as mixers in microwave superheterodyne receivers, they are mounted in coaxial lines or waveguides. A silicon rectifier mounted in a coaxial line holder is shown in Fig. 11–6. The mixer is designed for use at 3000 mc. The input tuning circuit of this unit consists of a coaxial transmission line element having a length of approxi-

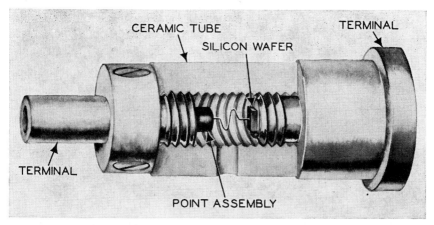

FIG. 11.4. Internal structure of a silicon crystal.

mately three-quarters of a wavelength at the input frequency. The silicon rectifier is connected at the high impedance end of this line while the

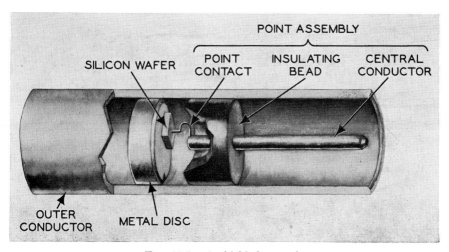

FIG. 11.5. A shielded crystal.

opposite end of this three-quarter wavelength coaxial line is shorted by a by-pass capacitor. This low impedance, reflected over the three-quarter wavelength line, presents a high impedance at the silicon rectifier. Note that this by-pass capacitor appears as a short circuit only for the input frequency and not for the i-f signal which is produced in the silicon rectifier.

The line carrying the input signal is coupled to this tuned circuit by a variable coupling probe. The beat oscillator input is, in turn, coupled capacitively to the input line, and thus the two beating signals are transferred to the silicon rectifier where the mixing occurs.

The output circuit, containing the i-f voltage, consists of the previously mentioned by-pass capacitor and an i-f transformer which is not shown.

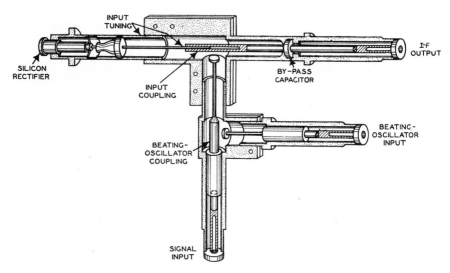

FIG. 11.6.   A 3000-mc crystal mixer.   (*Courtesy Bell System Technical Journal*)

At very high frequencies the input signal generally reaches the mixer through a waveguide, and in these instances the silicon crystal rectifier is mounted with its axis parallel to the electric lines of force, as shown in Fig. 11–7. To insure that the field, at this point, will be maximum, an adjustable shorting piston is inserted a quarter of a wave from this crystal. The electric field at the piston is zero, but at a distance of one-quarter wavelength it is maximum as established by the standing waves set up in the guide.

At another point along the guide, the output probe of a reflex klystron oscillator projects into the guide, radiating the local oscillator signals. Thus, this signal together with the input signal arrive at the crystal where the mixing process occurs. The i-f output is obtained from the coaxial line connected to the crystal terminal. At the point of connection, there is a choke consisting of a half wavelength section short-circuited at the far end. This is a half wavelength at the input signal frequency and prevents this signal from going into the i-f line. The intermediate frequency, being far removed from the input frequency, is relatively unaffected by this choke.

When this arrangement is to be used at one frequency, as it is in most applications, the piston is replaced by a fixed short circuit.

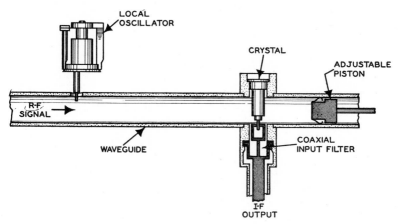

FIG. 11.7.   A crystal converter mounted in a waveguide.

Balanced Converters. In the foregoing converters or mixers, the coupling that existed between the local oscillator circuit and the incoming signal circuit was such that a certain amount of interaction existed between these two circuits. This permitted an appreciable amount of oscillator power to reach the antenna and radiate to near-by receivers, producing interference. It also resulted in variations in the local oscillator frequency whenever the impedance of the incoming signal circuit varied, causing variations in the load impedance of the local oscillator. Finally, each circuit lost useful power in the other circuit because of this coupling. To prevent, or at least minimize, each of these effects, a balanced type of converter has been developed.

The balanced converter, in nearly all instances, uses a magic-T section of waveguide. A magic T, as shown in Fig. 11–8, consists of a main waveguide with two other waveguides connected perpendicularly to it. One of the junctions (labeled 1 in Fig. 11–8) is at the narrow side of the waveguide and is known as an *H*-plane T-junction because the branching waveguide is in the plane of the magnetic field of the main guide. The effect of this connection, electrically, is the same as a parallel connection in a low-frequency circuit. Any signal fed in the branch guide will divide at the junction and move, in phase, along both arms (or in both directions) of the main waveguide.

The second junction (labeled 4) occurs at the broad side of the main waveguide and is known as an E-plane T-junction because this branching waveguide is in the plane of the electric field of the main guide. The effect of this junction, electrically, is the same as a series connection in a low-frequency circuit. Any signal fed into this branch guide will divide at the junction and move down the arms of the main guide out of phase with each other.

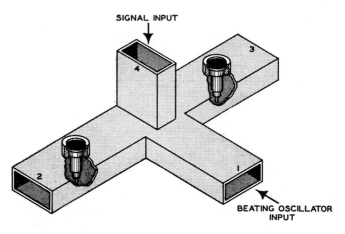

Fig. 11.8.   The placement of the silicon crystals in a balanced converter.

When both junctions are combined, as they are in the magic T, then the following actions occur. If a signal is fed into branch 1 of Fig. 11–8, and both arms of the main waveguide terminate in matched loads, then the signal will divide equally between arms 2 and 3 and no power will go to arm 4. By the same token, power fed into arm 4 will divide equally between arms 2 and 3 (if these contain matched loads) and no power will go into arm 1. Thus, by designing the impedances properly, we can prevent oscillator signal power from reaching the incoming signal guide and we can prevent signal power from being expended uselessly in the oscillator guide.

For use as a microwave converter, silicon crystals are placed at both ends of the main waveguide. The incoming signal is then sent into one branching arm, generally branch 4, while the local oscillator voltage is fed into branch 1. The incoming signal in branch 4 will divide at the junction with the main guide, half of the energy going to one crystal and half to the other. Because branch 4 is an E-plane T-junction connection, each crystal will receive the signal in opposite polarity—or differing from each other by 180 degrees.

The local oscillator voltage will also reach each crystal in equal amounts, except that these voltages will be in phase with each other because branch

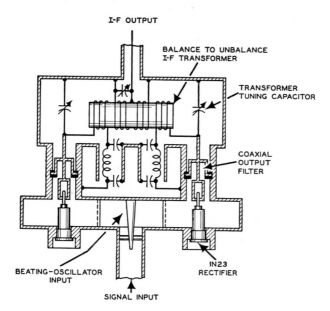

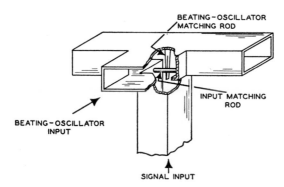

FIG. 11.9. A balanced crystal converter. (*Courtesy Bell System Technical Journal*)

1 is an *H*-plane T-junction. Because of the phase relationship between the mixing signals at each crystal, the i-f signals produced will differ from each other by 180 degrees. If these are now fed to a push-pull output circuit, the i-f voltages will add. However, the local oscillator

signals, being in phase with each other at each crystal, will be cancelled out. This serves to remove any noise introduced by the local oscillator and helps improve receiver sensitivity.

The complete circuit of a balanced crystal converter is shown in Fig. 11–9. At the junction of the two branch arms, certain impedance matching rods and plates are used in order to affect an impedance match between each branch arm and the main waveguide.

To those who find the magic-T operation somewhat puzzling, reference may be made to a low-frequency balanced modulation circuit shown in

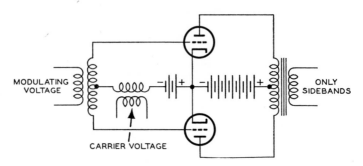

Fig. 11.10. A low-frequency balanced modulator circuit. In many respects the operation of this circuit is similar to that of Fig. 11.9.

Fig. 11–10. Here out-of-phase modulating voltages are fed to the grid of each tube while a carrier voltage is fed in phase to each grid. The voltages mix in each tube, producing modulated sidebands at the output. Since the output circuit is connected in push-pull, the carrier voltage is cancelled out in the output transformer, and only the sidebands remain.

In comparing Fig. 11–10 with Fig. 11–8, the carrier voltage is equivalent to the local oscillator voltage, while the modulating voltage is equivalent to the incoming r-f signal. The sideband output is equivalent to the i-f signal produced at the output of the microwave converter.

By isolating the local oscillator and incoming signal voltages from each other in the balanced converter, we avoid interaction between the circuits and its accompanying disadvantages.

Local Oscillators. Local oscillators for UHF receivers, in common with r-f amplifiers and mixers, can be divided according to the frequency to be generated. Up to approximately 1000 mc the negative-grid tube (that is, operated in the conventional manner) is employed as the local oscillator. Common tubes used are the 6C4, 6AF4, 6J6 and one of the lighthouse or other type of disk-seal triodes. Between 1000 mc and 3000 mc, the task is shared by either disk-seal tubes or the klystron; above

3000 mc, the klystron is used almost exclusively. Typical oscillator circuits at all these frequencies have been shown at various points in the preceding chapters, and no further discussion will be undertaken here.

I-F AMPLIFIERS

The signal, at the output of the mixer, is transferred to a group of i-f amplifiers whose characteristics determine the bandwidth and amplification of the entire receiver. To date three types of i-f amplifiers have been employed. These are:

1. Synchronous single-tuned.
2. Staggered single-tuned.
3. Double-tuned.

Synchronous Single-tuned. The circuit of a synchronous single-tuned amplifier is shown in Fig. 11–11. It consists simply of a parallel-tuned circuit together with a coupling capacitor and a grid resistor for the following stage. The type of bias generally employed is cathode bias, derived from the plate and screen current flowing through a cathode resistor. To prevent degeneration (if this is not desired), a shunting capacitor is placed across the cathode resistor. Essentially, then, we employ impedance coupling between stages, the name "synchronous" applying not so much to the type of tuning circuit as it does to the

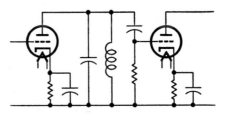

Fig. 11.11. The basic form of a synchronous single-tuned amplifier.

fact that if a group of such stages are connected together (that is, in cascade), all of the resonant circuits would be peaked to the same frequency.

To determine the effect of peaking all of the tuning circuits to the same frequency, let us consider the shape of one tuning curve. This is shown in Fig. 11–12. Note that the response is not uniform, but varies from point to point. At the resonant frequency (labeled F_0 in the illustration) the response of the circuit is at its peak, or maximum. From this point, in either direction, the response tapers off until it soon becomes negligible.

Now, this tuned circuit will permit a certain group of frequencies to pass. In other words, the circuit in which it is connected possesses a certain bandwidth. By definition, the bandwidth of a circuit has been defined as illustrated in Fig. 11–12. It is equal to the numerical difference in cycles between the two frequencies at which the impedance presented by the tuning circuit is equal to 0.707 of the impedance presented at F_0 (that is, the maximum impedance). Thus, in the response curve shown in Fig. 11–12, the impedance at points A–A' is 0.707 (or $1/\sqrt{2}$) of the impedance offered by the circuit at F_0. In this particular illustration, the bandwidth is 0.4 mc.

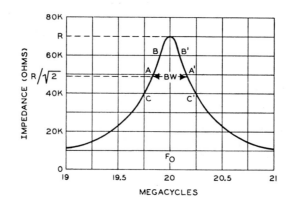

FIG. 11.12.   The tuning curve for a single parallel resonant circuit and its bandwidth (BW).

A further note of importance is the fact that, if the gain of the circuit is considered as equal to 1 at F_0, it is down 3 db at points A–A'. That this is so can be seen from the following.

The definition of the decibel is given by: db $= 20 \log (E_1/E_2)$ where E_1 here would be the voltage at F_0, and E_2 would be the voltage at points A–A'. For the sake of simplicity, let us assign a value of 1 volt to E_1. At either point A or point A' the impedance offered to the same signal is $1/\sqrt{2}$, or 0.707 times as great. Hence, the voltage developed at either of these two points will be 0.707 volt. Substituting these values in the formula we have: db $= 20 \log (1/0.707)$ or db $= 20 \log 1.414$, or about 3 db.

Points A–A' are also known as the "half power" points because $P = E_1{}^2/R$, and since $E_2 = E_1/\sqrt{2}$, then $P_{A-A'} = E_1{}^2/2R$, which is one-half the power developed across R at F_0, the peak of the curve.

With this concept of bandwidth in mind, let us consider two single-tuned amplifiers, both tuned to the same frequency. If these two amplifiers are in cascade (that is, follow each other), then the overall bandwidth is not equal to the bandwidth of either circuit, as one might expect, but to 64 per cent of this value. The reason for the shrinkage in bandwidth will be apparent from the following.

The response curve of the first amplifier, shown in Fig. 11–13A, has a maximum value of amplification of 1 at F_0, its peak, and 0.707 at the ends of the bandpass. Let us say that the mid-frequency is 10 mc, while the end frequencies of the bandpass are 9 and 11 mc respectively. If each of these three frequencies has an amplitude of 1 volt at the input to this tuned stage, then at the output they would possess the following

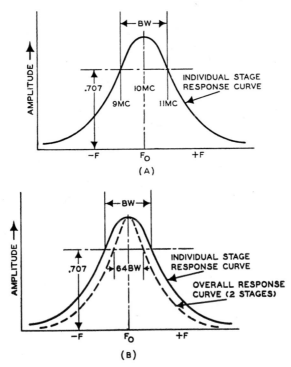

Fig. 11.13.   (A) The response curve of one single-tuned amplifier. (B) A comparison of the response curves of one and two single-tuned amplifiers.

values: at 9 mc—1 × 0.707, or 0.707 volt; at 10 mc, 1 volt; and at 11 mc, 1 × 0.707, or 0.707 volt.

These same three frequencies are now passed through the second tuned circuit. Since this second circuit possesses the same characteristics as its predecessor, here is the result at its output: At 9 mc—0.707 × 0.707, or 0.49 volt; at 10 mc—1 × 1, or 1 volt; and at 11 mc—0.707 × 0.707, or 0.49 volt. After passage through the two amplifiers, 9 and 11 mc are no longer within the 0.707 region about the resonant frequency of 10 mc. To find frequencies with voltages equal to at least 0.707 of the 10-mc voltage we must move closer to 10 mc. The result, of course, is a narrower bandpass; more accurately, 36 per cent narrower. (See Fig. 11–13B.)

A general formula which indicates the bandwidth of any number of synchronous single tuned stages is

$$\text{Bandwidth} = \frac{\sqrt{2^{1/N} - 1}}{2\pi R C_t}$$

where N = number of stages,

R = resistance of the total circuit,

C_t = total interstage capacitance.

A coil and capacitor, by themselves, will possess an extremely high impedance at resonance if neither branch contains an appreciable amount of resistance. The bandwidth of such a circuit would be quite narrow because of the sharply peaked response curve.   In order to achieve a certain bandwidth, a resistor is generally shunted across the circuit, its purpose being to broaden the peak so that the desired bandwidth is obtained.   Since this resistor (which may actually be shunted across the tuned circuit or may be the grid resistor of the following stage) is considerably lower in impedance than the value of the resonant circuit itself, the total interstage impedance will be very close to the value of the resistor.   It is this value which is indicated in the foregoing equation.

To determine how rapidly the over-all bandwidth of a group of synchronous single-tuned i-f amplifiers decreases with the addition of more and more stages, a table has been developed in which the value of $\sqrt{2^{1/N} - 1}$ is shown for values of n from 1 through 10.   (See Table 11-1.)   For one stage,

TABLE 11-1.   THE VALUE OF THE EXPRESSION $\sqrt{2^{1/N} - 1}$ FOR VALUES OF n FROM 1 TO 10.

N	$\sqrt{2^{1/N} - 1}$
1	1.00
2	0.64
3	0.51
4	0.44
5	0.39
6	0.35
7	0.32
8	0.30
9	0.28
10	0.27

of course, the value of $\sqrt{2^{1/N} - 1}$ is 1, which, when substituted in the equation, reveals the bandwidth to be equal to

$$\text{Bandwidth} = \frac{1}{2\pi R C_t}$$

Now, if two such stages are connected in cascade, the over-all bandwidth decreases to 0.64 of its bandwidth when only one stage was used. This was noted previously. With three stages, the total bandwidth narrows down to 0.51 of its value of one stage, or it is now roughly one-half the bandwidth of one tuned circuit used by itself. With the addition of successive stages, the bandwidth decreases, although not with the same rapidity that it did when only one or two stages were employed.

The over-all gain of a multistage amplifier employing synchronous single-tuned stages is given by

$$\text{Gain} = \left(\frac{g_m\sqrt{2^{1/N} - 1}}{2\pi C_t \text{BW}}\right)^N$$

where g_m = mutual conductance of the amplifier tube,

BW = over-all bandwidth desired.

The equation indicates that, in order to achieve high gain, the value of g_m should be high and that of C_t should be small. Since C_t is composed, in large measure, of the input (C_i) and output (C_o) capacitances of the tubes used as the amplifiers, it has been suggested that the ratio

$$\frac{g_m}{C_o + C_i}$$

of each tube be used as a "Figure of Merit" of that tube. The higher the value of this ratio, the more desirable the tube for use as an i-f amplifier.

The fact that the individual stage bandwidth must be widened, as the number of stages in the i-f string increases, in order to obtain a given over-all bandwidth is clearly indicated in Table 11–2. The over-all band-

TABLE 11–2. THE INTERSTAGE BANDWIDTH AND OVER-ALL GAIN
OF SYNCHRONOUS SINGLE-TUNED AMPLIFIERS.

No. of Amplifier Stages	Interstage Bandwidth (mc)	Over-all Gain (db)
1	5	24
2	7.8	37
4	11.5	61
6	14.3	80
8	16.6	96
10	18.7	110

width desired is 5 mc. If only one amplifier stage is used, then the bandwidth of its interstage tuning circuit is the required 5 mc. When a second stage is added, the bandwidth of each separate unit must now be increased to 7.8 mc in order that the over-all bandwidth be 5 mc. When four stages are used, the individual bandwidth required becomes 11.5 mc in order that the over-all bandwidth be 5 mc. The table reveals that for a ten-stage amplifier, the individual stage bandwidth is 18.7 mc in order that the over-all bandwidth be only 5 mc.

The advantages of synchronous single-tuned amplifier systems are the simplicity of construction and the ease with which such amplifiers can be aligned.   Actually, all we require for alignment purposes is a signal generator and a vacuum-tube voltmeter. The generator is attached between grid and ground of the last i-f amplifier, and the vacuum-tube voltmeter is connected across the load resistor of the second detector that follows the i-f amplifier strip. The generator frequency is set to the peak frequency of the individual tuning circuit. The coil is now adjusted (generally by a powdered-iron core) until the vacuum-tube voltmeter reading is maximum. The signal generator is then moved to the grid of the next preceding i-f amplifier, and the tuning coil in the plate of this tube is adjusted until the meter reading is again maximum. This procedure is repeated for each stage in the amplifier system.

The disadvantage of using synchronous single-tuned amplifiers lies in their poor efficiency. With each additional stage, the individual bandwidth must be broadened and this, in turn, acts to reduce the gain of the stage. In Table 11–2, the over-all gain (in db) is indicated for specified numbers of amplifier stages. It is seen that, as the number of stages increase, the rise in gain becomes less and less. Thus, in going from 4 to 6 stages, the over-all gain increased by 19 db. However, from 6 to 8 stages, the gain rise amounted only to 16 db, and from 8 to 10 stages, only 14 db. To obtain a gain of 14 or 16 db from two additional amplifiers is extremely poor efficiency. In the present instance this is due entirely to the very broad bandwidth required of the individual stages.

Stagger-tuned Amplifiers. An i-f system can be designed in which single-tuned circuits similar to those just described are employed, but where the various tuned circuits are not all peaked to the same frequency. This is known as stagger-tuning. In its most common form, alternate stages are resonated at frequencies above and below the desired mid-band i-f value.

An indication of the effect that stagger tuning has on the over-all response curve can be obtained from the following simple illustration.

Consider two single-tuned amplifiers, each with the same bandwidth, but with their peaks separated (or staggered) by an amount equal to their bandwidth. (See Fig. 11–14.) The result is a response in which the over-all bandwidth (to the 0.707 points) is 1.4 times the bandwidth of a single stage. The over-all gain, however, is now only one-half that of the two stages tuned to the same frequency. This is so because at the center frequency of the over-all response curve, the individual stage responses are only 0.707 of their peak response. The product of the stage gains is approximately one-half (0.707 × 0.707 = 0.5).

Now, to progress one step further. We have seen that by stagger-tuning two tuned circuits, we achieve 1.4 times the bandwidth of a single stage but with only one-half the gain. Suppose, however, we retain stagger tuning, but we decrease the bandwidth of each individual tuned circuit. The over-all bandwidth of the stagger-tuned system will still be 1.4 times the bandwidth of the individual stages. However, because we have

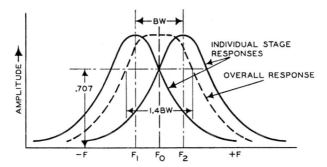

Fig. 11.14. By stagger-tuning two tuned circuits wide bandpass may be obtained. See text.

decreased the individual coil's bandwidth, 1.4 times this new figure will be less than 1.4 times the previous figure when each individual bandwidth was greater. The advantage of this is that we still get a greater bandwidth than if we had not stagger-tuned the circuits, and the over-all gain remains high.

A simple illustration will make this clearer. Suppose that the bandwidth of each individual stage is decreased to 0.707 of its original value. To do this, we raise the individual circuit Q's to 1.4 times their previous value, which will provide an increase in gain by 1.4 times. Now, when the stages are staggered by an amount equal to this reduced bandwidth, the over-all gain at the mid-frequency is one-half the product of 1.4 times 1.4. The answer is 1. Thus the over-all gain is now the same as with the previous amplifier where both circuits are tuned to the same frequency, but the bandwidth is greater.

If we carry this process further, and decrease the over-all bandwidth of the two stagger-tuned circuits so that it equals the narrow bandwidth obtained when two synchronous tuned amplifiers are used, the gain rises even higher. Stagger-tuning thus permits us to achieve the same bandwidth as the previous synchronous single-tuned system but with greater gain.

An important relationship and one which should be remembered by all radio men is the fact that bandwidth of any parallel resonant circuit (or an ordinary resistance-coupled amplifier) is inversely proportional to the amplification of that system. Expressed a little differently, we can say that bandwidth multiplied by gain equals a constant. Thus, if we increase the bandwidth of a system by 1.5 times, we decrease its gain by the same amount. For any individual tuning coil, bandwidth equals F_0/Q, where F_0 is its resonant frequency, and Q is the figure of merit of the coil. The expression tells us that, for any given resonant frequency,

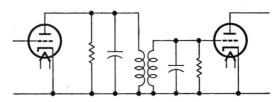

FIG. 11.15.   The basic diagram of a double-tuned i-f amplifier.

increasing the bandwidth can be accomplished only by decreasing the Q of the coil a proportional amount. However, if we raise the resonant frequency of the coil, maintaining Q constant, then the bandwidth will increase in like measure.

Double-tuned I-f Amplifiers. The schematic diagram of a double-tuned i-f amplifier is shown in Fig. 11–15. Energy is transferred from one circuit to another by the inductive coupling which exists between primary and secondary windings of each interstage transformer. Both sections of the transformer are tuned and, in general, both coils possess the same Q. The response curve for this type of amplifier will depend upon the degree of coupling between the primary and secondary windings of the transformer. If the separation of the windings is large and therefore the coupling is loose, a response curve similar to that of a single-tuned circuit is obtained. However, as the windings are moved closer together, the gain increases and, at the same time, the response curve broadens out. This process continues until a point known as critical coupling is reached, where the gain is maximum and the response curve is flat-topped. Moving the windings closer together beyond critical coupling causes the ends of the curve to spread out and become double-humped. This type of response curve, is, in most instances, undesirable since it destroys the uniformity of response of the circuit. Critical coupling is the point at which these transformers should be operated. (See Fig. 11–16.)

Since the response curve of this tuned circuit is flat-topped, connecting several of these stages in cascade results in a slower bandwidth reduction than is true of either of the two previous amplifier systems. Gain, too, is high because the shunting capacitances of plate circuit of one tube and the grid circuit of the following tube are separated from each other by the separate transformer windings, and the plate-to-grid coupling capacitor with its shunting capacitance (to ground) is also eliminated. A double-tuned system is thus preferable to either of the two previous types of amplifiers. Its chief disadvantage, however, is the relatively greater diffi-

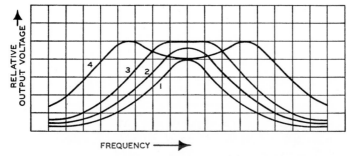

FIG. 11.16. The response curve of a double-tuned i-f amplifier depends upon the degree of coupling between the primary and secondary windings of the interstage transformer. Curves 1 and 2—undercoupled. Curve 3—critical coupled. Curve 4—overcoupled.

culty in aligning and adjusting such a system. Alignment by simple peaking is now no longer possible and a sweep generator, an oscilloscope, and special marker frequencies are required if the alignment is to be accomplished properly.

A comparison of the gains and bandwidths of synchronous single-tuned and double-tuned amplifiers is given in Table 11–3. The over-all bandwidth desired in each case is 5.0 mc. In order to achieve this, say with 6 amplifier stages, the individual bandwidth of each circuit in the synchronous single-tuned system must be 14.3 mc wide. On the other hand, using the double-tuned amplifiers, each stage need be only 8.6 mc wide. The result, as indicated, is that the gain of the synchronous system is 80 db, whereas the double-tuned system provides 125 db. The gain of a 6-stage stagger-tuned amplifier would be 116 db.

The construction of an i-f amplifier strip is shown in Fig. 11–17. It employs five 6AK5 stages followed by a second detector. Although this strip uses stagger tuning, the same arrangement of parts would prevail with either of the two other systems. Note the use of miniature tubes, and the compact placement of capacitors, coils, and resistors, to insure short leads with a minimum introduction of stray capacitance. Adjustment of the coils for peaking is accomplished with slotted screws extending above the chassis.

TABLE 11–3. A COMPARISON OF THE GAIN AND BANDWIDTH CHARACTERISTICS OF SYNCHRONOUS SINGLE-TUNED AND DOUBLE-TUNED I-F SYSTEMS. (*Courtesy B.S.T.J.*)

| No. of Amplifier Stages | Synchronous Single-Tuned Amplifiers | | Double-Tuned Amplifiers | |
	Interstage Bandwidth (mc)	Over-all Gain (db)	Interstage Bandwidth (mc)	Over-all Gain (db)
1	5	24	5	27
2	7.8	37	6.2	47
4	11.5	61	7.6	87
6	14.3	80	8.6	125
8	16.6	96	9.3	162
10	18.7	110	9.8	198

FIG. 11.17. The appearance and construction of a high-frequency i-f amplifier strip. (*Courtesy Bell System Technical Journal*)

Second Detectors. In UHF superheterodyne receivers, as in the better-known lower frequency sets, detection of the signal beyond the i-f system is accomplished most frequently by means of simple diodes or their equivalent, crystal detectors. A simple diode detector is shown in Fig. 11–18. If the i-f system employs either synchronous single-tuned circuits or stagger tuning, the coupling circuit between the last i-f amplifier stage and the detector will appear as indicated in Fig. 11–19. On the

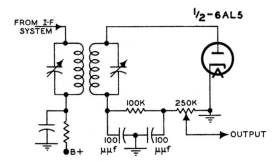

FIG. 11.18.   The schematic diagram of a simple diode detector.

other hand, if transformer coupling is utilized, the circuit will appear as shown in Fig. 11–18.

Current passes through the tube whenever its plate is positive with respect to its cathode. The electrons then travel through the coil and load

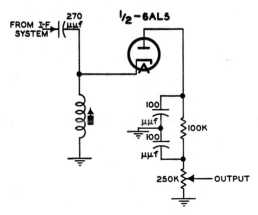

FIG. 11.19.   Another illustration of a simple diode detector employing another type of coupling.

resistors back to the tube again. The i-f voltages are by-passed around the load resistors by shunting capacitors, thus preventing the i-f voltages from reaching the succeeding amplifiers.

Just how extensive the detector circuit will be depends upon the frequency range of the signal to be received. If the bandwidth is narrow, perhaps 0.5 mc or less, then the detector circuits shown in Figs. 11–18 and 11–19 will work satisfactorily. However, if the desired bandwidth is greater, possibly to the extent of 3, 4, or more mc, as it is in television systems and most radar applications, then a more elaborate detector circuit is required.

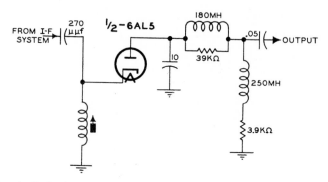

FIG. 11.20. A diode detector capable of passing signals having frequencies up to 4 mc.

Shunt and series peaking coils are inserted in the detector output circuit to maintain a uniform response up to the highest frequencies desired. (See Fig. 11–20.) The response of the detector load circuit, above 1 mc, is dependent largely upon the amount of capacitance present in the circuit.

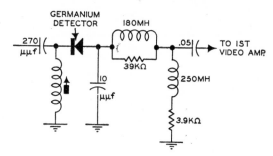

FIG. 11.21. A detector using a germanium crystal.

The purpose of the peaking coils is to neutralize this shunting capacitance as much as possible and therefore prevent the higher frequency components of the detected signal from being by-passed around the load resistor. More information concerning such peaking circuits will be given in the next section dealing with video amplifiers.

In place of a diode tube, it is also possible to use a crystal rectifier of the germanium type. (See Fig. 11–21.) In construction and operation, germanium and the silicon crystals previously described are very similar. In general, silicon crystals are employed as microwave mixers at the front end of the receiver, whereas germanium crystals are more useful as second detectors. This division of application is due entirely to the properties of the crystals. Silicon has much better rectifying properties at microwaves than germanium. On the other hand, germanium gives much better back-to-front ratios than silicon crystals. When a diode conducts, current flows in one direction only. In a crystal, current flows in both directions, although more current flows in one direction than another. To obtain the greatest efficiency, the ratio of the current flowing in the desired direction to the current flowing in the opposite direction should be as high as possible. For germanium crystals that are built to withstand the greater voltages at the second detector, the back-to-front ratio is better than it is for silicon crystals built to withstand the same voltage.

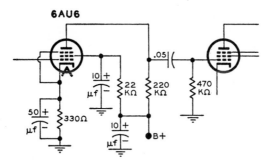

FIG. 11.22. An audio amplifier.

AUDIO AND VIDEO AMPLIFIERS

The signal, at the output of the second detector, is usually too weak to drive the output device used with the particular receiver and hence requires further amplification. To determine the type of amplifier to use, the nature of the received signal must be known. If, for example, an audio signal is to be received, then the usual audio amplifier is used. A typical stage is shown in Fig. 11–22. On the other hand, if a video or radar pulse type of signal is to be amplified, the amplifier form must be altered to be able to pass a wider range of frequencies. In the case of video signals, a uniform frequency response from 30 cps to 4.0 mc is required. For radar pulses, the extent of the frequency response may be less, perhaps extending to 2 mc. In the following pages we will consider what changes must be made to the conventional amplifier circuit to enable it to provide uniform amplification from 30 cps to 4.0 mc. If a narrower bandpass is required, the changes will be fairly obvious.

The type of amplifier that can be used to give the necessary 4-mc bandwidth is restricted, almost without exception, to resistance-capacitance coupled networks. Transformers and inductances, even if they could be built to possess a 4-mc width, would involve a disproportionate expense. On the other hand, r-c amplifiers have the advantage of small space and economy and are universally employed.

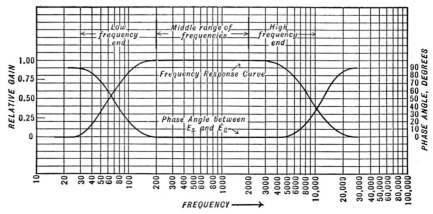

FIG. 11.23.   The frequency and phase response of a resistance-coupled amplifier.

From knowledge of conventional resistance-coupled amplifiers that the radio man possesses he knows that a flat response is obtained in the middle range of frequencies, say, from 200 cps up to approximately 3000 cps with ordinary circuits. A frequency response curve is illustrated in Fig. 11–23 and applies to any ordinary r-c amplifier. The frequency characteristics of the amplifier, throughout the middle range, are suitable for use in video amplifiers, and this section of the curve requires no further improvement. However, the responses at either end of the curve are far from satisfactory and corrective measures must be taken. Fortunately, any changes made in the circuit to improve the high- or low-frequency responses of the curve will not react on each other (with one limitation noted later), and each end may be analyzed separately and independently. Let us begin first with the high-frequency compensation.

When determining the high-frequency operation of a resistance-coupled amplifier, it is necessary to consider only the plate load resistor, the grid input resistor of the next stage, and any shunting capacitances that are present in the circuit. The coupling capacitor C_c offers negligible opposition to high-frequency alternating currents and can be disregarded. Fig. 11–24 shows the high-frequency equivalent circuit of an r-c amplifier.

Since R_L and R_g are both resistances and are both constant in value, any change in high-frequency response must be due to the shunting capacitance, C_T. The resistance of a capacitor decreases with frequency and, in effect, the total impedance of the parallel combination of R_L, R_g, and C_T becomes less as the frequency increases. The alternating voltage that is developed at the tube will divide between r_p, which is the internal tube plate resistance, and the parallel combination of R_g, R_L, and C_T. Since the value of the impedance of the parallel combination decreases, it means that with increasing frequency, more and more of the output voltage will be lost across the tube's plate resistance, r_p. If less voltage reaches the grid of the next tube, less is available for amplification.

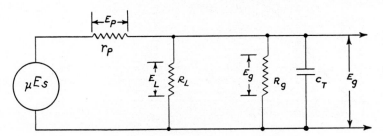

FIG. 11.24. The equivalent circuit, at the high frequencies, of the resistance-capacitance-coupled amplifier of Fig. 11.22.

To increase the gain at the high-frequency end of the response curve, it is obvious that the value of the shunting capacitances should be reduced. The shunting capacitance is composed of three components: (1) the output capacitance of the preceding tube, (2) the input capacitance of the following tube, and (3) the wiring capacitance to ground. For a typical video amplifier tube, the 6AC7, the output capacitance is 5 $\mu\mu$f. The wiring capacitance may run from about 5 $\mu\mu$f to 15 or 20 $\mu\mu$f, whereas the input capacitance of the next tube might well be about 10 $\mu\mu$f and, unless tube construction changes radically, will remain close to this figure for most tubes. The wiring or stray capacitance can be reduced if the amplifier is carefully constructed. The wiring capacitance will be kept at a minimum (about 5 $\mu\mu$f) if all leads are as short as possible, low-loss sockets are used, and the parts are intelligently placed.

With the foregoing reduction in the value of the capacitance, due perhaps in part to the use of tubes of small internal capacitance and in part to careful wiring, it is possible to increase the frequency response of an amplifier to .1 or .2 mc. The gain, however, especially near the end of the curve, is not uniform. To improve the response uniformity, the value of the load resistor can be lowered, probably close to the impedance presented by the shunting capacitance. In this manner, the effect of capacitor C_T is less, and it does not begin to destroy the linearity of the frequency response curve until some higher frequency. The results for several resistor values are shown in Fig. 11–25. As the resistance becomes less, the extent of the flat portion of the curve increases, but the stage gain decreases. For many of the amplifiers found in commercial receivers, values of R_L as low as 1500 ohms are used. This results in gains in the neighborhood of 20 or so per stage, which is not very high. Obviously, further extension of the frequency range of the amplifier by lowering the load resistance value is not very feasible.

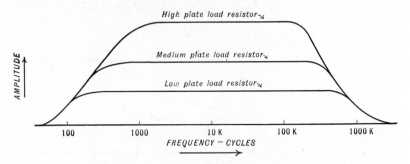

FIG. 11.25. By lowering the plate load resistor, it is possible to increase the extent of the flat portion of the response curve.

A more satisfactory method of increasing the flat response of the amplifier can be obtained through the insertion of a small inductance in series with the load resistor. The inductance is so chosen that it will neutralize the effect of the shunting capacitances at least to the extent that we may improve the amplifier response at the upper frequencies.

A circuit diagram using this compensating inductance is shown in Fig. 11–26. L is chosen to resonate with C_T at or slightly above the highest frequency at which flat response is desired. In this manner, the peaking inductance tends to compensate for the loss caused by the capacitance C_T and the curve remains flat. If too much peaking is resorted to, the curve will rise sharply at resonance (of L and C_T) and result in an undesirable hump.

A second method of improving the high-frequency response of an amplifier is to insert a small coil in series with the coupling capacitor, as illustrated in Fig. 11–27. This method gives higher gain and better phase response than shunt peaking, because the components of C_T are no longer lumped together in one unit, but have been separated. On the left-hand side of the series inductance there is the output capacitance of the preceding tube, while on the other side there is the input capacitanc of the next tube. By this separation, the load resistor R_L may be chosen higher in value because only C_o is directly across it now and not C_T. Since C_o is smaller than C_T, its capacitive reactance is greater and it will have less of a shunting effect on R_L. Hence, a larger value of R_L is possible. The series combi-

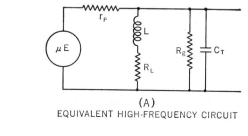

(A)
EQUIVALENT HIGH-FREQUENCY CIRCUIT

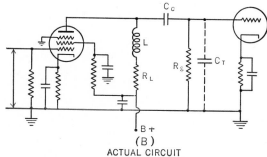

(B)
ACTUAL CIRCUIT

FIG. 11.26. High-frequency compensation for an r-c amplifier using shunt peaking.

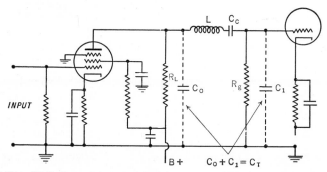

FIG. 11.27. High-frequency compensation by means of a series peaking coil.

nation of the inductance and the total capacitance is designed, by proper choice of L, to have a resonant frequency above the highest video frequency desired, generally 4 mc.

It is further possible to combine shunt and series peaking and obtain the advantages of both. The shunt coil is designed to neutralize the

output capacitance of the preceding tube while the series coil combines
with the input capacitance (and stray wiring capacitance) of the next
tube. With this double combination, it is possible to achieve 1.8 times
more gain than can be derived through the use of shunt peaking alone.
Furthermore, the phase distortion of the coupling network is lower than
either of the previous two types. An amplifier using combined shunt and
series peaking is shown in Fig. 11–28. A resistor is shunted across the series

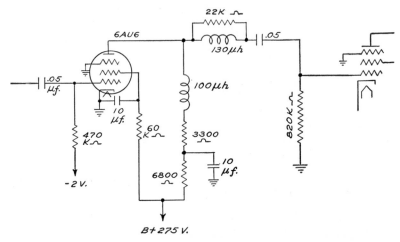

FIG. 11.28. A video amplifier employing series and shunt peaking.

coil to minimize any sharp increase in circuit response due to the combination
of the series coil inductance and its natural or inherent capacitance. The
coil is designed to have a natural frequency considerably above the highest
video frequency. In production, however, a certain number of coils will
be produced with natural resonant frequencies within the range covered
by the amplifier. The effect is a sharp rise in response. It is to prevent
this peak, if it occurs, that the shunting resistor is used. Its value is
generally four to five times the impedance of the series coil at the highest
video frequency.

Low-frequency Compensation. At the low-frequency end of the
band, it is possible to disregard the shunting capacities since their reactance,
given by

$$X_c = \frac{1}{2\pi f C}$$

is very high, and they do not affect the low-frequency signal voltages
in any way. Now, however, it becomes necessary to include the

coupling capacitor. The equivalent low-frequency circuit is shown in Fig. 11–29.

When an alternating voltage is applied to the input of V_1, an amplified version of this voltage will appear across R_L, due, of course, to the usual amplifier action of a tube. It is desired now to transfer this a-c voltage to the grid of V_2, and this is accomplished through the series combination of C_c and R_g. How much of the total voltage of R_L will appear across R_g is dependent on how great an opposition (or impedance) C_c presents to the a-c current flowing through this circuit. At low frequencies, the opposition of the capacitor is high and a large part of the a-c voltage

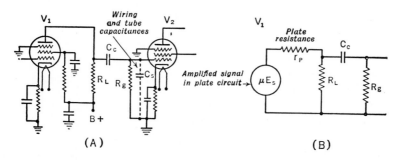

FIG. 11.29. A resistance-coupled amplifier (A) and its low-frequency equivalent circuit (B).

is lost. Less is available for R_g. This condition, as every radio man knows, is responsible for the poor low-frequency response of resistance-coupled amplifiers. Increasing the frequency will result in less voltage lost across C_c and more available for R_g.

The phase of the voltage at R_g is governed by the amount of opposition C_c offers to the a-c wave passing through the circuit. Consider, for example, what the phase of the a-c current would be if only C_c were present in the circuit. The current flowing would be 90 degrees ahead of the voltage. Now, add a resistor in series with the capacitor. The current flowing in the circuit becomes less than 90 degrees out of phase with the applied voltage. The voltage drop across the resistor is in phase with the current flowing through it and hence would also be less than 90 degrees out of phase with the applied voltage.

As the opposition that C_c offers to the current in the circuit becomes less and less (say, with increasing frequency), R_g becomes more important and the current approaches closer and closer in phase with E_L. At the middle range of frequencies, the opposition of C_c may be neglected entirely and E_g is in phase with E_L, similar to any other completely resistive circuit.

We see, then, that, when voltages of many frequencies and with no phase difference are applied at E_L, the voltages appearing across E_g have different phase relationships, the degree dependent upon each frequency.

The lowest frequency will have the greatest phase angle introduced while it is traveling from the output of the tube to the input of the next stage. As the frequency rises, the phase difference becomes less, gradually reaching zero.

A video wave, which contains many frequencies, will have its shape altered when it passes through the resistance-coupled amplifier network. With a change in shape, the effect of the wave at the grid of the picture tube must certainly be different and the resulting image is distorted to some extent. By distortion, we mean that the image is not an exact duplicate of the original. The amount of change introduced into the picture detail depends on the degree of phase distortion.

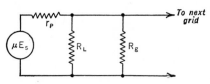

FIG. 11.30.   The equivalent circuit, at the middle frequencies, of the resistance-coupled amplifier of Fig. 11.29.

In the middle range of frequencies, from 200 to 2000 cps, C_c has no effect on the passing waves and can be disregarded. The equivalent circuit for the middle range now assumes the form shown in Fig. 11–30. Since only resistances are involved, there is no phase shift introduced between the voltages at R_L and R_g.

The operation of the circuit, as explained, shows that the lower the frequency, the greater the effect of the coupling capacitor. The response gradually falls off because the reactance of C_c soon becomes dominant and a large portion of the output voltage of T_1 is lost here. The phase delay of the signal begins to change, eventually becoming as great as 90 degrees.

To increase the linear response at the low frequencies, either C_c should be made larger so that it will have less reactance or R_g should be made larger. The limit of the size of either C_c or R_g is governed by several factors:

1. Too large a value of C_c increases the stray capacitance to ground and is certain to interfere with the high-frequency response.

2. A large coupling capacitor generally has an appreciable leakage current. This would permit the positive power supply voltage on the preceding plate to affect the grid of the following tube and bias it positively.

3. A large value of R_g could prove detrimental if the tube to which it is attached has even a slight amount of gas.

4. Finally, high values of R_g and C_c result in "motor boating" (or oscillations) because of the slow building up and leaking off of charge across the combination.

It is possible to improve the low-frequency response without making either R_g or C_c too large by inserting a resistor and capacitor in the plate circuit of tube V_1, as indicated in Fig. 11–31. R_f and C_f are two added components and they form the low-frequency compensation circuit. Through the addition of this resistor and capacitor, the impedance in the

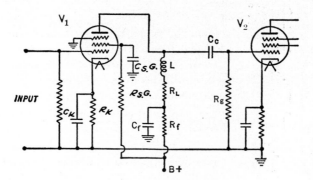

FIG. 11.31.   Low-frequency compensation (R_f, C_f) of an r-c amplifier.

plate circuit is increased for the lower frequencies and greater gain results. At the high frequencies, C_f by-passes R_f and effectively nullifies it.   Furthermore, C_f and R_f serve as a decoupling filter which aids in stabilizing the stage by preventing any low-frequency oscillations or "motor boating" from feedback between stages by way of the power supply.

The value of C_f in Fig. 11–31 is obtained from the expression:

$$R_L C_f = C_c R_g$$

where R_L, C_c, and R_g have previously been assigned values. R_L will be determined by the highest frequency to be passed by the amplifier, and C_c and R_g will be as large as possible but within the limitations noted above.   Finally, R_f should have a resistance which is at least twenty times greater than the impedance of C_f at the lowest frequency to be passed.

C_f and R_f provide the greatest amount of compensation, but there are additional factors which influence the extent of the low-frequency response. One of these is the screen-grid dropping resistor and by-pass capacitor. For best results, R_{sg} and C_{sg} should have a time constant which is at least three times as long as the period $(1/f)$ of the lowest video frequency to be passed by the amplifier.   A second governing factor is the cathode resistor R_k and the cathode by-pass capacitor C_k.   These should be chosen so that they satisfy the following expression:

$$R_k C_k = R_f C_f$$

Admittedly, the latter two compensating circuits are not quite as important

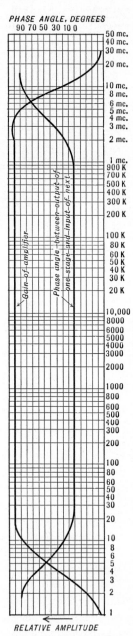

PHASE ANGLE, DEGREES

RELATIVE AMPLITUDE

Fig. 11.32. The frequency response of a fully compensated resistance-coupled amplifier.

as the decoupling resistor and capacitor, C_f and R_f, but they should be considered in the amplifier design.

In the design procedure of video amplifiers, the values of the high-frequency compensating components are chosen first. These include R_L, L_s, and L_c. Next, the low-frequency compensating components, C_f and R_f, are computed, then R_{sg} and C_{sg}, and finally R_k and C_k. The values of each of the latter three resistors must fall within the operating characteristics of the tube as recommended by the manufacturer. This imposes a limitation. However, since we are concerned with a time constant in each instance (as $C_f \times R_f$, $R_{sg} \times C_{sg}$, and $R_k \times C_k$) rather than the individual value of each part, we can usually satisfy all the required conditions.

When both high- and low-frequency compensation is applied to a video amplifier, the result appears as shown in Fig. 11–31. The frequency and phase response of this amplifier are plotted in Fig. 11–32.

UHF RECEIVERS

The officially designated limits of the UHF band extend from 300 mc to 3000 mc. Actually, for our discussion here we can include frequencies above 3000 mc since the basic form of the receiver remains the same.

In the lower section of the UHF region, from 300 mc to roughly 1000 mc, most of the spectrum has been set aside for television broadcasting (470–890 mc). Between 300 and 470 mc there are a variety of commercial and governmental allocations together with a 30-mc band of frequencies (from 420 to 450 mc) which is available to amateurs.

Amateurs who have worked these frequencies have employed converters to reduce the 420-mc signal to some frequency within the r-f range of a VHF communications receiver. This permits the amateur to utilize the receivers he already possesses with only a minimum amount of additional equipment.

An illustration of a 420-mc converter* is shown in Fig. 11–33. The incoming signal is fed directly into the grid circuit of a 6J6 balanced mixer. An oscillator signal is inductively coupled into the same circuit. The two signals combine in the mixer and the difference or i-f frequency is then transferred to an i-f amplifier. The i-f value chosen depends on the local oscillator. The frequency most often recommended is 30 mc, since this falls within one of the ranges which amateur receivers cover.

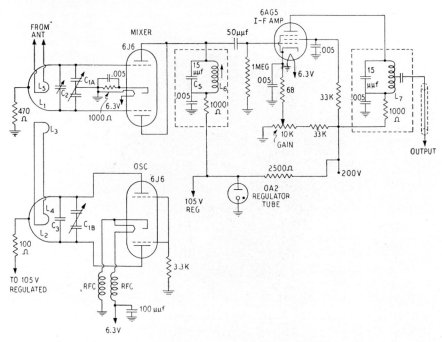

Fig. 11.33. Schematic diagram of a converter for 420 mc. (*Courtesy QST Magazine*)

After the i-f signal has been amplified by an i-f amplifier in the converter, it is transferred to a communications receiver where it is treated as any other received signal.

The tuning circuits of the mixer and oscillator are similar, consisting of small inductances (L_1 and L_2) which are cut from sheet copper in U shape and soldered directly onto the stator assemblies of the tuning capacitor. The latter is a two-section ganged split-stator unit, 6.75 $\mu\mu$f-per-section stator to stator. Brackets are supplied with the tuner on which the 6J6 tube sockets may be mounted. (See Fig. 11–34.) This permits short, direct connections between the tubes and their respective tuning circuits, which is highly essential at these frequencies.

* "Better Results On 420 Mc," by E. P. Tilton. *QST Magazine*, August 1950.

Energy from the oscillator is link-coupled into the mixer circuit. L_6 and C_5 form the output resonant circuit of the mixer, and it is adjusted to 30 mc or whatever i-f value is desired. The signal is then amplified by the 6AG5 and made available to a receiver tuned to the i-f frequency. An 0A2 voltage regulator is incorporated to stabilize convertor operation.

R-f amplifiers are seldom found in UHF equipment because of the scarcity of suitable low-priced tubes. Other factors which enter and

Fig. 11.34.   Photograph of 420-mc converter.   (*Courtesy of QST Magazine*)

complicate the picture are: (1) the low gain obtainable even from the few tubes that can be used; (2) the difficulty of constructing simple tuning circuits; and (3) the increase in mechanical complexity which develops when the r-f, mixer, and oscillator tuning elements are ganged together. In UHF television converters, no r-f amplifiers have as yet been used. In amateur applications where continuous tuning is not as important, some r-f amplifiers have been developed and used, but they are definitely in the minority.

An illustration of an r-f amplifier* which was developed for the 420-mc amateur band is shown in Fig. 11–35. The amplifier is of the grounded-grid variety in which the grid is at r-f ground potential while the signal is received by the cathode. The cathode circuit is untuned since the

* "R.F. Amplifiers For 420 Mc," by E. P. Tilton. *QST Magazine*, January 1952.

low impedance present here would load down a tuned circuit and reduce its gain to 1.

Any one of three tubes may be used. The 5675 is a pencil tube; the 6J4 and 6AF4 are miniature twin triodes. Of these, the 5675 is the most stable, with the 6J4 requiring some neutralization (to keep it from oscillating) and the 6AF4 requiring even more. The neutralizing circuit consists of a small loop (L_3) connected to the cathode and positioned near the plate end of the output tuning circuit. The loop transfers a

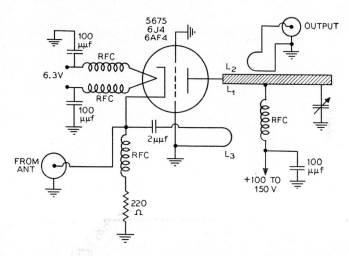

FIG. 11.35. Schematic diagram of r-f amplifier for 420 mc. (*Courtesy QST Magazine*)

small voltage from the output to the cathode circuit in such phase as to suppress any tendency of the tube to oscillate.

The tuning circuit for the amplifier is found in the plate circuit and consists of a coaxial line one-half wavelength long. It is loaded down by the tube's output capacitance at one end and tuned with a small copper plate capacitor at the other. Energy is coupled out of the plate circuit by positioning a small loop of wire near the plate end of the line. The r-f current is high here and provides a strong magnetic field for signal transfer. B+, via an r-f choke and a by-pass capacitor, is also fed into the line at the plate end.

Fig. 11–36 contains two views of the amplifier and its components. The coaxial plate line is made by using a rectangular outer conductor with a removable bottom plate. This permits access to the circuit components which are mounted at one end of the line. The inner conductor of the coaxial line is a rod of ⅝-inch diameter held in position at the center

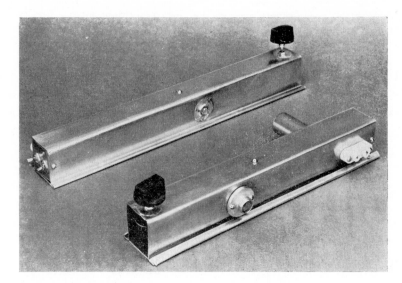

Fig. 11.36A.   Two coaxial-line r-f amplifiers for 420 mc.   The shorter one, in the foreground, uses a 6J4 triode; the larger one, a 5675 pencil tube.   (*Courtesy QST Magazine*)

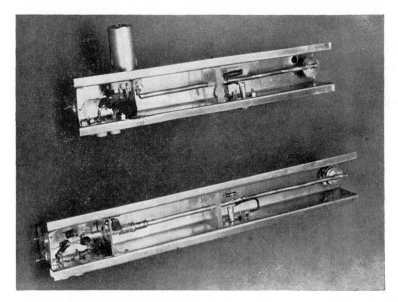

Fig. 11.36B.   Underside view of the two r-f amplifiers shown in Fig. 11.36A. (*Courtesy QST Magazine*)

by a polystyrene block. At the tube end, the rod is fastened to the plate terminals; at the opposite end, it is connected to the circular stator plate of the tuning capacitor.

It will be noted that a longer coaxial line is required with the pencil tube than with the miniature twin triodes. This is because of the lower output capacitance and lead inductance of the pencil triode.

Fig. 11.37. An RCA microwave relay showing the relay receiver and its parabolic antenna. The relay transmitter employs a similar arrangement. (*Courtesy RCA*)

Microwave Relays. Relatively small, low-powered microwave relays are extensively employed for the handling of programs originating outside the studio or as a means of transferring studio signals to a distant transmitter. The latter situation is quite common to F–M and television stations. Studios, for example, are required in the city, whereas the transmitter is situated atop some near-by mountain in order to provide a usable signal over a wide area. Coaxial cable could be employed between the studio and transmitter, but the installation cost is frequently prohibitive and a microwave relay presents a more economical solution.

The power output requirements of microwave relays are very nominal because of the high gain of the transmitting antennas and the relatively short distances to be covered. As an illustration, the RCA Model TTR-1B microwave relay provides an output signal of only 100 milliwatts. When this signal is beamed from a parabolic reflector, an equivalent power output of 500 watts is obtained. This is because the parabolic reflector has a gain of 5000 over a standard half-wave dipole.

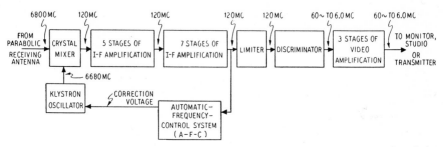

F_IG. 11.38. Block diagram of a microwave relay. It is extensively employed for the handling of programs originating outside the studio or for transferring studio signals to a distant transmitter.

The RCA relay was designed principally for the beaming of remote TV programs to the studio. Its maximum range is specified as 15 miles, although it has been used over greater distances. The relay contains two sections. One section, the transmitter, is set up at the remote location from which the program is originating. The other section, the receiver, is placed at the studio (or station transmitter). (See Fig. 11–37.) Both sections use parabolic reflectors, the transmitter for beaming the signal and the receiver for picking it up.

A block diagram of the receiver portion of this relay is shown in Fig. 11–38. The received signal at the parabolic reflector is transferred to a 1N23B crystal mixer mounted at the end of the waveguide coming from the parabolic reflector. (See Fig. 11–39.) A Western Electric type 2K26 klystron oscillator also feeds a signal into the waveguide, and when the two signals mix, a difference frequency signal of 120 mc is produced. This is the i-f signal.

Five stages of i-f amplification follow the mixer. With a sufficient input to give a satisfactory signal-to-noise ratio, a signal level of at least 50 milliwatts can be obtained at the output. The signal is now led through a coaxial cable to another section of the receiver where there are seven more i-f stages. The signal, by this time, has been amplified to a considerable degree.

Since frequency modulation is used at the transmitter, a limiter and discriminator arrangement are employed at the receiver to demodulate the signal. Following this, there are three stages of video-frequency amplification, after which the signal is available for monitors, the studio control room, and the transmitter.

The receiver also contains an automatic-frequency-control (a-f-c) system whose function it is to keep the receiver in tune for a change in transmitter frequency of plus and minus 20 mc, provided there is no

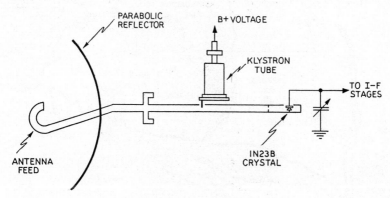

Fig. 11.39. Input circuit arrangement of the microwave relay of Fig. 11.38.

interruption of input signal to the receiver. If the signal is interrupted, the a-f-c system may be expected to lock in automatically when the transmitter oscillator comes within plus or minus 10 mc of the normal frequency of the receiver.

The receiver input circuit is untuned, and thus it is the frequency generated by the klystron oscillator that actually determines what signal will be fed to the i-f system. The klystron signal must mix with whatever signal is received to produce a difference frequency of 120 mc. The correction voltage from the a-f-c system will, within the limits just mentioned, alter the klystron frequency so that the 120-mc i-f will be produced. Should the transmitter signal frequency be too far off, no output at all will be obtained from the receiver.

Inter-city Relays. A somewhat more extensive application of the microwave relay is its use in connecting two or more cities into one network. As an illustration, consider the relay route between Boston and New York. This is shown in Fig. 11–40 and extends over a distance of 220 miles. Not counting the New York and Boston terminals, there are seven relay stations separated from each other at some points by as much as 35 miles. The transmitted power between successive repeater stations is incredibly low, being somewhat less than 1 watt. However, metallic lens antennas are used for both reception and transmission, and each has a gain of 10,000. Antenna beam width is only 2 degrees.

There are four repeaters at each relay station. Each repeater is a broad-band amplifier system capable of handling almost any type of signal having a bandwidth up to 5 mc. Since each repeater is separate and

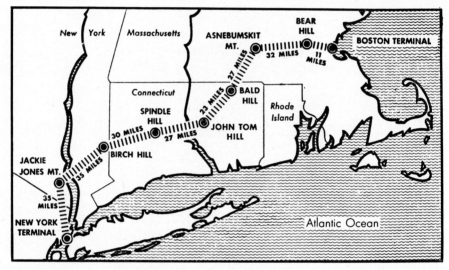

FIG. 11.40. The 220-mile Bell Telephone System microwave relay route between Boston and New York. Each of the black dots represents location of a relay station.

distinct from the others at each station, four channels are available. In normal use, this provides two video channels in each direction. Fig. 11–41 shows, in block diagram form, the arrangement at each relay station and at both terminal stations. This particular relay system operates in the 3700 to 4200-mc band, and the frequencies specifically used between relay stations are chosen so as not to interfere with each other. For example, in the relay station shown in Fig. 11–41, the signals coming from New York into the two upper repeaters have frequencies of 3930 and 4130 mc respectively. Both signals are received by the same lens antenna and fed down a waveguide to a branching filter. Here they are separated (by their 200-mc difference) and each is routed to its respective repeater.

At the output ends of the repeaters, the 4130-mc signal is now 4170 mc, and the 3930-mc signal has been converted to a 3970-mc signal. Both signals are combined by another branching filter and beamed out by a single lens antenna.

The equipment which is contained at the receiving and transmitting terminals and at each repeater station is shown in Fig. 11–42. At the receiving terminal, Fig. 11–42A, the incoming signal, at a frequency of say 4170 mc, is mixed with a locally generated signal of 4235 mc to provide a difference frequency of 65 mc. This is then sent through a series of 65-mc i-f amplifiers and through an F–M receiver where the video signal intelligence is extracted from the incoming carrier. The video signal receives additional video-frequency amplification beyond the detector and then is transferred to a local TV station to be broadcast locally.

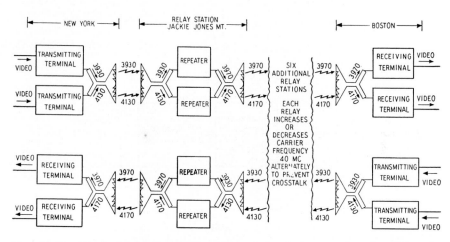

Fig. 11.41. Block diagrams of Boston–New York microwave relay showing equipment at a typical relay station and equipment at each end. (*Courtesy Electronics Magazine*)

The circuits in a repeater section are indicated in Fig. 11–42B. The incoming signal, from a previous station, is received and fed to a balanced converter. A signal frequency of 3930 mc is assumed here. Also feeding into the same converter* is a 3865-mc signal. The two voltages mix, and the resulting difference frequency is 65 mc. This is amplified by a number of i-f stages and then applied to a balanced modulator to which a 3905-mc signal is also fed. The two combine, and this time it is the *sum* frequency of 3970 mc which is amplified and then led up to a metallic lens antenna for transmission to the following station.

An interesting feature of the repeater station circuitry is the manner in which a single klystron oscillator is employed for mixing with the incoming and outgoing signals. The oscillator frequency in the illustration is 3905 mc. This signal is combined in a balanced modulator with a crystal-generated 40-mc signal to provide an output frequency of 3905 —

---

* The terms converter and modulator are frequently used interchangeably.

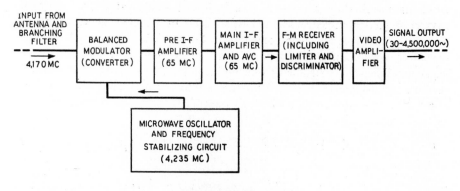

(A) RECEIVING TERMINAL

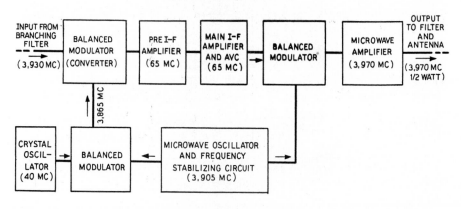

(B) REPEATER

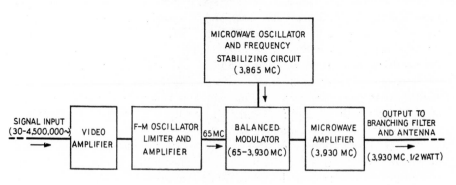

(C) TRANSMITTING TERMINAL

Fig. 11.42.   Block diagrams of the circuitry contained at the receiving and transmitting terminals and at each repeater station of a microwave relay network.

40 or 3865 mc. It is this latter signal which is then sent to combine with the incoming 3930-mc signal to produce the 65-mc i-f voltage.

At the other end of the repeater system, when the signal is to be transmitted, the 65-mc voltage is combined directly with the 3905-mc oscillator signal to produce the necessary 3970-mc signal for transmission to the next station, be it a repeater or the receiving terminal.

The difference between the frequencies of the received and transmitted signals is 40 mc, and this can be traced back to the crystal-controlled 40-mc oscillator. Along the way, each repeater station increases or decreases the carrier frequency 40 mc alternately to prevent crosstalk.

Views of the inside of one of these repeater stations is shown in Fig. 11–43. Most of these stations are set up so that they will operate without anyone in attendance.

2660-Mc Train Communication System.* Two-way microwave communication systems are particularly adaptable to industries engaged in some phase of transportation. An interesting example of one such installation is that employed by a major railroad. The system is designed to provide communication from the engine to the rear of the train and to wayside stations. It is not a replacement for existing communication facilities employed by the railroad but an adjunct to such facilities in order to improve and widen the scope of railroad operation.

Frequency modulation is chosen as the mode of operation because klystrons are employed in the transmitter and these tubes lend themselves more easily to frequency modulation than to amplitude modulation. This is true of many microwave systems.

A block diagram of both transmitter and receiver are shown in Fig. 11–44. The transmitter is crystal-controlled, using a crystal which has a frequency of 4.925925 mc. The oscillator is followed by a buffer which, in turn, feeds the signal into the frequency-modulating network. The Armstrong System of producing F–M is employed here.† Once the signal has been modulated, it is passed through a tripler, a doubler, and two triplers to raise its frequency to 266 mc. The signal now enters a klystron multiplier where a tenfold multiplication occurs, bringing the frequency to its final value of 2660 mc. An additional klystron stage, this time functioning as a straight amplifier, increases the signal power to the nominally rated output of 10 watts.

The antenna to which the signal is fed is unique in design. A structure was required which could be mounted on top of the train, yet which did not protrude so high that it could not clear the roofs of tunnels through

---

* *Electronics,* January 1946, p. 118.

† For further details on the operation of this system, see the author's *F-M Simplified,* published by D. Van Nostrand Company, Inc., New York, 1951.

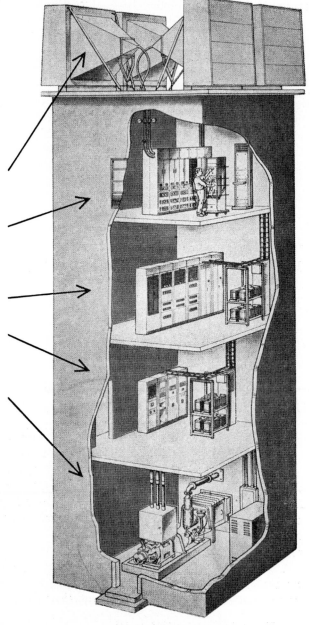

ON THE ROOF are the lens antennas, each with its horn tapering into a waveguide which leads down to equipment

ON THE TOP FLOOR, where the signal is amplified, changed to a different carrier-channel and sent back to another antenna on the roof. Here are testing and switching facilities. Normally unattended, the station is visited periodically for maintenance.

ON THE THIRD FLOOR are the plate voltage power supplies for several score electron tubes.

ON THE SECOND FLOOR are filament power supplies. Storage batteries on both floors will operate the station in an emergency for several hours, but

ON THE GROUND FLOOR is an engine-driven generator which starts on anything more than a brief power failure.

FIG. 11.43. View of inside of a typical repeater station.

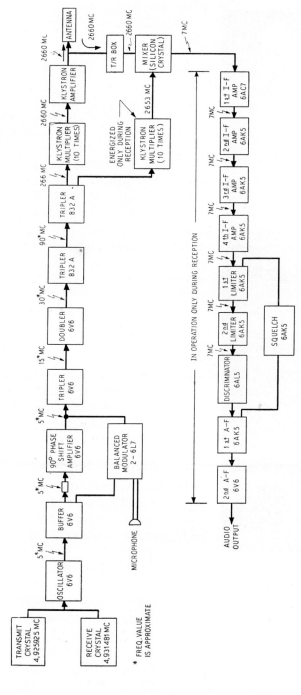

Fig. 11.44. A block diagram of both transmitter and receiver of train microwave system. *(Courtesy Electronics Magazine)*

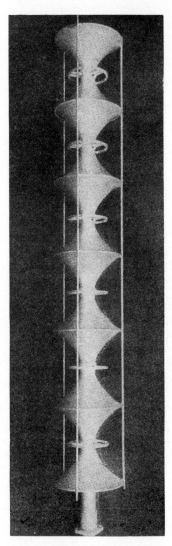

FIG. 11.45. Antenna array used with 2660-mc train communication system. (*Courtesy Electronics Magazine*)

which the train had to pass. A nondirectional pattern was desired since the front and back cars on a train are not always on a direct line with each other; furthermore, a directional pattern would be impractical for communicating with wayside stations as the train sped by.

The antenna which was eventually evolved is shown in Fig. 11–45. It is a 6-bay array, with each bay containing three radial dipoles. The circular dipole construction produces an essentially nondirectional signal. To help concentrate the signal in the horizontal plane, each bay is fitted with a biconical parabolic reflector. This construction, together with the use of 6 bays, produces a nondirectional signal in the horizontal plane having a gain approximately 10 times greater than a simple dipole.

From the block diagram it is seen that the receiver connects to the same antenna as the transmitter. To prevent damage to the receiver when the transmitter is operating, a T–R switch tube is inserted between the receiver and the antenna. The T–R (or Transmit-Receive) tube is a high-speed gaseous switch which permits the received signals to enter the receiving system, yet prevents the transmitter power from doing the same thing and causing destruction to the receiver input circuit.

During reception, the incoming signal is applied to a silicon mixer crystal. To this is added a signal frequency of 2653 mc from the local oscillator to produce a difference or i-f value of 7 mc. Four i-f amplifiers and two limiters then follow the mixer. An F–M discriminator demodulates the signal, after which it is passed through audio voltage and power amplifiers and then to a loud-speaker. The circuit line-up here is similar to that found in any low-frequency F–M receiver. Possibly a greater number of i-f amplifiers are used here, but this is not significant so far as the circuit is concerned.

An interesting feature of the receiver section is the manner in which the local oscillator frequency of 2653 mc is developed. When the receiver is in operation, the transmitter section is not and this permits us to use the latter circuits for the development of the 2653-mc mixing signal. During reception, a separate crystal having a frequency of 4.931481 mc is substituted in the transmitter oscillator circuit for the 4.925925-mc crystal. The 4.931481-mc frequency is then multiplied until it reaches a value of 2653 mc. It is then fed to the silicon mixer crystal where it combines with the received signal.

The klystron multiplier used for the receiver serves only this purpose. It is not used during transmission.

Summary. From the representative UHF receivers which have been discussed in this chapter the reader can see that they all possess a number of features in common. When the received frequency is so high that r-f amplifiers become impractical, the incoming signal is fed directly to a crystal mixer. A klystron oscillator is almost always used to provide the mixing signal. The i-f amplifiers follow the mixer, and the number used is dependent principally on the bandwidth required by the signal. When the bandwidth is wide, the gain per stage is correspondingly low and more i-f amplifiers are required. With a narrow bandwidth, the gain per stage can be made greater, permitting the use of fewer stages.

Limiters follow the i-f system when the signal is frequency-modulated. Then comes an F–M discriminator. With amplitude modulation, the signal goes directly to a 2nd detector. Finally, one or more amplifiers are employed beyond the detector before the signal is sent to the loudspeaker or the cathode-ray tube.

There may be special circuits, such as automatic gain control and squelch systems, but basically the sequence followed is that indicated above.

QUESTIONS

1. What type of receiver is employed most extensively at the ultra-high frequencies? Why?

2. Describe briefly the operation of the receiver mentioned in answer to question 1.

3. Many UHF receivers operating above 1000 mc do not contain an r-f amplifier. Why?

4. Name two types of mixers that have been used in UHF circuits. Indicate the range of frequency operation of each.

5. Define noise figure. What is its significance?

6. What is the origin of receiver noise? Describe each type of noise component briefly.

7. What factors determine whether or not an r-f amplifier stage is used in a UHF receiver?

8. Draw the equivalent circuit of a 1000-mc converter.

9. Describe the internal construction of a silicon crystal rectifier.

10. Draw a rough sketch showing how mixing of signals is achieved in wave-guides.

11. What properties of a magic T section make it useful for use with balanced converters?

12. Describe the arrangement of components in a balanced converter.

13. Discuss the type of local oscillators used in UHF receivers.

14. Name three types of i-f amplifiers used in UHF superheterodyne receivers.

15. Draw the basic circuit of a synchronous single-tuned amplifier.

16. What electrical features does the amplifier of question 15 possess?

17. What advantages and disadvantages does a synchronous single-tuned i-f amplifier system possess?

18. Indicate briefly how the bandwidth in a synchronous single-tuned amplifier system changes with the addition of more tuned circuits. Why?

19. How does a stagger-tuned i-f system differ from a single-tuned system? Compare the advantages and disadvantages of these two systems.

20. Which of the three i-f systems described in this chapter provides the greater gain? What factors prevent its use in all instances?

21. Draw the circuit of a simple half-wave detector.

22. How can the frequency response of this simple circuit be widened? Illustrate.

23. Draw the circuits of two compensated second detectors, one receiving its signal from a double-tuned i-f system, the other attached to a stagger-tuned i-f system.

24. Describe how the type of signal to be received will determine the design of the amplifiers following the second detector.

25. What factors tend to reduce the high-frequency amplification of an audio amplifier?

26. Draw the equivalent high- and low-frequency circuits of an audio amplifier.

27. What is a peaking coil? Why is it useful in video amplifiers?

28. Draw the circuit of a video amplifier containing high-frequency compensation.

29. Explain and illustrate the differences between series peaking, shunt peaking, and a combination of the two.

30. Why can we disregard all shunting capacitances when designing the low-frequency compensation network.

31. Without adding any additional components to an audio amplifier, how can we partially improve its low-frequency response? What limitations exist to this method?

32. Draw the circuit of a video amplifier containing low-frequency compensation.

33. Specify the various points in an amplifier where low-frequency compensation can be applied. Indicate the compensation suggested in each instance.

34. A video amplifier is to use a single shunt peaking coil. The response is to extend to 4.0 mc. If the load resistor is 2000 ohms and the total shunting capacitance is 20 $\mu\mu$f, what value should the peaking coil have?

35. In the same video amplifier, the coupling capacitor (C_c) has a value of 0.1 μf and the grid resistor of the following stage a value of 250,000 ohms. What value should C_f have in the low-frequency compensation network?

36. Explain how the low-frequency compensation networks accomplish their purpose.

Chapter 12

UHF TELEVISION

From 1946 until the spring of 1952, television broadcasting and reception were confined to 12 channels within the VHF region. Channels 2 through 6 occupied a band extending from 54 to 88 mc; channels 7 through 13 were placed between 174 and 216 mc. When it became evident, after several years of operation, that more channels would be required, plans were made to allot frequencies to television in the ultra-high-frequency region. This was officially done in 1952. Now, television channels 14 through 83 extend from 470 mc to 890 mc.

By the time UHF television appeared on the scene, close to 18 million VHF television receivers had been manufactured and sold. Obviously something had to be done to permit these sets to receive UHF signals.

The industry brought forth several solutions to this problem. The most flexible was the construction of converters. These receive the UHF

Fig. 12.1. A UHF converter manufactured by the General Instrument Corporation.

signal, convert it down in frequency to one of the VHF channels, and then transfer this signal to the input terminals of a VHF receiver where it is treated as any other VHF signal. Most converters have their own cabinets and are self-powered. (See Fig. 12–1.) Some converters are especially designed by some receiver manufacturers for their own VHF sets, and in these instances power for the converter can be obtained from the VHF receiver power supply. In still other modifications, the UHF converters are designed to fit inside the VHF receiver cabinet. Tuning of

385

FIG. 12.2A.   Front view of the P. R. Mallory UHF converter.   (*Courtesy P. R. Mallory Co.*)

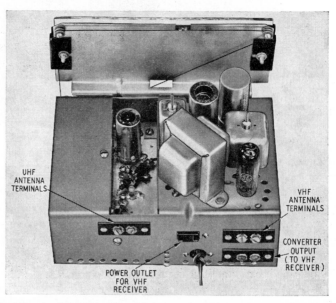

FIG. 12.2B.   Rear view of same unit.   For convenience, both UHF and VHF antennas can be connected to rear of UHF converter.   A front-panel switch then routes the desired signal to VHF receiver.

the converter can then be accomplished either by mechanical linkage to the VHF tuner (if such provision has been made) or by using a separate front panel dial.

A second solution for adapting VHF receivers to UHF reception is by the addition of auxiliary tuning elements to the VHF tuner. Examples of this are the UHF channel strips that can be substituted for unused VHF strips in turret tuners (see Chapter 1). Zenith and Standard Coil are advocates of this approach because their tuners fall within this category.

At the time of this writing, one overall 82-channel VHF-UHF tuner has just been developed. What particular success this unit will have is difficult to predict, although, in time, combination tuners will undoubtedly be widely used.

In the sections to follow, several representative UHF converters will be examined to determine how they function. UHF tuning strips for turret tuners will also be considered.

CONVERTERS

P. R. Mallory Converter. One of the first UHF converters to become available commercially was the P. R. Mallory converter shown in Figs. 12–2A and 12–2B. Electrically, it contains a double-tuned preselector

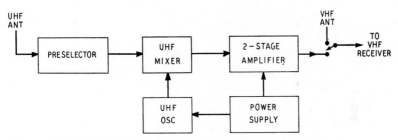

Fig. 12.3. Block diagram of P. R. Mallory UHF converter.

circuit, a crystal mixer, a 6AF4 oscillator, and a two-stage i-f amplifier. The block diagram is shown in Fig. 12–3 and the schematic diagram in Fig. 12–4. The absence of an r-f amplifier stems primarily from the fact that a good low-cost tube is not available. A number of r-f amplifier tubes have been manufactured, but their cost is too high in competitive converters.

Examining the circuit in detail, the input is balanced with an impedance of 300 ohms. This particular value was chosen to match the 300-ohm twin lead transmission lines widely used in television installations. If a coaxial cable, with an impedance of 75 ohms is used, it can be connected between one terminal and ground of the converter.

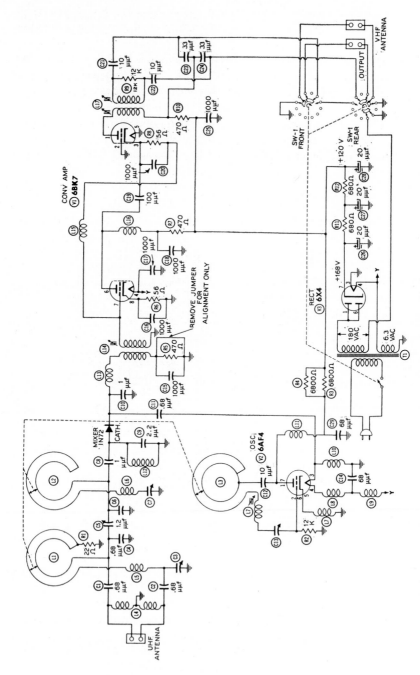

FIG. 12.4. Schematic diagram of P. R. Mallory UHF converter. (*Courtesy H. W. Sams & Co.*)

The input tuned network, known as the preselector, is double-tuned by two concentric line tuning elements (L_1 and L_2 in Fig. 12–4). These tuning elements are outgrowths of the P. R. Mallory VHF Inductuner (shown in Chapter 1). They consist of two metal strips which are placed in parallel circular grooves extending for 270 of the total 360 degrees. (See Fig. 12–5.) The far end of the two concentric lines are permanently shorted together; the other ends are the points which connect into the

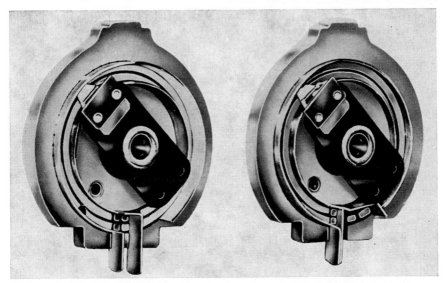

Fig. 12.5.   The tuning elements of the P. R. Mallory UHF tuner.

circuit.   To tune the lines, a movable shorting bar is employed. Where several sections are employed, the shorting bars of all are ganged together and turned by a common front panel control. Tracking over the tuning range is obtained by varying the shape of the various tuning elements.

In addition to the tuning elements in the preselector circuit, there also exists here a high-pass filter which is designed to attenuate all signals below the UHF band. This is primarily directed against harmonics of powerful VHF-TV or F–M broadcast stations, although it will also discriminate against image response.

Following the preselector is a crystal mixer stage. This combines the incoming signal with a locally generated oscillator voltage. The result is a difference frequency which, in this instance, falls within VHF channel 5 or channel 6 (as desired). The channel chosen is the one most free of other signals. In any community where one channel might be employed for local broadcasts, the other would not.

The 1N72 mixer is a germanium crystal chosen for its low noise level. A vacuum tube at this point would provide some gain, but it would also introduce more noise than a crystal. Furthermore, the crystal is cheaper and its circuit simpler.

The local oscillator is of the ultraudion variety, this being a modification of the Colpitts. The principal tuning element is another concentric-line section whose shorting bar is mechanically linked to the preselector shorting bars. C_{13} is an adjustment trimmer, designed to enable the oscillator tuning line (L_3) to track with the other lines. C_{12} is used for temperature compensation. Coupling between the oscillator and the mixer is achieved by a 0.68-$\mu\mu$f capacitor. Note that at the oscillator this capacitor connects to the 6AF4 heater (pin 3). The capacitance between heater and cathode is about 2.7 $\mu\mu$f, and a portion of the oscillator signal travels through this capacitance to the 0.68-$\mu\mu$f unit to the mixer. In this manner it is hoped that variations in the mixer circuit would have a minimum effect on the oscillator stability and output.

The frequency generated by the oscillator must be below the incoming signal frequency by an amount equal to the desired difference frequency. (Here this is TV channel 5 or channel 6.) This is necessary in order that the video carrier frequency, after mixing, remain below the sound carrier frequency. It must be remembered that the output of this converter goes to a VHF television receiver, and the relative positions of the two carriers must be the same as they are in directly received VHF television signals.

The signal at the mixer output is now applied to two amplifiers (sometimes called converter i-f amplifiers). The first stage is a conventionally operated triode, with the signal being received at the grid and appearing, after amplification, at the plate. The second stage is a grounded-grid amplifier wherein the signal is received in the cathode circuit. Coil L_{15} is inserted to stabilize the circuit and decrease its tendency to oscillate. It is also useful in reducing the noise generated in the circuit.

The output of the second amplifier is now transferred to the output terminals of the converter where it will be conducted to the input terminals of a VHF receiver.

Power for the converter is supplied by a 6X4 half-wave rectifier. The filtering network consists of C_{26}, C_{27}, C_{28}, and R_{11}, R_{12}. D-c voltage output is +120 volts, this being sufficient to power the various tubes in this unit.

At the left-hand side of the converter chassis (Fig. 12–2A) there is a three-position rotary switch. The three positions are: OFF, VHF, and UHF.

In the OFF position, power to the converter is off.

In the VHF position, power is turned on. In addition, any signal applied to the VHF terminals at the rear of the converter are transferred directly to the output terminals of the unit. This is done so that the lead-in line from the VHF antenna can be connected to the UHF converter. Then only one line will be required from the converter to the VHF receiver. Now, if it is desired to receive a VHF signal, turning the converter switch to the VHF position will act to transfer this signal automatically (from the VHF antenna) to the VHF receiver. The converter circuitry, in this instance, is by-passed.

In the UHF position, the output terminals of the converter are set to receive the signal from the converter and to transfer this to the VHF set.

This particular arrangement, followed more or less by all converter manufacturers, simplifies the routing of signals between the various antennas and the converter and VHF receiver.

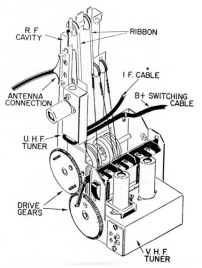

It is also customary to provide an a-c outlet on the back of the converter. The power line plug from the VHF set is then inserted into this outlet so that when the power for the converter is turned on, the VHF set also receives its power. Thus, one switch turns both units on or off.

Raytheon Converter. Another approach to UHF conversion is demonstrated by the Raytheon UHF tuner. This unit is not mounted in a separate cabinet, as the other converters were, but rather is installed directly on the VHF receiver chassis. To make the installation, the VHF chassis is removed from its cabinet, a drive gear is fitted onto the VHF tuner, and then the UHF

Fig. 12.6. The Raytheon UHF converter is installed on the VHF tuner assembly.

unit is fastened to the VHF chassis with four screws. (See Fig. 12–6.) With the drive gears, both UHF and VHF units can be tuned by the same front panel knob. (This arrangement was devised especially by Raytheon for the conversion of their own VHF television receivers.)

Connection between the UHF tuner and the VHF chassis is made by two cables. One cable couples the converted signal to the VHF i-f section while the other cable is used for switching B plus voltage to either the UHF or VHF tuners. The converted UHF signal does not pass through the VHF tuner section (as it did in the previous converter), but instead feeds directly to the video i-f amplifiers of the VHF receiver. This represents a single-conversion process in distinction to the double-conversion procedure employed in the preceding converter. In order to do this, however, the UHF section must step the incoming UHF signal down to

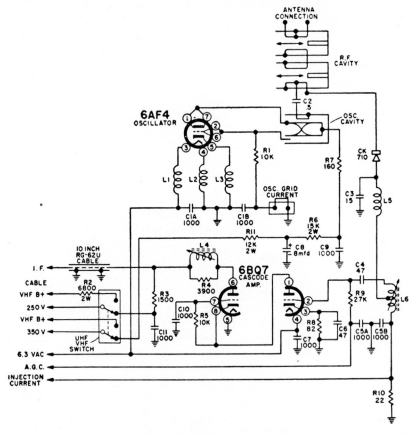

FIG. 12.7. Schematic diagram of the Raytheon UHF converter. (*Courtesy Raytheon*)

the video i-f value of the VHF receiver. In Raytheon sets, this is 45.75 mc. The reason this can be done in this instance, of course, is that the UHF tuner is being used with a specific type of set. If it were designed to be used with *all* makes of television receivers, it would have to follow the conversion method of the previous converter.

Schematically, the tuner contains a preselector input circuit, a crystal mixer, a 6AF4 ultraudion oscillator, and a 6BQ7 cascode amplifier. (See Fig. 12–7.) Frequency tuning is accomplished by a double-tuned coaxial-line or r-f cavity. These tuning circuits are basically nothing more than quarter-wave lines shorted at one end. The electrical length of the lines is varied by a ribbon which is attached to a dial cord and pulley arrangement. Signal transfer between preselector tuning sections is by inductive coupling furnished by short loops of wire.

The oscillator resonant circuit is similar to that of the preselector. Here a quarter-wave shorted parallel-wire transmission line is used, and a shorting bar varies the electrical length of the line. There is provision in the grid circuit of the oscillator for inserting a microamp meter to measure grid current. This serves to indicate not only whether the oscillator is functioning but also how well.

The mixer receives both the oscillator voltage and the incoming signal and from them produces a difference frequency equal to the video i-f. This signal is fed to the 6BQ7 cascode amplifier where it is amplified and then transferred to the i-f section of the VHF receiver through 10 inches of RG-62U coaxial cable.

The cascode amplifier, mentioned above, is a fairly recent development. It consists, essentially, of two triodes connected in series, that is, the plate of the first section goes directly to the cathode of the second section. Frequently this connection between the two sections is direct, which means that the same current flows through both tubes. However, it is also possible for the two sections to be capacitively coupled.

This type of amplifier, it has been found, is capable of good gain and low noise. A single triode, by itself, has better noise characteristics than even a well-constructed, high-frequency pentode; however, the pentode is capable of greater gain. By combining two triodes as indicated, we achieve both good gain and low noise.

The input impedance of this UHF tuner is 300 ohms and the overall bandwidth is 6 to 8 mc. Since there is no r-f amplifier ahead of the mixer, the sensitivity of the receiver on UHF will be less than it is on VHF.

General Instrument UHF Converter. The General Instrument (or G.I.) UHF converter is designed around a transmission line tuner which differs considerably from any of the other line tuners previously considered in this book. Basically this unit is derived from the rectangular line shown in Fig. 12-8. The inner conductor, while depicted as being solid, can just as well be hollow. At ultra-high frequencies, current flow is along the outer surface of a conductor. Depth penetration is exceedingly slight.

To tune this transmission line, a variable capacitor is placed across one end. By varying the capacitance we are, in effect, varying one of the reactive components of the line and this will cause a frequency change.

With this as a background, we can now examine the final form of this UHF tuner. (See Fig. 12–9.) The line is shaped as shown in Fig. 12–8, except that the top plates of both the outer and inner rectangular con-

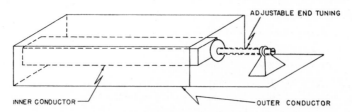

FIG. 12.8.   The basic rectangular section from which the General Instrument tuner is derived.

ductors have been removed. The line still functions in the same manner except that the energy is not as closely confined.

One end of each line (which is a quarter wavelength long) is shorted; the other end contains the tuning capacitors. Four plates are provided for each line. The two outer plates are slotted to permit point-by-point

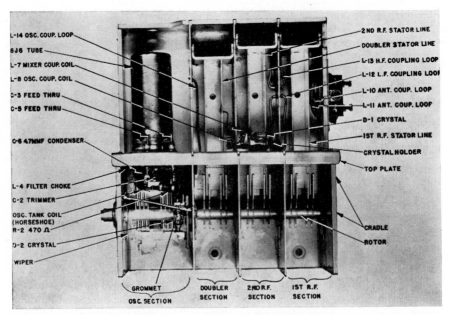

FIG. 12.9.   The General Instrument UHF tuner construction. The rectangular transmission line sections are shown at the right. Three are used: 1st r-f, 2nd r-f, and osc. doubler. Schematic diagram of unit shown in Fig. 12.10.

corrections over the tuning range. The two inner plates are solid. All capacitor plates are mounted on a common rod, permitting simultaneous tuning of all sections at the same time.

Coupling between the 1st r-f section and the 2nd r-f section is accomplished by means of two coupling loops. (L_{12} and L_{13} in Fig. 12.10.) The larger loop takes care of the coupling at the low end of the UHF band, whereas the smaller loop provides adequate coupling at the high end. The overall bandwidth of these two sections is approximately 10 mc for any setting of the variable capacitor elements. Incoming signals are coupled into the 1st r-f section by means of two loops, L_{10} and L_{11}. The input impedance is 300 ohms balanced. However, either side to ground will provide 75 ohms unbalanced. (Inductance of a coil is proportional to the square of the number of turns. Using half the number of turns on a coil reduces inductance by one-fourth and, at the same frequency, one-fourth the impedance: 75 is one-fourth of 300.)

The oscillator used in this unit is a push-pull affair operating at one-half the frequency required to mix with each incoming signal. The oscillator output is coupled from L_{15} to L_{14} where the 1N82 crystal produces a number of harmonics. Of particular interest is the second harmonic, and this is accentuated by the oscillator doubler tuning section. The designers of this unit felt that, by this arrangement, it would be possible to obtain adequate injection voltage to the crystal mixer, low drift, and low shift with temperature and voltage changes and trouble-free operation.

The incoming signal reaches the crystal mixer through L_7; the oscillator voltage arrives at the mixer via L_8. The resultant difference frequency, in either channel 5 or 6, feeds into a broad double-tuned circuit which is compensated for any changes in crystal impedance with frequency. This double-tuned circuit (between D_1 and the input grid of V_1) is about 12 mc wide peak-to-peak, and it feeds a low-noise cascode amplifier using a 6BQ7 tube. Switch S_2 permits changing from a center frequency of 79.5 mc (channel 5) to a center frequency of 85.5 mc (channel 6).

The power supply employs a selenium rectifier, D_3, to provide $+130$ volts output to the 6BQ7 and the same voltage to the oscillator.

This same tuner can be used without the 6BQ7 amplifiers. By adjusting the tuning range of the 6J6 oscillator, a difference frequency in the 40-mc range can be obtained from the crystal mixer, D_1. This output could then be fed directly to the video i-f system of any television receiver. When used in this manner, the UHF tuner can be mechanically coupled to the General Instrument VHF tuner as shown in Fig. 12–11. This now permits one front panel control for both units.

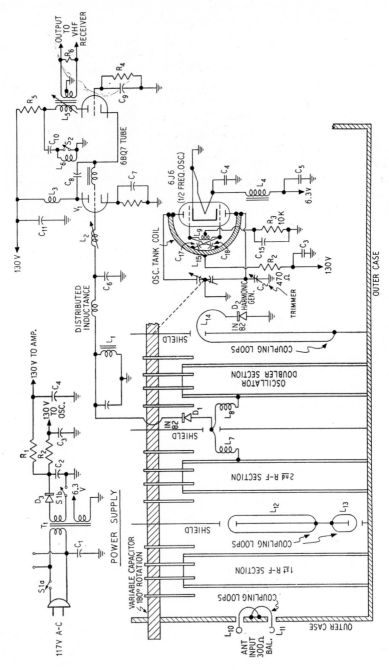

FIG. 12.10.   Schematic diagram of General Instrument UHF converter.

FIG. 12.11. The G. I. UHF tuner can be mechanically coupled to the G. I. VHF tuner, as shown.

TUNER STRIPS

The second approach to UHF conversion is by means of tuner strips. In Chapter 1 it was stated that one type of VHF television tuner widely employed was the turret tuner. The example used was the Standard Coil tuner in which the r-f tuning elements are mounted on strips which can be removed from the tuner drum. There are two strips for every channel, from No. 2 to No. 13.

Now, in any one locality, no more than seven VHF channels would be allocated. That means that five channels are unused and, if desired, UHF strips could be substituted in their place. Fig. 12–12 shows the Standard Coil tuner, together with one set of VHF tuning strips and one set of alternate UHF strips. One UHF set would be required for each UHF station to be received.

The block and schematic diagrams of the circuits contained on the Standard Coil UHF strips are shown in Fig. 12–13. The incoming signal is received by a preselector circuit which is designed to pass the desired frequencies and attenuate all others. The signal is then transferred to a crystal-mixer where it is combined with a locally generated signal. The resulting difference frequencies are then fed to the r-f amplifier of the Standard Coil tuner. After passing through the r-f amplifier, the signal goes on to the mixer stage of the tuner where it is again combined with an oscillator voltage.   The result of this second mixing is a signal possessing a frequency equal to the video i-f frequencies of the television receiver.

Now, superficially, this sequence of events may appear to be similar to those encountered in a self-contained converter. Actually, several significant differences exist between the two. The UHF strips do not

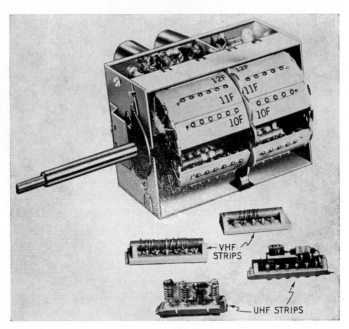

Fig. 12.12.   The Standard Coil turret tuner.   The UHF strips, shown at the bottom of the illustration, would replace the two VHF strips shown just above.
(*Courtesy Standard Coil*)

contain their own oscillator circuit. Instead, for the sake of economy, the local oscillator of the Standard Coil VHF tuner is used. However, for the initial mixing with the UHF signal in the crystal mixer, the fundamental of the tuner oscillator is *not* used, but a harmonic instead. Here is how this works.

Suppose the UHF strip is designed to receive a UHF station operating on channel 16. The frequencies for this channel extend from 482 mc to 488 mc. The video carrier is located at 483.25 mc and the sound carrier is at 487.75 mc. With these strips in place, the tuner local oscillator is operating at 127.25 mc. This frequency is passed through a crystal (not the UHF mixer) where harmonics of 127.25 mc are produced. A multiplier-tuned circuit is peaked to the third harmonic, insuring that this frequency will predominate over all the other harmonics. This third harmonic, which

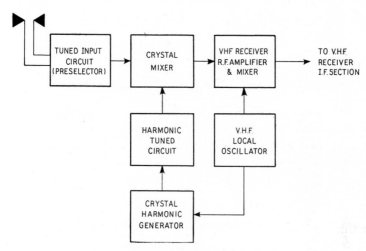

FIG. 12.13A. Block diagram of the UHF circuits contained on the Standard Coil plug-in strips.

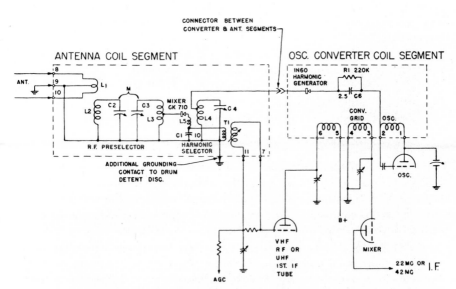

FIG. 12.13B. Schematic diagram of the components on Standard Coil UHF strips. (*Courtesy Standard Coil*)

is 381.75 mc, is now combined with the incoming UHF signal. The result is:

(a) For the video carrier:

$$483.25 \text{ mc} - 381.75 \text{ mc} = 101.50 \text{ mc}$$

(b) For the sound carrier:

$$487.75 \text{ mc} - 381.75 \text{ mc} = 106.00 \text{ mc}$$

These two signals are then accepted by the r-f amplifier, amplified and fed to the regular VHF mixer where it beats with the fundamental frequency generated by the local VHF oscillator. This frequency is 127.25 mc and the result of this second beating is as follows:

For the video carrier:

$$127.25 - 101.50 = 25.75 \text{ mc}$$

For the sound carrier:

$$127.25 - 106.00 = 21.25 \text{ mc}$$

Thus, at the output of the VHF mixer, the video and carrier i-f values are what they normally are for a directly received VHF signal.

It will be noted that since the tuner strips determine what circuits the VHF r-f amplifier, mixer, and oscillator will have, the frequencies of these circuits can be of *any* desired value. In the foregoing example, the VHF oscillator operated at 127.25 mc; the r-f amplifier was tuned to accept a frequency band extending from 101 mc to 106 mc.

The actual circuitry of the Standard Coil UHF strips is shown in Fig. 12–13B.

The UHF signals garnered by the UHF antenna are applied to terminals 8 and 10 of the tuner strips. The impedance here is 300 ohms. The incoming signal is transferred from L_1 to L_2 to L_3 via inductive coupling. These three circuits, particularly L_2, C_2 and L_3, C_3, provide the initial selectivity of the strip, selecting the desired signal and attenuating all others. The selectivity is not particularly sharp, encompassing two or three adjacent channels (12 to 18 mc), but it does offer sufficient discrimination beyond these limits to be definitely worth while.

A crystal mixer taps down on L_3 (for best impedance match) receiving the incoming signal from the preselector circuit. At the same time, the mixer also receives from L_4 (via L_5) a harmonic of the oscillator signal. L_4 and C_4 are tuned to this harmonic in order to accentuate it and, at the same time, depress the fundamental oscillator frequency and whatever other harmonics may be present. To aid in the development of the oscillator harmonics, a special multiplier crystal is inserted between the oscillator and L_4, C_4. The crystal distorts the oscillator current and, of the harmonics thus produced, one is chosen by L_4, C_4.

Both signals are now mixed and the difference frequency signal is passed on to the grid of the normal r-f amplifier of the VHF receiver. The signal is amplified here, then transferred to the mixer where it combines with the fundamental frequency signal of the VHF oscillator. The result of this second mixing is the normal VHF intermediate frequency of the receiver. In some sets this will be in the 20-30 mc range; in others it will fall within the 40-50 mc range.

Another UHF strip, to date, is the one developed by Zenith for use in its VHF turret tuners. The method of approach is somewhat similar to that described above, except that incoming UHF signals are immediately reduced to their video i-f values (either in the 20- or 40-mc ranges). The signal is then amplified by the VHF r-f amplifier (which is now operating at the video i-f frequencies) and the mixer. This latter stage has also been converted to an i-f amplifier. Following this, the signal is transferred into the normal VHF i-f system. On UHF operation, the VHF oscillator functions only for the UHF crystal mixer; its signal is not required for the VHF mixer tube since this is now a straight amplifier.

OVER-ALL VHF–UHF TUNERS

As mentioned earlier in this chapter, one overall 82-channel VHF-UHF TV tuner has been developed. This is shown in Fig. 12–14. It consists of a separate VHF section, located at the rear, and a separate UHF section, at the front, which are mechanically and electrically ganged to each other. The VHF section is essentially similar to the Standard Coil VHF turret tuner shown in Fig. 1–17, Chapter 1. In the present unit a 6BZ7 double triode is employed as a cascode r-f amplifier and a 6U8 as a triode oscillator and pentode mixer. The UHF section of the tuner uses a 6T4 (or 6AF4) oscillator and a 1N82 germanium crystal as the mixer.

Each section has its own antenna input terminals. All power connections are made to the VHF section, and then the B + and heater power is brought from the VHF to the UHF section by using two short connecting wires.

When the tuner is set to receive a VHF signal, the ouput path from the UHF to the VHF sections is open. However, when the unit is set for UHF reception, this path is closed, and then any UHF signals received are stepped down in frequency to the i-f value of the receiver, either in the 20-mc or 40-mc band. This i-f signal is then applied first to the r-f amplifier in the VHF section which, by the use of appropriate circuits, is now operating at the i-f level. The signal is then next applied to the

VHF mixer, which is likewise functioning at the i-f frequency. During UHF reception, the VHF oscillator is made nonoperative.

The foregoing description is, of necessity, brief. Actually, many of the operating features of this tuner are built around a fairly extensive cam-switching arrangement which serves to effect the change-over from VHF to UHF as required.

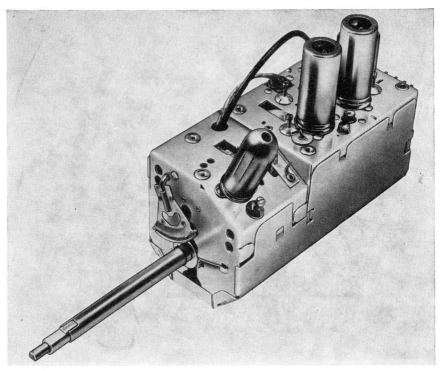

FIG. 12.14. The Standard Coil VHF-UHF tuner designed for television receivers.

The use of the ultra-high frequencies for television transmission and reception is still comparatively new and we can expect to see a number of changes before any semblance of standardization is achieved. UHF converters and tuning strips, for example, are transitional devices and will, in time, disappear. In the meantime, they serve the very useful purpose of adapting all VHF sets to UHF reception when UHF broadcasting commences in any locality. Eventually all sets will come equipped with VHF and UHF tuners capable of receiving any signal from channel 2 to channel 83.

QUESTIONS

1. What general solutions did the television industry adopt to permit VHF television receivers to receive UHF signals?

2. Draw the block diagram of a UHF TV converter.

3. Why do converters lack r-f amplifiers?

4. What type of tuning elements does the P. R. Mallory UHF converter employ? Describe how they operate.

5. Wherein does the Raytheon converter differ from the Mallory converter? (Disregard difference in tuning elements themselves.)

6. Could the Raytheon converter be used with every VHF television receiver? Explain.

7. What is the reason for using two coupling loops in the preselector section of the General Instrument tuner?

8. How do UHF tuning strips differ from UHF converters?

9. Draw the block diagram of the Standard Coil UHF tuning strip.

10. Describe briefly the operation of the tuning strip circuits.

INDEX